Middle School 3-2
중간고사 완벽대비

KB087569

적중100

영어 기출 문제집

중3

미래 | 최연희

Best Collection

구성과 특징

교과서의 주요 학습 내용을 중심으로 학습 영역별 특성에 맞춰 단계별로 다양한 학습 기회를 제공하여
단원별 학습능력 평가는 물론 중간 및 기말고사 시험 등에 완벽하게 대비할 수 있도록 내용을 구성

Words & Expressions

Step1 Key Words 단원별 핵심 단어 설명 및 풀이
Key Expression 단원별 핵심 숙어 및 관용어 설명
Word Power 반대 또는 비슷한 뜻 단어 배우기
English Dictionary 영어로 배우는 영어 단어

Step2 실력평가 단원별 수시평가 대비 주관식, 객관식 문제풀이

Step3 서술형 대비 학업성취도 및 수행능력평가 대비 서술형 문제풀이

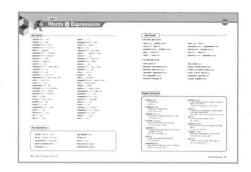

Conversation

Step1 핵심 의사소통 소통에 필요한 주요 표현 방법 요약
핵심 Check 기본적인 표현 방법 및 활용능력 확인

Step2 대화문 익히기 교과서 대화문 심층 분석 및 확인

Step3 교과서 확인학습 빈칸 채우기를 통한 문장 완성 능력 확인

Step4 기본평가 시험대비 기초 학습 능력 평가

Step5 실력평가 단원별 수시평가 대비 주관식, 객관식 문제풀이

Step6 서술형 대비 학업성취도 및 수행능력평가 대비 서술형 문제풀이

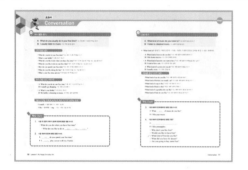

Grammar

Step1 주요 문법 단원별 주요 문법 사항과 예문을 알기 쉽게 설명
핵심 Check 기본 문법사항에 대한 이해 여부 확인

Step2 기본평가 시험대비 기초 학습 능력 평가

Step3 실력평가 단원별 수시평가 대비 주관식, 객관식 문제풀이

Step4 서술형 대비 학업성취도 및 수행능력평가 대비 서술형 문제풀이

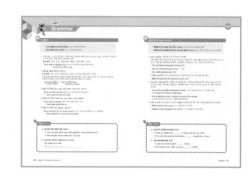

Reading

Step1 구문 분석 단원별로 제시된 문장에 대한 구문별 분석과 내용 설명
확인문제 문장에 대한 기본적인 이해와 인지능력 확인

Step2 확인학습A 빈칸 채우기를 통한 문장 완성 능력 확인

Step3 확인학습B 제시된 우리말을 영어로 완성하여 작문 능력 키우기

Step4 실력평가 단원별 수시평가 대비 주관식, 객관식 문제풀이

Step5 서술형 대비 학업성취도 및 수행능력평가 대비 서술형 문제풀이
교과서 구석구석 교과서에 나오는 기타 문장까지 완벽 학습

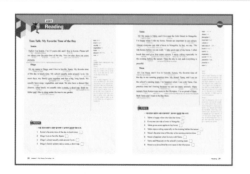

Composition

|영역별 핵심문제|

단어 및 어휘, 대화문, 문법, 독해 등 각 영역별 기출문제의 출제 유형을 분석하여 실전에 대비하고 연습할 수 있도록 문제를 배열

|단원별 예상문제|

기출문제를 분석한 후 새로운 시험 출제 경향을 더하여 새롭게 출제될 수 있는 문제를 포함하여 시험에 완벽하게 대비할 수 있도록 준비

|서술형 실전 및 창의사고력 문제|

학교 시험에서 점차 늘어나는 서술형 시험에 집중 대비하고 고득점을 취득하는데 만전을 기하기 위한 학습 코너

|단원별 모의고사|

영역별, 단계별 학습을 모두 마친 후 실전 연습을 위한 모의고사

on the textbook

교과서 파헤치기

- **단어Test1~3** 영어 단어 우리말 쓰기, 우리말을 영어 단어로 쓰기, 영영풀이에 해당하는 단어와 우리말 쓰기
- **대화문Test1~2** 대화문 빈칸 완성 및 전체 대화문 쓰기
- **본문Test1~5** 빈칸 완성, 우리말 쓰기, 문장 배열연습, 영어 작문하기 복습 등 단계별 반복 학습을 통해 교과서 지문에 대한 완벽한 습득
- **구석구석지문Test1~2** 지문 빈칸 완성 및 전문 영어로 쓰기

This Is Korea

🔑 의사소통 기능

- 궁금한 것 묻고 답하기
  A: I wonder why he is running.
  B: I think he is late for school.

- 설명 요청하기
  A: Could you explain what this is?
  B: It's a traditional Korean hat. It's called a gat.

🔑 언어 형식

- '과거완료' had + 과거분사
  She kept laughing even after she **had been** in the water for over five hours.

- 간접의문문
  They didn't understand **why I wanted to take their pictures**.

교과서
Words & Expressions

Key Words

- □ **ad** [æd] 몡 광고 (= advertisement)
- □ **attend** [əténd] 동 참석하다
- □ **audience** [ɔ́:diəns] 몡 청중
- □ **audio guide** 음성 안내기
- □ **bakery** [béikəri] 몡 빵집
- □ **beat** [bi:t] 몡 (북 등을 치는) 소리, (심장의) 고동
- □ **black-and-white** 혱 (사진, TV 등) 흑백의
- □ **bookstore** [búkstɔr] 몡 서점
- □ **breadwinner** [brédwinər] 몡 생계를 책임지는 사람, 가장
- □ **breathe** [bri:ð] 동 호흡하다
- □ **bridge** [bridʒ] 몡 교량, 다리
- □ **community** [kəmjú:nəti] 몡 지역 공동체
- □ **complete** [kəmplí:t] 동 완성[완료]하다
- □ **continue** [kəntínju:] 동 계속하다
- □ **copy machine** 복사기
- □ **destroy** [distrɔ́i] 동 파괴하다
- □ **device** [diváis] 몡 기구
- □ **diver** [dáivər] 몡 잠수부
- □ **environment** [inváiərənmənt] 몡 환경
- □ **exhibition** [èksəbíʃən] 몡 전시회, 박람회
- □ **female** [fí:meil] 혱 여성의
- □ **good harvest** 풍년
- □ **greenhouse** [grí:nhàus] 몡 온실
- □ **harvest** [há:rvist] 동 수확하다
- □ **heritage** [héritidʒ] 몡 유산
- □ **intangible** [intǽndʒəbl] 혱 무형의, 만질 수 없는

- □ **jellyfish** [dʒélifiʃ] 몡 해파리
- □ **marine** [mərí:n] 혱 해양의, 바다의
- □ **moved** [mu:vd] 혱 감동받은
- □ **nationwide** [néiʃənwàid] 혱 전국적인
- □ **overseas** [óuvərsiz] 부 해외로, 해외에
- □ **overwork** [óuvərwərk] 동 과로하다
- □ **past** [pæst] 혱 지나간 몡 과거
- □ **path** [pæθ] 몡 경로, 길
- □ **photographer** [fətágrəfər] 몡 사진작가
- □ **press** [pres] 동 누르다 몡 언론, 기자
- □ **promote** [prəmóut] 동 홍보하다, 촉진하다
- □ **realize** [rí:làiz] 동 깨닫다, 인식하다
- □ **seafood** [sí:fud] 몡 해산물
- □ **several** [sévərəl] 혱 몇몇의
- □ **suitable** [sú:təbl] 혱 적합한, 적절한
- □ **sunshine** [sʌ́nʃain] 몡 햇빛
- □ **tightly** [táitli] 부 단단히, 꽉
- □ **traditional** [trədíʃənl] 혱 전통적인
- □ **trail** [treil] 몡 좁은 길
- □ **underground** [ʌndərgráund] 혱 지하의
- □ **underwater** [ʌndərwɔ́tər] 혱 수중의, 물속에서
- □ **volcanic** [vɑlkǽnik] 혱 화산의, 화산 작용에 의한
- □ **waterfall** [wɔ́tərfɔl] 몡 폭포
- □ **wetsuit** [wétsu:t] 몡 잠수용 고무옷, 잠수복
- □ **worldwide** [wɔ́rldwaid] 부 세계적으로

Key Expressions

- □ **a couple of** 두 서너 개의
- □ **a little bit** 조금, 약간
- □ **an intangible cultural treasure** 무형문화재
- □ **be good for** ~에 유익하다
- □ **be suitable for** ~에 적절하다
- □ **check ~ out** ~을 확인하다, ~을 조사하다
- □ **cheer up** 힘을 북돋아 주다, 격려하다
- □ **get into** ~에 들어가다
- □ **give (someone) a call** 전화를 걸다
- □ **give (someone) a hand** 거들어 주다, 돕다
- □ **give a presentation** 발표하다

- □ **give a talk** 강의하다, 연설하다
- □ **go on vacation** 휴가 가다
- □ **happen to** 우연히 ~하다
- □ **keep -ing** 계속해서 ~하다
- □ **make double-sided copies** 양면 복사를 하다
- □ **take a photo** 사진을 찍다
- □ **walk along** ~을 따라 걷다
- □ **Why don't we ~?** ~하는 것이 어때?
- □ **Why not?** 왜 안 되겠어?, 좋고말고.
- □ **wish for** ~을 기원하다
- □ **would like to** ~하고 싶다

Word Power

※ 서로 비슷한 뜻을 가진 어휘

- □ **ad** 광고(**advertisement**) : **commercial** 광고
- □ **device** 기구 : **tool** 도구
- □ **moved** 감동받은 : **touched** 감동받은
- □ **several** 몇몇의 : **a few** 몇몇의

- □ **borrow** 빌리다 : **rent** 임대하다
- □ **environment** 환경 : **surroundings** 환경
- □ **path** 경로, 길 : **trail** 좁은 길
- □ **suitable** 적합한, 적절한 : **proper** 적절한

※ 서로 반대되는 뜻을 가진 어휘

- □ **borrow** 빌리다 ↔ **lend** 빌려주다
- □ **nationwide** 전국적인 ↔ **local** 지역적인

- □ **female** 여성의 ↔ **male** 남성의
- □ **suitable** 적합한 ↔ **unsuitable** 부적절한

※ 동사 - 명사

- □ **attend** 참석하다 - **attendance** 참석
- □ **continue** 계속하다 - **continuity** 연속
- □ **explain** 설명하다 - **explanation** 설명
- □ **realize** 깨닫다 - **realization** 깨달음

- □ **breathe** 호흡하다 - **breath** 호흡
- □ **destroy** 파괴하다 - **destruction** 파괴
- □ **promote** 홍보하다 - **promotion** 홍보

※ 형용사 - 명사

- □ **good** 좋은 - **goodness** 선량함
- □ **aware** 알고 있는 - **awareness** 인식
- □ **weak** 약한 - **weakness** 약함
- □ **polite** 예의 바른 - **politeness** 예의 바름
- □ **sad** 슬픈 - **sadness** 슬픔

- □ **ill** 아픔 - **illness** 질병
- □ **fair** 공정한 - **fairness** 공정함
- □ **kind** 친절한 - **kindness** 친절
- □ **happy** 행복한 - **happiness** 행복
- □ **dark** 어두운 - **darkness** 어둠

English Dictionary

- □ **ad** 광고 (= **advertisement**)
  → a picture, set of words, or a short film, intended to persuade people to buy
  사람들이 사도록 설득하려고 의도된 사진, 어구, 또는 짧은 영상

- □ **beat** (북 등을 치는) 소리
  → one of a series of regular movements or hitting actions 일련의 규칙적인 움직임 또는 치는 동작 중의 하나

- □ **breadwinner** 생계를 책임지는 사람, 가장
  → the member of a family who earns the money to support the others 가족을 부양하려고 돈을 버는 가족 구성원

- □ **breathe** 호흡하다
  → to take air into your lungs and send it out again
  폐로 공기를 들여보내고 그것을 다시 내보내다

- □ **community** 지역 공동체
  → the people who live in the same area, town, etc.
  같은 지역이나 마을 등에 사는 사람들

- □ **heritage** 유산
  → the traditional beliefs, values, customs of a family, country, or society
  한 가족, 국가, 사회의 전통적인 믿음, 가치관, 관습

- □ **intangible** 무형의, 만질 수 없는
  → having value but not existing physically
  가치가 있지만 물리적으로 존재하지는 않는

- □ **overseas** 해외의
  → to or in a foreign country that is across the sea
  바다 건너 있는 외국으로 가거나 외국에 있는

01 다음 짝지어진 단어의 관계가 같도록 빈칸에 알맞은 말을 쓰시오.

> female : male = _____ : borrow

02 다음 영영풀이가 가리키는 것을 고르시오.

> having value but not existing physically

① underground   ② traditional
③ volcanic   ④ marine
⑤ intangible

03 다음 중 밑줄 친 부분의 뜻풀이가 바르지 <u>않은</u> 것은?

① All the <u>audience</u> stood up and gave the performer a big hand. (청중)
② We can't <u>breathe</u> in outer space. (호흡하다)
③ It is an important part of <u>community</u> life. (공동체)
④ She invited me to her photo <u>exhibition</u>. (전시회)
⑤ The trip was a great <u>experience</u>. (실험)

서답형

04 다음 우리말에 맞게 빈칸에 알맞은 말을 쓰시오. (철자가 주어진 경우, 그 철자로 시작하여 쓸 것.)

(1) 심해 잠수를 위해 잠수복을 가져와라.
➡ Bring a w_____ for deep sea diving.
(2) 그 영화는 전세계적으로 유명해졌다.
➡ The movie has become famous w_____.

(3) 그들은 지역 신문에 광고를 실었다.
➡ They put an _____ in the local paper.
(4) 우리는 강 위에 놓인 다리를 건넜다.
➡ We crossed the _____ over the river.

서답형

05 다음 문장의 빈칸에 들어갈 말을 〈보기〉에서 골라 알맞은 형태로 쓰시오.

> ──┤ 보기 ├──
> cheer up / wish for / get into / be good for / walk along

(1) Walking _____ your health.
(2) I _____ lots of interests for our new products.
(3) _____! You can do better next time.
(4) If you _____ the street, you can find the post office.
(5) It is hard to _____ the medical school.

06 다음 주어진 문장의 밑줄 친 press와 같은 의미로 쓰인 것은?

> Please <u>press</u> the start button.

① Jack blamed the <u>press</u> photographers for violating his privacy.
② Which switch should I <u>press</u> to turn it off?
③ Some people don't believe the <u>press</u> reports.
④ They are fighting for the freedom of the <u>press</u>.
⑤ The car accident in my town was reported in the <u>press</u>.

01 다음 짝지어진 단어의 관계가 같도록 빈칸에 알맞은 말을 쓰시오.

> thin : thick = future : _____

02 다음 우리말에 맞게 빈칸에 알맞은 말을 쓰시오. (철자가 주어진 경우, 그 철자로 시작하여 쓸 것.)

(1) 길은 단풍잎으로 덮여 있었다.
➡ The p_____ was covered with colorful leaves.

(2) 전 지역 공동체가 바이러스에 대해 걱정했다.
➡ The whole _____ was concerned about the virus.

(3) 그 밴드는 그들의 새로운 앨범을 홍보할 필요가 있다.
➡ The band needs to p_____ their new album.

(4) 해파리를 본 적이 있나요?
➡ Have you ever seen the _____?

03 다음 우리말과 일치하도록 주어진 단어를 모두 배열하여 완성하시오.

(1) 우리는 작년에 풍년이 들었다.
(last / harvest / had / we / a / good / year)
➡ _____

(2) 돈이 항상 행복을 가져다주지는 않는다.
(does / happiness / money / not / bring / always)
➡ _____

(3) 우리의 국가적 유산이 화재에 의해 파괴되었다.
(was / by / the / our / heritage / destroyed / fire / national)
➡ _____

04 다음 우리말을 주어진 단어를 이용하여 영작하시오.

(1) 우리는 한 시간 동안 길을 따라 걸었다. (along, for, street)
➡ _____
_____

(2) 이 책은 초등학생들에게 적합하다. (suitable, elementary)
➡ _____
_____

(3) 종이를 절약하기 위해 양면 복사를 하자. (let's, save)
➡ _____
_____

05 다음 문장의 빈칸에 들어갈 말을 〈보기〉에서 골라 쓰시오.

> ┤ 보기 ├
> realize / promote / underwater / volcanic / several

(1) This campaign will _____ the education for all ages.
(2) He didn't _____ that he was acting differently.
(3) I go hiking _____ times a month.
(4) The _____ photographer is diving into the sea.
(5) Dokdo was created from _____ activity.

Conversation

① 궁금한 것 묻고 답하기

> **A** I wonder why he is running. 왜 그가 달리고 있는지 궁금해.
> **B** I think he is late for school. 내 생각엔 그가 학교에 늦은 것 같아.

- 궁금증을 표현할 때 wonder(궁금하다), curious(궁금한, 호기심이 많은), want to know(알고 싶다) 등의 표현을 이용하여 'I wonder ~.'라고 말한다. 이때 어순은 'I wonder+의문사+주어+동사 ~.', 'I wonder+if/whether+주어+동사 ~.'이다. 또한 궁금한 내용을 'I want to know ~.', 'I don't know why ~.'로 표현할 수 있다.

- 'Can I ~?', 'Can/Could you ~?' 등과 같이 요구/요청을 나타내는 조동사 표현을 사용하여 'Can I ask you ~?' 또는 'Can you tell me ~?'와 같이 궁금한 점에 대하여 물어볼 수 있다. 그 외에 궁금증을 나타낼 때는 'Do you know ~?' 등을 사용할 수도 있다.

- 궁금함을 나타낼 때 'I wonder ~.' 대신에 쓸 수 있는 표현으로 'I'm curious ~.' 또는 'I want to know ~.' 등이 있다. 'I'm curious'와 명사구를 같이 쓸 때는 'I'm curious about+명사구'이고, 명사절과 함께 쓸 때는 'I'm curious if/whether ~.' 또는 'I'm curious 의문사+주어+동사'이다.

궁금한 것 묻고 답하기

- I'm wondering + if/whether 주어+동사/의문사절. ~인지 궁금하다.
- Can you tell me ~? ~에 대해 말해 줄 수 있니?
- Can I ask you + 의문사절? ~에 대하여 물어봐도 되니?
- I'm curious if/whether 주어+동사. ~가 궁금하다.
- I want to know 명사구/명사절. ~을 알고 싶다.
- I'd be very interested to ~. 나는 ~에 매우 관심이 많다.

핵심 Check

1. 밑줄 친 우리말을 괄호 안에 주어진 어휘를 이용하여 영작하시오.

   G: Wow, look at the bridge in this ad.
   어디에서 찍은 사진인지 궁금하네. (the photo, taken)

   B: That's Gwangandaegyo in Busan.

   G: How do you know that?

   B: I went there with my family last summer.

   ➡ _____

② 설명 요청하기

A Could you explain what this is? 이게 무엇인지 설명해 줄 수 있니?

B It's a traditional Korean hat. It's called a gat. 그것은 한국의 전통적인 모자야. 갓이라고 불러.

■ 상대방에게 궁금한 내용에 대한 설명을 요청할 때는 '설명하다, 말하다'의 의미를 가지는 동사 'explain', 'tell' 또는 'give information' 등의 표현을 사용하여 'Could/Can you explain 의문사절?', 'Could/Can you tell me more about ~?'라고 표현한다. Could 대신 Would, Can, Will 등을 사용할 수 있고, 'Do you mind if I ask you to explain ~?'이라고 말할 수도 있다.

■ 상대방의 말을 듣고 추가로 더 많이 설명해 달라고 할 때는 'Could/Can you tell me more about it?'이라고 한다. 좀 더 공손하게 표현하여 Can 대신에 Could나 Would를 사용할 수도 있다. tell 대신에 explain을 써서 'Could/Can you explain that more, please?'라고 할 수 있다.

■ 상대방이 말하는 의도를 모르거나 사용하는 단어의 뜻을 몰라서 설명을 요청할 때 쓰는 표현은 'What does that mean?(그것이 무슨 뜻입니까?)', 'What do you mean by that?(그것이 무슨 뜻이니?)' 등이다. 상대방의 말을 알아듣지 못했을 때는 'I'm not following you.(잘 알아듣지 못하겠습니다.)', 'I don't get it.(제대로 이해를 못하겠어요.)' 등의 표현을 사용하여 상대방이 다시 설명을 하도록 요청할 수도 있다.

설명 요청하기

- Could/Can you explain what this is? 이게 무엇인지 설명해 줄 수 있니?
- Could/Can you tell me more about it? 그것에 대해 좀 더 말해 줄 수 있니?
- I think I need some more information about it. 그것에 대해 정보가 더 필요한 것 같아.
- Could you give me more information? 좀 더 정보를 주시겠습니까?
- Could you be more specific? 좀 더 구체적으로 말해 주시겠습니까?
- What is the meaning of that exactly? 그게 정확하게 무슨 뜻입니까?

핵심 Check

2. 다음 대화를 자연스러운 순서로 배열하시오.

B: Excuse me, I'd like to use a copy machine.

(A) Sure. Press the button for double-sided copies, and then press the start button.

(B) Could you explain how to make double-sided copies?

(C) O.K. You can use this machine.

B: Thank you.

➡ _____

Listen & Speak 1 A-2

B: Look over there. ❶I wonder why there are so many people waiting in line.

G: They're waiting to ❷get into the new bakery there.

B: Why? Is ❸it famous?

G: Yes. ❸It was on a TV program.

B: Really? We should try their bread then.

G: Sure.

B: 저기 좀 봐. 왜 저렇게 많은 사람들이 줄을 서서 기다리고 있는지 궁금하네.

G: 새로 생긴 제과점에 들어가려고 기다리고 있는 거야.

B: 왜? 유명한 곳이야?

G: 맞아. TV 프로그램에 나왔어.

B: 정말? 그럼 우리 저곳의 빵을 먹어 봐야겠다.

G: 그래.

❶ 궁금한 것을 묻는 표현으로 'I want to know why there are so many people waiting in line.' 등으로 바꾸어 쓸 수 있다.

❷ get into: ～에 들어가다

❸ It은 The new bakery를 가리킨다.

Check(√) True or False

(1) The boy wants to know why there are lots of people waiting in line.   T ☐ F ☐

(2) The new bakery became famous after it was on a TV program.   T ☐ F ☐

Communicate A

Jaden: Do you hear that? I wonder where that music is coming from.

Yuri: I think it's coming from over there. Do you want to go and ❶check it out?

Jaden: Yes, I love that strong beat. Is it ❷traditional Korean music?

Yuri: Yes, it's called nongak. It's a kind of ❸community band music.

Jaden: Nongak? ❹Could you explain a little bit more about it?

Yuri: It's traditionally used to ❺cheer up farmers and ❻wish for a good harvest.

Jaden: I see. Look! Some people are dancing to the rhythm.

Yuri: Yes, that's a big part of nongak. Dancing together completes the music.

Jaden: Let's join them.

Yuri: Sure. Why not?

Jaden: 저거 들리니? 저 음악이 어디서 오는 것인지 궁금하네.

유리: 저기서 나오는 것 같은데. 가서 확인해 볼래?

Jaden: 그래. 저 강한 비트가 마음에 들어. 이게 한국의 전통 음악이니?

유리: 맞아. 농악이라고 해. 공동체 악단 음악의 한 종류야.

Jaden: 농악? 그것에 대해 좀 더 설명해 줄래?

유리: 그건 전통적으로 농부들의 힘을 북돋아 주고 풍년을 기원하기 위해 사용되었어.

Jaden: 그렇구나. 봐! 몇몇 사람들이 리듬에 맞춰 춤추고 있어.

유리: 그래, 그게 농악의 큰 부분이야. 함께 춤추는 것이 음악을 완성하지.

Jaden: 저들과 함께 하자.

유리: 물론이야. 왜 안 되겠어?

❶ check (something) out: ～을 확인하다, 조사하다   ❷ traditional: 전통적인   ❸ community: 지역 공동체

❹ 상대방에게 궁금한 내용에 대한 설명을 요청할 때 쓰는 표현으로 'Could you tell me a little bit more about it?' 등으로 바꾸어 쓸 수 있다.

❺ cheer up: 격려하다   ❻ wish for: ～을 기원하다

Check(√) True or False

(3) Jaden and Yuri are listening to nongak.   T ☐ F ☐

(4) The strong beat is a big part of nongak.   T ☐ F ☐

Listen & Speak 1 A-1

G: Wow, look at the ❶bridge in this ❷ad. I wonder where the photo was taken.

B: That's Gwangandaegyo in Busan.

G: How do you know that?

B: I went ❸there with my family last summer.

❶ bridge: 다리
❷ ad(= advertisement): 광고
❸ there는 Gwangandaegyo in Busan을 가리킨다.

Listen & Speak 2 A-1

W: Excuse me, ❶I'd like to ❷borrow ❸an audio guide.

M: Here you are.

W: ❹Could you explain how to use ❺it?

M: Sure. Press this button, and it'll tell you what to do.

❶ would like to ~: ~하고 싶다
❷ borrow: 빌리다
❸ audio guide: 음성 안내기
❹ 'Could you tell me how to use it?' 등으로 바꾸어 표현할 수 있다.
❺ it은 the audio guide를 가리킨다.

Listen & Speak 2 A-2

B: Are you going somewhere this summer?

G: I'm going to Jejudo to ❶walk along the Jeju Olle Trail.

B: The Jeju Olle Trail? Could you explain what ❷that is?

G: It's a long hiking ❸path around Jejudo.

B: Oh, I see. I hope you enjoy your trip!

❶ walk along: ~을 따라 걷다
❷ that은 the Jeju Olle Trail을 가리킨다.
❸ path: 길

Progress Check 1

W: Look over there. ❶I wonder why there are so many cars on the road.

M: Lots of people are ❷going on vacation this weekend.

W: Really? Then, ❸why don't we go somewhere, too?

M: O.K.

❶ 궁금한 것을 묻는 표현으로 'Could you tell me why there are so many cars on the road?'로 바꾸어 표현할 수 있다.
❷ go on vacation: 휴가를 가다
❸ why don't we ~? = how about ~? = what about ~? = ~하는 게 어때?

Progress Check 2

B: Excuse me, I'd like to use a ❶copy machine.

W: O.K. You can use ❷this machine.

B: Could you explain how to ❸make double-sided copies?

W: Sure. ❹Press the button for double-sided copies, and then press the start button.

B: Thank you.

❶ copy machine: 복사기
❷ this machine은 복사기를 가리킨다.
❸ make double-sided copies: 양면 복사를 하다
❹ press: 누르다

● 다음 우리말과 일치하도록 빈칸에 알맞은 말을 쓰시오.

Listen & Speak 1 A-1

G: Wow, look at the _____ in this _____. I wonder _____
_____ _____ _____ _____.

B: That's Gwangandaegyo in Busan.

G: _____ do you know that?

B: I went there _____ my family _____ _____.

해석

G: 와, 이 광고에 나오는 다리 좀 봐. 어디에서 찍은 사진인지 궁금하네.
B: 부산의 광안대교야.
G: 그걸 어떻게 아니?
B: 작년 여름에 우리 가족들과 그곳에 갔었거든.

Listen & Speak 1 A-2

B: Look over there. _____ _____ _____ there are so many people _____ _____ _____.

G: They're waiting to _____ _____ the new bakery there.

B: Why? Is it _____?

G: Yes. It was _____ a TV program.

B: Really? We should _____ their bread then.

G: Sure.

B: 저기 좀 봐. 왜 저렇게 많은 사람들이 줄을 서서 기다리고 있는지 궁금하네.
G: 새로 생긴 제과점에 들어가려고 기다리고 있는 거야.
B: 왜? 유명한 곳이야?
G: 맞아. TV 프로그램에 나왔어.
B: 정말? 그럼 우리 저곳의 빵을 먹어 봐야겠다.
G: 그래.

Listen & Speak 2 A-1

W: Excuse me, _____ _____ _____ _____ an audio guide.

M: Here you are.

W: Could you _____ _____ _____ _____ _____?

M: Sure. _____ this button, and it'll tell you _____ _____ _____.

W: 실례합니다, 음성 가이드를 대여하고 싶은데요.
M: 여기 있습니다.
W: 어떻게 사용하는지 설명해 주실 수 있나요?
M: 물론이죠. 이 버튼을 누르면, 무엇을 해야 할지 말해 줄 겁니다.

Listen & Speak 2 A-2

B: Are you going _____ this summer?

G: I'm going to Jejudo to _____ _____ the Jeju Olle Trail.

B: The Jeju Olle Trail? _____ _____ _____ what that is?

G: It's a _____ _____ _____ around Jejudo.

B: Oh, I see. I hope you _____ _____ _____!

B: 이번 여름에 어디 갈 거야?
G: 제주 올레길을 따라 걸으러 제주도에 갈 거야.
B: 제주 올레길? 그게 무엇인지 설명해 줄래?
G: 제주도 둘레에 있는 긴 하이킹 코스야.
B: 오, 그렇구나. 즐거운 여행이 되길 바랄게!

Communicate A

Jaden: Do you hear that? _____ _____ _____ that music is coming from.

Yuri: I think it's coming from over there. Do you want to go and _____ _____ _____?

Jaden: Yes, I love that _____ _____. Is it _____ Korean music?

Yuri: Yes, it's called nongak. It's a kind of _____ band music.

Jaden: Nongak? _____ _____ _____ a little bit more about it?

Yuri: It's _____ used to _____ _____ farmers and wish for a _____ _____.

Jaden: I see. Look! Some people are dancing to the _____.

Yuri: Yes, that's a big part of nongak. Dancing together _____ the music.

Jaden: Let's join them.

Yuri: Sure. _____ _____?

Progress Check 1

W: Look over there. _____ _____ _____ _____ _____ _____ _____ _____ on the road.

M: Lots of people are _____ _____ _____ this weekend.

W: Really? Then, _____ _____ _____ go somewhere, too?

M: O.K.

Progress Check 2

B: Excuse me, I'd like to use a _____ _____.

W: O.K. You can use this machine.

B: Could you explain _____ _____ _____ _____ _____?

W: Sure. _____ the button for double-sided copies, and then _____ the start button.

B: Thank you.

[01~02] 다음 대화를 읽고 물음에 답하시오.

G: Wow, look at the bridge in this ad. (A)I wonder where was the photo taken.

B: That's Gwangandaegyo in Busan.

G: (B)그걸 어떻게 아니?

B: I went there with my family last summer.

01 위 대화의 밑줄 친 (A)를 어법상 바르게 고치시오.

➡ _____

02 위 대화의 밑줄 친 우리말 (B)를 5 단어로 영작하시오.

➡ _____

[03~04] 다음 대화를 읽고 물음에 답하시오.

Tom: Are you going somewhere this summer?

Jane: I'm going to Jejudo to walk along the Jeju Olle Trail.

Tom: The Jeju Olle Trail? (A)Could you explain what that is? (tell)

Jane: It's a long hiking path around Jejudo.

Tom: Oh, I see. I hope you enjoy your trip!

03 위 대화의 밑줄 친 (A)와 의미가 같도록 주어진 단어를 사용하여 바꿔 쓰시오.

➡ _____

04 위 대화의 내용과 일치하지 <u>않는</u> 것은?

① Jane은 이번 여름에 제주도에 갈 예정이다.

② Jane은 제주도에서 올레길을 걸을 것이다.

③ 올레길은 제주도 둘레에 있는 긴 하이킹 코스이다.

④ Tom은 Jane이 즐거운 여행을 하길 바란다.

⑤ Tom은 이미 올레길에 대해 잘 알고 있다.

서답형

01 다음 대화가 자연스럽게 이어지도록 순서대로 배열하시오.

> Look over there. I wonder why there are so many people waiting in line.

> (A) Sure.
> (B) Yes. It was on a TV program.
> (C) Why? Is it famous?
> (D) Really? We should try their bread then.
> (E) They're waiting to get into the new bakery there.

➡ _____

중요

02 다음 대화의 빈칸 (A)에 들어갈 말로 적절하지 않은 것은?

> W: Excuse me, I'd like to borrow an audio guide.
> M: Here you are.
> W: _____ (A) _____
> M: Sure. Press this button, and it'll tell you what to do.

① Could you explain how to use it?
② Can you tell me how to use it?
③ Could you give me more information about how to use it?
④ Could you be more specific about how to use it?
⑤ What do you mean by that?

[03~04] 다음 대화를 읽고 물음에 답하시오.

> G: Wow, ⓐlook at the bridge in this ad. I wonder where the photo ⓑtook.
> B: That's Gwangandaegyo ⓒin Busan.
> G: How do you know ⓓthat?
> B: I went ⓔthere with my family last summer.

서답형

03 위 대화의 밑줄 친 ⓐ~ⓔ 중 어법상 틀린 것을 찾아 바르게 고치시오.

➡ _____

중요

04 위 대화의 내용과 일치하지 않는 것은?

① The girl and the boy are watching the ad.
② There is a bridge in the ad.
③ The girl wants to know where the photo of the bridge was taken.
④ The boy visited Busan with his family last summer.
⑤ The girl wants to take a photo of the bridge.

[05~06] 다음 대화를 읽고 물음에 답하시오.

> Brian: Look over there. I wonder why there are so many people (A)[waited / waiting] in line.
> Sujin: They're waiting to (B)[get into / get out] the new bakery there.
> Brian: Why? Is it famous?
> Sujin: Yes. It was (C)[on / off] a TV program.
> Brian: Really? We should try their bread then.
> Sujin: Sure.

05 위 대화의 (A)~(C)에 들어갈 말로 바르게 짝지어진 것은?

	(A)	(B)	(C)
①	waited	get into	on
②	waited	get out	off
③	waiting	get out	on
④	waiting	get out	off
⑤	waiting	get into	on

06 위 대화의 내용과 일치하지 <u>않는</u> 것은?

① Brian은 왜 많은 사람들이 줄을 서서 기다리고 있는지 궁금하다.
② 새로 생긴 제과점에 들어가려고 많은 사람들이 줄을 서 있다.
③ 새로 생긴 제과점이 TV 프로그램에 나왔다.
④ Brian은 새로 생긴 제과점의 빵을 먹어 보고 싶다.
⑤ Brian과 수진은 함께 제과점 앞에서 줄을 서서 기다리고 있었다.

서답형

07 다음 대화가 자연스럽게 이어지도록 순서대로 배열하시오.

(A) Thank you.
(B) O.K. You can use this machine.
(C) Excuse me, I'd like to use a copy machine.
(D) Could you explain how to make double-sided copies?
(E) Sure. Press the button for double-sided copies, and then press the start button.

➡ _____

[08~09] 다음 대화를 읽고 물음에 답하시오.

Jaden: Do you hear that? (a)<u>I wonder where that music is coming from.</u>
Yuri: I think it's coming from over there. Do you want to go and check it out?
Jaden: Yes, I love that strong beat. Is it traditional Korean music?
Yuri: Yes, it's called nongak. It's a kind of community band music.
Jaden: Nongak? Could you explain a little bit more about it?
Yuri: It's traditionally used to cheer up farmers and wish for a good harvest.
Jaden: I see. Look! Some people are dancing to the rhythm.

Yuri: Yes, that's a big part of nongak. (b)<u>함께 춤추는 것이 음악을 완성하지</u>. (together)
Jaden: Let's join them.
Yuri: Sure. Why not?

08 위 대화의 밑줄 친 (a)와 바꾸어 쓸 수 있는 것을 고르시오.

① I don't know where that music is coming from.
② I'm sure where that music is coming from.
③ It's not certain where that music is coming from.
④ I want to know where that music is coming from.
⑤ I've been told where that music is coming from.

09 위 대화의 밑줄 친 (b)를 주어진 단어를 사용하여 5 단어로 영작하시오.

➡ _____

10 다음 짝지어진 대화가 <u>어색한</u> 것은?

① A: Look at the boy. I wonder why he is running.
   B: I think he is late for school.
② A: Look at her. I wonder why she looks surprised.
   B: I think she saw a celebrity.
③ A: Could you explain what this is?
   B: It's a traditional Korean hairpin. It's called a binyeo.
④ A: Can you tell me how to use this machine?
   B: Sure. Press this button first.
⑤ A: I want to know where the photo was taken.
   B: Thank you for your great efforts.

[01~02] 다음 대화를 읽고 물음에 답하시오.

W: Excuse me, I'd like to borrow an audio guide.

M: Here you are.

W: _____

M: Sure. Press this button, and it'll tell you what to do.

01 위 대화의 빈칸에 들어갈 말을 주어진 단어를 배열하여 영작하시오.

you / how / it / could / to / explain / use

➡ _____

02 What does the woman get to know after pressing the button?

➡ _____

03 다음 대화의 내용과 일치하도록 빈칸을 완성하시오.

Brian: Look over there. I wonder why there are so many people waiting in line.

Sujin: They're waiting to get into the new bakery there.

Brian: Why? Is it famous?

Sujin: Yes. It was on a TV program.

Brian: Really? We should try their bread then.

Sujin: Sure.

Brian and Sujin saw many people (A)_____ in front of (B)_____. People wanted to (C)_____ there. The new bakery was so popular because (D)_____. Brian and Sujin wanted to try its bread together.

[04~05] 다음 대화를 읽고 물음에 답하시오.

Jaden: Do you hear that? I wonder where that music is coming from.

Yuri: I think it's coming from over there. Do you want to go and check it out?

Jaden: Yes, I love that strong beat. Is it traditional Korean music?

Yuri: Yes, it's called nongak. It's a kind of community band music.

Jaden: Nongak? Could you explain a little bit more about it?

Yuri: It's traditionally used to cheer up farmers and wish for a good harvest.

Jaden: I see. Look! Some people are dancing to the rhythm.

Yuri: Yes, that's a big part of nongak. Dancing together completes the music.

Jaden: Let's join them.

Yuri: Sure. Why not?

04 위 대화를 읽고 빈칸에 알맞은 말을 써 넣으시오.

VISIT Korea

About Korea | **Culture** | Food | Travel | More

Nongak ...
• is a community ___(1)___ music
• has ___(2)___ beats
• cheers up ___(3)___
• wishes for a good ___(4)___

➡ (1) _____ (2) _____ (3) _____
(4) _____

05 What are Jaden and Yuri going to do after the conversation?

➡ _____
_____

Grammar

① '과거완료' had + 과거분사

- Until then, I **had** only **seen** black-and-white photos of haenyeo.
그때까지, 나는 흑백 사진 속의 해녀만 보았었다.

그녀는 다섯 시간이 넘도록 물속에 있은 후에도 계속 웃었다.
- She kept laughing even after she **had been** in the water for over five hours.

■ 과거완료시제는 'had+과거분사' 형태로 표현하며, 과거의 어느 시점을 기준으로 그 이전에 일어난 동작이나 상태를 나타낸다.

   • Somi went shopping at the local market after she **had gone** swimming at Hyeopjae Beach.
   소미는 협재 해변으로 수영하러 간 후, 지역 시장으로 쇼핑하러 갔다.

■ 과거의 특정 시점을 기준으로 그 이전에 일어난 동작의 완료, 경험, 계속, 결과를 나타낸다.

   (1) 완료: '막 ~했었다'는 의미로 과거 이전에 시작된 동작이 과거의 어느 시점에 완료된 일을 나타낸다. 보통 already, yet 등의 부사와 함께 쓰인다.

   • When I arrived, the class **had** already **begun**. 내가 도착했을 때, 수업이 벌써 시작됐다.

   (2) 경험: '~한 적이 있었다'는 의미로 과거 이전부터 과거의 어느 시점까지의 경험을 나타낸다. 보통 never, ever, once, twice, before 등의 부사(구)와 함께 쓰인다.

   • Barbara recognized the suspect immediately, for she **had met** him online before.
   Barbara는 그 용의자를 즉시 알아봤는데, 전에 온라인상에서 그를 만난 적이 있었기 때문이었다.

   (3) 결과: '(과거 이전에) ~해서, 그 결과 …했다'는 의미로 과거 이전의 동작이 과거의 어느 시점의 결과에 영향을 미치는 것을 나타낸다.

   • He **had gone** to work when I called. 내가 전화했을 때, 그는 (이미) 출근했다.

   (4) 계속: '계속 ~하고 있었다'는 의미로 과거 이전부터 과거의 어느 시점까지 계속되는 동작이나 상태를 나타낸다. 보통 since, for 등과 함께 쓰인다.

   • Tiffany **had waited** for her brother for 2 years when he returned.
   그녀의 오빠가 돌아왔을 때, Tiffany는 오빠를 2년 동안이나 기다렸었다.

■ 부정문은 'had+not[never]+과거분사', 의문문은 'Had+주어+과거분사 ~?', 과거 어느 시점을 기준으로 전부터 진행 중인 동작을 강조할 때는 과거완료진행형 'had+been+V-ing'을 쓴다.

   • She **had never won** an Academy Award by then. 그녀는 그 때까지 아카데미상을 탄 적이 없었다.

   • **Had they met** the director before? 그들이 전에 감독을 만난 적이 있었나요?

   • I **had been watching** a movie until you came to see me. 당신이 나를 보러올 때까지 나는 영화를 보고 있었다.

핵심 Check

1. 괄호 안에서 알맞은 말을 고르시오.

   (1) My family (has / had) lived in Seoul before we moved to Busan.

   (2) Suji had never seen wild animals until she (visits / visited) the zoo.

② 간접의문문

> • They didn't understand **why I wanted to take their pictures.**
> 그들은 내가 왜 그들의 사진을 찍으려고 하는지 이해하지 못했다.
>
> • Please tell us **what you're planning to do in the future.**
> 앞으로 계획하고 있는 것에 대해 말씀해 주세요.

■ 간접의문문은 의문문이 다른 문장의 일부가 된 형태로 '의문사+주어+동사' 형태로 쓰며, 이때 의문사가 접속사 역할을 한다.

• I want to know. + Where is he from?

→ I want to know **where he is from.** 나는 그가 어디에서 왔는지 알고 싶다.

• I wonder. + Why did she leave so early?

→ I wonder **why she left so early.** 나는 그녀가 왜 그렇게 빨리 떠났는지 궁금하다.

■ 의문문의 '동사+주어'의 어순이, 간접의문문에서 '주어+동사'의 어순이 되지만, 의문사가 주어인 의문문은 어순의 변화가 생길 수 없다.

• My teacher will tell us. + Who called the police?

→ My teacher will tell us **who called the police.**
나의 선생님은 누가 경찰에게 전화를 했는지 우리에게 말해 줄 것이다.

■ 의문사가 없는 경우, if 또는 **whether**가 '~인지 (아닌지)'라는 의미의 명사절을 이끈다.

• I don't know. + Does she like me?

→ I don't know **if[whether] she likes me.** 나는 그녀가 나를 좋아하는지 알지 못한다.

• Tell us. + Is the lady married or not?

→ Tell us **if[whether] the lady is married or not.** 그 숙녀분이 결혼했는지 안 했는지를 우리에게 말해 주시오.

■ 생각이나 추측, 상상, 믿음 등을 나타내는 동사들(think, believe, guess, suppose, imagine)이 쓰인 문장에서 의문사가 이끄는 간접의문문이 목적어가 될 때, 간접의문문의 의문사를 문장 맨 앞으로 보낸다. 이 경우, 의문사가 문두로 가도, 어순은 '주어+동사'이다.

• Do you believe? + What does he have in his bag?

→ **What** do you believe **he has in his bag?** 당신은 그의 가방 속에 그가 무엇을 가지고 있다고 생각합니까?

• Do you think? + Who is going to marry you?

→ **Who** do you think **is going to marry you?** 당신은 누가 당신과 결혼할 것이라고 생각합니까?

핵심 Check

2. 다음 문장에서 어법상 틀린 부분을 찾아 바르게 고쳐 쓰시오.

(1) I wonder when will she make us the cookie. ➡ _____

(2) Nobody knows why was Sarah so upset. ➡ _____

01 다음 빈칸에 들어갈 말로 알맞은 것은?

> Parker was sure he _____ his laptop on the table last night, but he couldn't find it.

① put　　　　② puts　　　　③ has put
④ to put　　　⑤ had put

02 다음 두 문장을 한 문장으로 바꿔 쓸 때, 빈칸에 들어갈 말로 가장 적절한 것은?

> • Does Andy know?
> • Is that bus going to the airport?
> → Does Andy know _____ that bus is going to the airport?

① where　　② but　　③ if　　④ how　　⑤ so

03 다음 밑줄 친 부분 중 어법상 옳은 것을 고르시오.

① The old man had lived in the town for 40 years until now.
② The plane has already taken off when I reached the airport.
③ The police had found his wallet that was left under the desk.
④ She opened the box that Miles had sent a week before.
⑤ Nora has gone to London before her husband came back.

04 다음 두 문장을 간접의문문을 이용하여 한 문장으로 만들 때, 빈칸에 알맞은 말을 써 넣으시오.

(1) The reporter asked.
　　How did she become interested in taking photos?
　　➡ The reporter _____ _____ _____ _____ _____ in
　　taking photos.

(2) Could you tell us?
　　What is so special about haenyeo?
　　➡ Could you _____ _____ _____ _____ _____ ➡
　　_____ about haenyeo?

01 밑줄 친 부분이 어법상 **어색한** 것은?

① After all the animals <u>had left</u> the burning woods, she felt relieved.
② The violinist <u>played</u> such a beautiful song that the audience gave her an endless applause that night.
③ Lucy asked the man how to fix the phone that <u>has broken</u> down.
④ The professor <u>had</u> just <u>left</u> the hall when the politician appeared.
⑤ Caroline ate the cookies that her grandma <u>had made</u> for her.

[02~03] 다음 우리말을 어법상 알맞게 영작한 것을 고르시오.

02

> 그게 무엇인지 설명해 주시겠어요?

① Could you explain that what it is?
② Could you explain that what that is?
③ Could you explain what is that?
④ Could you explain that what is that?
⑤ Could you explain what that is?

03 중요

> 왜 저렇게 많은 사람들이 줄을 서서 기다리고 있는지 궁금하다.

① I wonder why so many people there waiting in line.
② I wonder why are there so many people waiting in line.
③ I wonder why do so many people are waiting in line.
④ I wonder why there are so many people waiting in line.
⑤ I wonder why there are so many people are waiting in line.

[04~05] 다음 중 어법상 옳은 것을 고르시오.

04 ① Jinsu had read the article about the history of Jeju for the last 3 years.
② William lived in New York before he had moved to San Francisco.
③ Kevin required that Minsu had completed the report.
④ He lost the watch which he had bought the day before.
⑤ I am hungry since I had not eaten anything so far.

05 중요 ① Could you tell us more about what so special is about haenyeo?
② Does Julie know which subject do I like?
③ Do you imagine how old she is?
④ Tell me what is your favorite food.
⑤ Do you want to ask your English teacher what the sentence means?

서답형

06 다음 문장에서 어법상 **어색한** 단어 한 개를 찾아서 고치시오.

> It had been raining since Miranda went to Spain to learn tango.

_____ ➡ _____

07 다음 두 문장을 의미가 같도록 한 문장으로 바꿔 쓸 때 적절하지 않은 것은?

① I'd like to know. + When did Louise apply for the scholarship?
→ I'd like to know when Louise applied for the scholarship.

② May I ask you? + How much are the souvenir photos?
→ May I ask you how much the souvenir photos are?

③ David asked Emma. + Why was she angry with him?
→ David asked Emma why she was angry with him.

④ Could you tell us? + What did Frank buy at the mall?
→ Could you tell us what Frank bought at the mall?

⑤ Susan is wondering. + Who took away her kids' toys?
→ Susan is wondering who her kids' toys took away.

08 다음 중 밑줄 친 과거완료의 용법이 〈보기〉와 같은 것은?

┌─ 보기 ─┐
He had already found out the secret of the mystery cube when I asked him.
└────────┘

① Tiffany had lived in Busan for 7 months before she moved to Daegu.

② Anna had never been fat by the time she started learning swimming.

③ My cousin had been sick in bed for a week when I visited him.

④ I didn't know how long he had waited for me at the gate the other day.

⑤ Jordan had not finished the work when everyone was about to go out.

09 다음 중 밑줄 친 부분의 쓰임이 〈보기〉와 같은 것은?

┌─ 보기 ─┐
Chanho should not miss such a good opportunity if he wants to win the game.
└────────┘

① Does anybody know if the handsome guy over there has a girlfriend?

② I'm sure the company will succeed if it expands their market in Asia.

③ All of us were not sure if Peter's answer was right or wrong.

④ Taste the food to determine if more salt is required.

⑤ Sarah wondered if Ted would come to the party without the invitation.

10 다음 두 문장을 한 문장으로 만들 때 가장 적절한 것은?

┌────────────────────────┐
• Do you think?
• Why did the haenyeo look happy?
└────────────────────────┘

① Do you think why did the haenyeo look happy?

② Do you think why the haenyeo looked happy?

③ Why do you think did the haenyeo look happy?

④ Why do you think the haenyeo looked happy?

⑤ Why do you think the haenyeo did looked happy?

[11~12] 다음 중 어법상 옳은 문장은?

11
① Cecilia had lost the necklace which I bought for her.
② You can't see the snowman anymore as it had melted this morning.
③ When we were about to leave home, my uncle had already arrived.
④ The passengers have been seated before the plane took off.
⑤ William has never seen the wallaby until he visited Australia.

12 중요
① Do you think where Clara first met her husband?
② Could you please tell us what did your action mean?
③ I wonder whether did anyone see the boy walking along the beach.
④ Do you know how the writer of these books old is?
⑤ Let me know what they are drinking.

서답형
[13~14] 우리말과 일치하도록 괄호 안에 주어진 어구를 바르게 배열하시오.

13

기자는 많은 고객들이 돈가스를 먹으려고 줄을 서서 상당한 시간을 보냈다고 말했다. (돈가스: pork cutlet)
→ The reporter said that (lining up, time, had spent, in order to, quite a long, many, eat, customers, pork cutlet).

➡ The reporter said that _____
_____
_____.

14

당신은 그 절들이 왜 유명하다고 생각합니까?
(the temples, you, famous, why, are, do, think)?

➡ _____

서답형
15 다음 그림을 보고 자연스러운 문장이 되도록 괄호 안에 주어진 어구를 바르게 배열하여 빈칸을 완성하시오.

(1)

➡ Jiho _____
_____. (fly, could, asked, people, in the sky, his sister, why, not)

(2)

➡ Pooh _____
_____. (a hive, told, touched, he, that morning, his friend, had, that)

01 다음 우리말과 일치하도록 괄호 안에 주어진 어구를 바르게 배열하여 문장을 완성하시오.

(1) 그 기업은 몇몇 프랑스인들이 전에 훔쳐갔었던 한국의 많은 보물들을 수집했다.

➡ The company _____

_____.

(before, French, stolen, collected, many, that, had, Korean treasures, some)

(2) 수민이는 어떻게 자신이 해녀를 전 세계적으로 홍보할 수 있을지 궁금하다.

➡ Sumin _____

_____. (the haenyeo, wonders, can, worldwide, promote, how, she)

(3) Jim이 출장에서 돌아왔을 때, 그는 누군가가 자신의 집에 침입했었던 것을 발견했다.

➡ When Jim came back from a business trip, _____

_____. (his house, found, broken, he, someone, into, had)

(4) 그 사진 작가가 어디에서 이 사진들을 찍었는지 추측할 수 있습니까?

➡ _____

these pictures? (guess, took, can, the photographer, where, you)

02 다음 〈보기〉와 같이 간접의문문을 활용하여 빈칸을 채우시오.

┌─ 보기 ─────────────────┐
When does the post office close?
→ Do you know when the post office closes?
└───────────────────────┘

(1) How could they get to the meeting on time?

➡ Do you know _____

_____?

(2) Which boy did the girl next to Jane choose at the blind date?

➡ Can you tell me _____

_____?

(3) Hasn't Shrek learned German yet?

➡ Do you know _____

_____?

(4) Where did Alex find the baby tiger?

➡ Let her figure out _____

_____.

(5) How old does the new employee look?

➡ How old do you think _____

_____?

03 다음 사진을 참고하여 우리말에 맞게, 괄호 안에 주어진 어구를 활용하되, 과거완료시제를 써서 빈칸을 채우시오.

그 날까지 나는 흑백 사진들 속의 아주 지친 모습의 해녀만 봤었다. (who, haenyeo, photos, only see, black-and-white photos)

➡ Until the day, I _____

_____

looked very tired.

04 다음 문장에서 어법상 어색한 것을 바르게 고쳐 다시 쓰시오.

(1) Can you tell me where was the magician when he disappeared?

➡ _____

_____

(2) Does the young student know how the hotel is far?

➡ _____

_____

(3) Do you know could I take pictures of haenyeo?

➡ _____

_____

(4) They didn't understand why did the girl want to take their pictures.

➡ _____

_____

(5) Tell me what did Zin Kim promise the haenyeo.

➡ _____

_____

(6) I wonder why is Jejudo not suitable for farming.

➡ _____

_____

05 주어진 우리말을 〈조건〉에 맞게 영작하시오.

┌─── 조건 ───
│ 1. 부정 의미의 과거완료시제를 쓸 것.
│ 2. The haenyeo를 포함, 총 18 단어로 쓸 것.
│ 3. 숫자도 영어로 쓸 것.
│ 4. the photographer, think, her picture, pretty, until, that, she, take 등을 활용할 것.
│ 5. ago를 가장 마지막 단어로 할 것.
└

그 사진작가가 12년 전에 그녀의 사진을 찍을 때까지, 그 해녀는 자신이 예쁘다고 생각하지 않았었다.

➡ _____

_____

06 괄호 안에 주어진 어휘를 활용하여 글자 수대로 다음 우리말을 영작하시오.

(1) Tom은 해녀들이 어떤 호흡장치도 없이 어떻게 물속에 그렇게나 오래 머무를 수 있는지 궁금했다. (how, stay, wonder, so long, without, breathing devices, haenyeo, for, any, could, 16 단어)

➡ _____

_____

(2) 그들은 너무 많은 해양 생물을 채취하는 것이 바다를 어떻게 파괴할 수 있는지 연구하고 있다. (how, can, are, study, marine life, destroy, catching, too much, the ocean, 13 단어)

➡ _____

_____

(3) 마녀는 거울에게 세상에서 가장 아름다운 여자가 누구인지 물었다. (who, woman, the witch, in the world, beautiful, was, ask, the mirror, 14 단어)

➡ _____

_____

(4) 엄마 염소는 아기들이 늑대에게 언제 문을 열어 준 것인지 몰랐다. (when, to, the door, the mother goat, open, not know, the wolf, the babies, 15 단어)

➡ _____

_____

Reading

Haenyeo, Female Divers of Korea

For the past several years, the underwater photographer Zin Kim has promoted the culture of Jeju haenyeo worldwide. Haenyeo are Korean female divers who harvest seafood without any breathing devices. Their culture made UNESCO's Intangible Cultural Heritage list in 2016. At her studio last week, Zin Kim was interviewed about her experience of taking pictures of haenyeo.

Q. How did you become interested in taking photos of haenyeo?

One day, I happened to take pictures of a haenyeo. I was surprised to find that she was enjoying her job. Until then, I had only seen black-and-white photos of haenyeo who looked very tired. However, she kept laughing even after she had been in the water for over five hours. I realized then that I should take pictures of haenyeo.

Q. You take beautiful pictures of them, but isn't it difficult to take pictures of haenyeo?

At first, they didn't understand why I wanted to take their pictures. They didn't think they looked pretty in their wetsuits. So, I said to them, "You're very special. I want to show your culture to the world." They opened up to me then. Of course, I also promised them that I would make them look beautiful in my pictures.

female 여성의, 암컷의
past 지난간
several 몇몇의
underwater 수중의, 물속에서
photographer 사진작가
promote 홍보하다, 촉진하다
worldwide 세계적으로
breathe 호흡하다
intangible 무형의, 만질 수 없는
heritage 유산
experience 경험
happen to 우연히 ~하다
black-and-white (사진, TV 등) 흑백의
realize 깨닫다, 인식하다
wetsuit 잠수용 고무 옷

확인문제

- 다음 문장이 본문의 내용과 일치하면 T, 일치하지 않으면 F를 쓰시오.

1 Zin Kim is the underwater photographer. ☐

2 Haenyeo are Korean female divers who harvest seafood with breathing devices. ☐

3 At first, haenyeo understood why Zin Kim wanted to take their pictures. ☐

4 Haenyeo didn't think they looked pretty in their wetsuits. ☐

5 Zin Kim wants to show the culture of Korea to the world. ☐

Q. Could you tell us more about haenyeo? What's so special about them?

I can tell you three things. First, haenyeo are a symbol of strong women. Jejudo, which is a volcanic island, is not suitable for farming,
계속적 용법의 관계대명사. which가 Jejudo를 받아서 그에 대한 추가 설명을 덧붙이고 있다.
so many haenyeo have become the breadwinners for their families. Second, haenyeo form their own communities and help each other. For example, more-experienced haenyeo train less-experienced haenyeo.
more(부사)+experienced(형용사)가 haenyeo를 꾸며 주고 있음.   less(부사)+experienced(형용사)가 haenyeo를 꾸며 주고 있음.
Third, because they stay in the water without any breathing devices, haenyeo can't catch a lot of seafood. This is good for the underwater
be good for: ~에 좋다
environment. Catching too much marine life at one time in one place
동명사 주어   = It can destroy the ocean to catch too much marine life at one time
can destroy the ocean.   in one place.

Q. Lastly, please tell us what you're planning to do in the future.
'What are you planning to do ~?'라는 의문문이 tell의 직접목적어로 쓰여 간접의문문이 된 형태
I once attended an overseas exhibition with a couple of haenyeo
attended at(×)   2~3명[개]
to give a talk about their lives. When I finished my talk, one of the
to부정사의 부사적 용법(목적)
haenyeo held my hand tightly. She said to me, "Thank you so much.
= me by the
I've never known in my whole life that I was such a special person."
경험 용법   such+a+형용사+명사
She was crying with happiness. Everyone in the audience was deeply
moved. I can never forget that moment, so I'll continue to take pictures
= touched   = taking
of haenyeo. I want to tell more beautiful stories about them to many
tell은 to를 사용하여 3형식으로 바꿀 수 있다.
more people in the world.

 **확인문제**

● 다음 문장이 본문의 내용과 일치하면 T, 일치하지 <u>않으면</u> F를 쓰시오.

1 Many haenyeo have become the breadwinners for their families. ☐

2 Haenyeo can catch a lot of seafood at one time. ☐

3 Catching too much marine life at one time in one place can destroy the ocean. ☐

4 A couple of haenyeo attendeded an overseas exhibition and gave a talk about their lives. ☐

5 One of the haenyeo said that she had never known in her whole life that she was such a special person. ☐

---

volcanic 화산의, 화산 작용에 의한

suitable 적합한, 적절한

breadwinner 생계를 책임지는 사람, 가장

experienced 경험이 있는

marine 해양의, 바다의

once 한 번, 한때, 옛날

attend 참석하다

overseas 해외의

exhibition 전시회, 박람회

give a talk 강의하다, 연설하다

tightly 단단히, 꽉

audience 청중

● 우리말을 참고하여 빈칸에 알맞은 말을 쓰시오.

1 Haenyeo, _____ _____ of Korea

2 For the past several years, the _____ _____ Zin Kim _____ _____ the culture of Jeju haenyeo worldwide.

3 Haenyeo are Korean female divers who harvest seafood _____ _____ _____ _____.

4 Their culture _____ _____ _____ _____ _____ _____ in 2016.

5 At her studio last week, Zin Kim _____ _____ about her experience of taking pictures of haenyeo.

6 Q. How did you _____ _____ _____ taking photos of haenyeo?

7 One day, I _____ _____ take pictures of a haenyeo.

8 I _____ _____ _____ _____ that she was enjoying her job.

9 Until then, I had only seen black-and-white photos of haenyeo who _____ _____ _____.

10 However, she _____ _____ even after she had been in the water for over five hours.

11 I realized then that I _____ _____ pictures of haenyeo.

12 Q. You take beautiful pictures of them, but _____ _____ _____ to take pictures of haenyeo?

13 At first, they didn't understand _____ _____ _____ to take their pictures.

14 They didn't think they looked pretty _____ _____ _____.

15 So, I said to them, "You're _____ _____.

16 I want to _____ your culture _____ the world."

17 They _____ _____ to me then.

18 Of course, I also promised them that I would _____ _____ look _____ in my pictures.

1 해녀, 한국의 여성 잠수부

2 지난 몇 년 동안, 수중 사진작가 Zin Kim은 제주 해녀 문화를 전 세계에 홍보해 왔다.

3 해녀는 어떤 호흡 장치도 사용하지 않고 해산물을 채취하는 한국의 여성 잠수부들이다.

4 그들의 문화는 2016년에 유네스코 무형문화유산에 등재되었다.

5 지난주 그녀의 작업실에서, Zin Kim과 해녀의 사진을 찍는 그녀의 경험에 대해 인터뷰를 했다.

6 Q. 어떻게 해녀의 사진을 찍는 것에 관심을 가지게 되었나요?

7 어느 날, 저는 우연히 한 해녀의 사진을 찍게 되었어요.

8 저는 그녀가 자신의 일을 즐겁게 하는 것을 보고 놀랐습니다.

9 그때까지, 저는 흑백 사진 속의 아주 지친 모습의 해녀만 봐 왔죠.

10 하지만, 그녀는 다섯 시간이 넘도록 물속에 있은 후에도 계속 웃었어요.

11 저는 그때 해녀의 사진을 찍어야겠다고 깨달았어요.

12 Q. 작가님은 아름다운 해녀 사진들을 찍으시는데, 그들의 사진을 찍는 것이 어렵진 않으신가요?

13 처음에, 그들은 제가 왜 자신들의 사진을 찍으려고 하는지 이해하지 못했어요.

14 그들은 잠수복을 입은 자신들의 모습이 예뻐 보인다고 생각하지 않았으니까요.

15 그래서, 제가 그들에게 말했죠, "여러분은 아주 특별해요.

16 저는 여러분의 문화를 세계에 알리고 싶어요."

17 그들은 그때 제게 마음을 열었어요.

18 물론, 저 또한 그들에게 제 사진 속에서 그들을 아름답게 보이도록 하겠다고 약속했지요.

19 Q. Could you tell us _____ _____ haenyeo?

20 What's _____ _____ about them?

21 I _____ _____ _____ three things.

22 First, haenyeo are a symbol of _____ _____.

23 Jejudo, which is a volcanic island, _____ _____ _____ _____ farming, so many haenyeo have become _____ _____ _____ their families.

24 Second, haenyeo _____ their own communities and help _____ _____.

25 For example, _____ haenyeo train _____ haenyeo.

26 Third, because they stay in the water _____ any breathing devices, haenyeo _____ _____ a lot of seafood.

27 This _____ _____ _____ the underwater environment.

28 Catching too much marine life _____ _____ _____ _____ _____ _____ can destroy the ocean.

29 Q. Lastly, please tell us what you're _____ _____ _____ in the future.

30 I once _____ an overseas exhibition with a couple of haenyeo to _____ _____ _____ about their lives.

31 When I finished my talk, one of the haenyeo _____ _____ _____ tightly.

32 She said to me, "Thank you _____ _____."

33 I've never known in my whole life that I was _____ _____ _____ _____."

34 She was crying _____ _____.

35 Everyone in the audience _____ _____ _____.

36 I _____ _____ _____ that moment, so I'll continue to take pictures of haenyeo.

37 I want to tell _____ _____ _____ _____ _____ to many more people in the world.

19 Q. 해녀에 대해서 더 말씀해 주시겠어요?

20 그들은 무엇이 그렇게 특별한가요?

21 세 가지를 말씀 드릴게요.

22 첫 번째로, 해녀들은 강인한 여성의 상징이에요.

23 제주도는 화산섬이고, 이는 농사에 적합하지 않아서 많은 해녀들이 가족들의 생계비를 버는 가장이 되어 왔어요.

24 둘째로, 해녀들은 그들 자신의 공동체를 조직하고 서로 도와요.

25 예를 들어, 경험이 더 많은 해녀들이 경험이 적은 해녀들을 훈련시키지요.

26 세 번째로, 어떤 호흡 장치도 사용하지 않고 물속에 머물기 때문에, 해녀는 많은 해산물을 채취할 수가 없어요.

27 이것은 수중 환경에 좋은 것이지요.

28 한 번에 한 장소에서 너무 많은 해양생물을 채취하는 것은 바다를 파괴할 수 있으니까요.

29 Q. 마지막으로, 앞으로 계획하고 있는 것에 대해 말씀해 주세요.

30 예전에 두 명의 해녀들과 함께 그들의 삶에 대해 이야기하기 위해 해외에서 열리는 박람회에 참가한 적이 있어요.

31 제가 연설을 마쳤을 때, 해녀 중 한 분이 제 손을 꼭 잡았어요.

32 그분이 말했죠, "너무 고마워.

33 내 평생 내가 이렇게 특별한 사람이라는 걸 미처 알지 못했어."

34 그녀는 행복해서 울고 있었어요.

35 청중들 모두가 깊은 감동을 받았어요.

36 전 그 순간을 절대 잊을 수가 없기 때문에 해녀의 사진을 계속해서 찍을 거예요.

37 저는 그들에 대한 더 많은 아름다운 이야기들을 세계의 더 많은 사람들에게 알려 주고 싶어요.

● 우리말을 참고하여 본문을 영작하시오.

1 해녀, 한국의 여성 잠수부
➡ _____

2 지난 몇 년 동안, 수중 사진작가 Zin Kim은 제주 해녀 문화를 전 세계에 홍보해 왔다.
➡ _____
_____

3 해녀는 어떤 호흡 장치도 사용하지 않고 해산물을 채취하는 한국의 여성 잠수부들이다.
➡ _____

4 그들의 문화는 2016년에 유네스코 무형문화유산에 등재되었다.
➡ _____

5 지난주 그녀의 작업실에서, Zin Kim과 해녀의 사진을 찍는 그녀의 경험에 대해 인터뷰를 했다.
➡ _____

6 Q. 어떻게 해녀의 사진을 찍는 것에 관심을 가지게 되었나요?
➡ _____

7 어느 날, 저는 우연히 한 해녀의 사진을 찍게 되었어요.
➡ _____

8 저는 그녀가 자신의 일을 즐겁게 하는 것을 보고 놀랐습니다.
➡ _____

9 그때까지, 저는 흑백 사진 속의 아주 지친 모습의 해녀만 봐 왔죠.
➡ _____

10 하지만, 그녀는 다섯 시간이 넘도록 물속에 있은 후에도 계속 웃었어요.
➡ _____

11 저는 그때 해녀의 사진을 찍어야겠다고 깨달았어요.
➡ _____

12 Q. 작가님은 아름다운 해녀 사진들을 찍으시는데, 그들의 사진을 찍는 것이 어렵진 않으신가요?
➡ _____

13 처음에, 그들은 제가 왜 자신들의 사진을 찍으려고 하는지 이해하지 못했어요.
➡ _____

14 그들은 잠수복을 입은 자신들의 모습이 예뻐 보인다고 생각하지 않았으니까요.
➡ _____

15 그래서, 제가 그들에게 말했죠, "여러분들은 아주 특별해요.
➡ _____

16 저는 여러분의 문화를 세계에 알리고 싶어요."
➡ _____

17 그들은 그때 제게 마음을 열었어요.
➡ _____

18 물론, 저 또한 그들에게 제 사진 속에서 그들을 아름답게 보이도록 하겠다고 약속했지요.
➡ _____

19 Q. 해녀에 대해서 더 말씀해 주시겠어요?
➡ _____

20 그들은 무엇이 그렇게 특별한가요?
➡ _____

21 세 가지를 말씀 드릴게요.
➡ _____

22 첫 번째로, 해녀들은 강인한 여성의 상징이에요.
➡ _____

23 제주도는 화산섬이고, 이는 농사에 적합하지 않아서 많은 해녀들이 가족들의 생계비를 버는 가장이 되어 왔어요.
➡ _____
_____

24 둘째로, 해녀들은 그들 자신의 공동체를 조직하고 서로 도와요.
➡ _____

25 예를 들어, 경험이 더 많은 해녀들이 경험이 적은 해녀들을 훈련시키지요.
➡ _____

26 세 번째로, 어떤 호흡 장치도 사용하지 않고 물속에 머물기 때문에, 해녀는 많은 해산물을 채취할 수가 없어요.
➡ _____
_____

27 이것은 수중 환경에 좋은 것이지요.
➡ _____

28 한 번에 한 장소에서 너무 많은 해양생물을 채취하는 것은 바다를 파괴할 수 있으니까요.
➡ _____

29 Q. 마지막으로, 앞으로 계획하고 있는 것에 대해 말씀해 주세요.
➡ _____

30 예전에 두 명의 해녀들과 함께 그들의 삶에 대해 이야기하기 위해 해외에서 열리는 박람회에 참가한 적이 있어요.
➡ _____

31 제가 연설을 마쳤을 때, 해녀 중 한 분이 제 손을 꼭 잡았어요.
➡ _____

32 그분이 말했죠, "너무 고마워.
➡ _____

33 내 평생 내가 이렇게 특별한 사람이라는 걸 미처 알지 못했어."
➡ _____

34 그녀는 행복해서 울고 있었어요.
➡ _____

35 청중들 모두가 깊은 감동을 받았어요.
➡ _____

36 전 그 순간을 절대 잊을 수가 없기 때문에 해녀의 사진을 계속해서 찍을 거예요.
➡ _____

37 저는 그들에 대한 더 많은 아름다운 이야기들을 세계의 더 많은 사람들에게 알려 주고 싶어요.
➡ _____

[01~03] 다음 글을 읽고 물음에 답하시오.

For the past several years, the underwater photographer Zin Kim has promoted the culture of Jeju haenyeo worldwide. Haenyeo are Korean female divers ⓐ harvest seafood without any breathing devices. Their culture ⓑmade UNESCO's Intangible Cultural Heritage list in 2016. At her studio last week, Zin Kim was interviewed about her experience of taking pictures of haenyeo.

01 위 글의 빈칸 ⓐ에 들어갈 알맞은 말을 <u>모두</u> 고르시오.

① which   ② who   ③ what
④ that   ⑤ whom

02 위 글의 밑줄 친 ⓑmade와 같은 의미로 쓰인 것을 고르시오.

① She made her own clothes.
② He always made me laugh.
③ She made him her assistant.
④ They made me repeat the whole story.
⑤ Jones made a professor in five years.

03 According to the passage, which is NOT true?

① Zin Kim is an underwater photographer.
② Zin Kim has promoted the culture of Jeju haenyeo worldwide for the past several years.
③ Haenyeo are Korean female divers.
④ Haenyeo harvest seafood with the help of breathing devices.
⑤ Haenyeo's culture has been UNESCO's Intangible Cultural Heritage since 2016.

[04~06] 다음 글을 읽고 물음에 답하시오.

Q. _____ⓐ_____

One day, I happened to take pictures of a haenyeo. I was surprised to find that she was enjoying her job. Until then, I had only seen black-and-white photos of haenyeo who looked very tired. However, she kept _____ⓑ_____ even after she ⓒhad been in the water for over five hours. I realized then that I should take pictures of haenyeo.

04 위 글의 빈칸 ⓐ에 들어갈 알맞은 질문을 고르시오.

① Could you tell us more about haenyeo?
② What's so special about haenyeo?
③ How did you become interested in taking photos of haenyeo?
④ What do you want to do in the future?
⑤ Is it difficult to take pictures of haenyeo?

서답형
05 위 글의 빈칸 ⓑ에 laugh를 알맞은 형태로 쓰시오.

➡ _____

06 아래 〈보기〉에서 위 글의 밑줄 친 ⓒhad been과 과거완료의 용법이 <u>다른</u> 것의 개수를 고르시오.

┌─── 보기 ───┐
① I <u>had</u> just <u>finished</u> my homework when she came.
② He <u>had lived</u> there for ten years when his father died.
③ I found that I <u>had lost</u> my wallet on the subway.
④ The train <u>had</u> already <u>left</u> when he got to the station.
⑤ They <u>had</u> never <u>met</u> a student like him before.
└────────────┘

① 1개   ② 2개   ③ 3개   ④ 4개   ⑤ 5개

[07~09] 다음 글을 읽고 물음에 답하시오.

Q. **You take beautiful pictures of them, but isn't it difficult to take pictures of haenyeo?**

(①) At first, ⓐ그들은 제가 왜 자신들의 사진을 찍으려고 하는지 이해하지 못했어요. (②) They didn't think they looked pretty in their wetsuits. (③) So, I said to them, "You're very special. (④) I want to show your culture to the world." (⑤) Of course, I also promised them that I would make them look beautiful in my pictures.

07 위 글의 흐름으로 보아, 주어진 문장이 들어가기에 가장 적절한 곳은?

They opened up to me then.

①　　②　　③　　④　　⑤

08 위 글의 제목으로 알맞은 것을 고르시오.

① Why Do You Want to Take Pictures of Haenyeo?
② Wow! Haenyeo Let Me Show Their Culture through Pictures!
③ Why Is It Important to Show Haenyeo's Culture?
④ Are You Interested in Taking Pictures of Haenyeo?
⑤ How Can You Make Haenyeo Look Beautiful in Your Pictures?

09 위 글의 밑줄 친 ⓐ의 우리말에 맞게 주어진 어휘를 이용하여 10 단어로 영작하시오.

why, their pictures

➡ _____
_____

[10~13] 다음 글을 읽고 물음에 답하시오.

Q. **Lastly, please tell us what you're planning to do in the future.**

I once (A)[attended / attended to] an overseas exhibition with a couple of haenyeo to give a talk about their lives. When I finished my talk, one of the haenyeo held my hand tightly. She said to me, "Thank you so much. ⓐI've never known in my whole life that I was (B)[so / such] a special person." She was crying with happiness. Everyone in the audience was deeply moved. I can never forget that moment, (C)[as / so] I'll continue to take pictures of haenyeo. I want to tell more beautiful stories about them to many more people in the world. <I: Zin Kim>

서답형
10 위 글의 괄호 (A)~(C)에서 문맥이나 어법상 알맞은 낱말을 골라 쓰시오.

➡ (A) _____ (B) _____ (C) _____

11 위 글의 분위기로 가장 알맞은 것을 고르시오.

① confusing　　② interesting
③ depressing　　④ boring
⑤ touching

12 Which question CANNOT be answered after reading the passage?

① With whom did Zin Kim attend an overseas exhibition?

② Why did Zin Kim attend an overseas exhibition?

③ When Zin Kim finished her talk, what did one of the haenyeo tell her?

④ How long has Zin Kim taken pictures of haenyeo?

⑤ What does Zin Kim want to tell to many more people in the world?

13 위 글의 밑줄 친 ⓐ의 현재완료와 용법이 같은 것을 모두 고르시오.

① I have just bought my watch.

② I have been to England twice.

③ Have you ever seen a panda?

④ Have you finished it yet?

⑤ Alice has lived in New York since January.

[14~17] 다음 글을 읽고 물음에 답하시오.

Q. Could you tell us more about haenyeo? What's so special about them?

I can tell you three things. First, haenyeo are a symbol of strong women. (A)Jejudo, that is a volcanic island, is not suitable for farming, so many haenyeo have become the ⓐ for their families. Second, haenyeo form their own communities and help each other. For example, more-experienced haenyeo train less-experienced haenyeo. Third, because they stay in the water without any breathing devices, haenyeo can't catch a lot of seafood. (B)This is good for the underwater environment. Catching too much marine life at one time in one place can destroy the ocean.

서답형

14 주어진 영영풀이를 참고하여 빈칸 ⓐ에 철자 b로 시작하는 단어를 쓰시오.

the people who earn the money that the family need for essential things

➡ _____

서답형

15 위 글의 밑줄 친 (A)에서 어법상 틀린 부분을 찾아 고치시오.

_____ ➡ _____

서답형

16 위 글의 밑줄 친 (B)This가 가리키는 것을 본문에서 찾아 쓰시오.

➡ _____

17 위 글의 주제로 알맞은 것을 고르시오.

① haenyeo as the subject of pictures

② what is special about haenyeo

③ haenyeo as a symbol of strong women

④ the hard lives of the breadwinners

⑤ the way haenyeo form their own communities

[18~21] 다음 글을 읽고 물음에 답하시오.

Q. ①You take beautiful pictures of them, but isn't it difficult to take pictures of haenyeo?

At first, ②they didn't understand why I wanted to take ③their pictures. They didn't think they looked pretty ⓐ their wetsuits. So, I said to ④them, "⑤You're very special. I want to show your culture ⓑ the world." They opened up to me then. Of course, ⓒI also promised them that I would make them looking beautiful in my pictures.

<I: Zin Kim>

18 위 글의 빈칸 ⓐ와 ⓑ에 들어갈 전치사가 바르게 짝지어진 것은?

	ⓐ	ⓑ			ⓐ	ⓑ
①	for	from		②	in	by
③	in	to		④	on	to
⑤	for	by				

19 밑줄 친 ①~⑤ 중에서 가리키는 대상이 나머지 넷과 다른 것은?

①   ②   ③   ④   ⑤

서답형

20 위 글의 밑줄 친 ⓒ에서 어법상 틀린 부분을 찾아 고치시오.

_____ ➡ _____

중요

21 자신들의 사진을 찍는 것에 대한 해녀들의 심경 변화로 가장 알맞은 것을 고르시오.

① hopeful → nervous
② delighted → upset
③ bored → agreeing
④ puzzled → consenting
⑤ confused → disappointed

[22~25] 다음 글을 읽고 물음에 답하시오.

Q. Could you tell us more about haenyeo? What's so special about them?

I can tell you three things. First, haenyeo are a symbol of strong women. (A)Jejudo, which is a volcanic island, is suitable for farming, so many haenyeo have become the breadwinners for their families. Second, haenyeo form their own communities and help each other. ____ⓐ____, more-experienced haenyeo train less-experienced haenyeo. Third, because they stay in the water without any (B)breathing devices, haenyeo can't catch a lot of seafood. This is good for the underwater environment. (C)Catching too much marine life at one time in one place can destroy the ocean.

22 위 글의 빈칸 ⓐ에 들어갈 알맞은 말을 고르시오.

① Therefore   ② However
③ For example   ④ Moreover
⑤ As a result

서답형

23 위 글의 밑줄 친 (A)에서 흐름상 어색한 부분을 찾아 고치시오.

_____ ➡ _____

중요

24 위 글의 밑줄 친 (B)breathing과 문법적 쓰임이 다른 것을 모두 고르시오.

① He is a walking dictionary.
② Where is my sleeping bag?
③ She is in the waiting room.
④ If you want to smoke, you need to go to a smoking room in the lobby.
⑤ Look at the dancing girl over there.

서답형

25 위 글의 밑줄 친 (C)를 다음과 같이 바꿔 쓸 때 빈칸에 들어갈 알맞은 말을 두 단어로 쓰시오.

➡ It can destroy the ocean _____ too much marine life at one time in one place.

[01~03] 다음 글을 읽고 물음에 답하시오.

> **Q. How did you become interested in taking photos of haenyeo?**
> ⓐOne day, I happened to take pictures of a haenyeo. I was surprised to find that she was enjoying her job. ⓑUntil then, I have only seen black-and-white photos of haenyeo who looked very tired. However, she kept laughing even after she had been in the water for over five hours. I realized then that I should take pictures of haenyeo. <I: Zin Kim>

01 위 글의 밑줄 친 ⓐ를 다음과 같이 바꿔 쓸 때 빈칸에 들어갈 알맞은 말을 두 단어로 쓰시오.

➡ One day, I took pictures of a haenyeo _____ (또는 _____).

02 위 글의 밑줄 친 ⓑ에서 어법상 틀린 부분을 찾아 고치시오.

_____ ➡ _____

03 다음 빈칸 (A)와 (B)에 알맞은 단어를 넣어 Zin Kim이 해녀의 사진을 찍는 것에 관심을 가지게 된 계기를 완성하시오.

> When Zin Kim happened to take pictures of a haenyeo, she was (A)_____ her job and kept (B)_____ even after she had been in the water for over five hours. Zin Kim was surprised at that and decided to take pictures of haenyeo.

[04~06] 다음 글을 읽고 물음에 답하시오.

> (A)[During / For] the past several years, the underwater photographer Zin Kim has promoted the culture of Jeju haenyeo worldwide. Haenyeo are Korean female divers who harvest seafood without (B)[any / no] breathing devices. ⓐTheir culture made UNESCO's (C)[Tangible / Intangible] Cultural Heritage list in ⓑ2016. At her studio last week, Zin Kim was interviewed about her experience of taking pictures of haenyeo.

04 위 글의 괄호 (A)~(C)에서 문맥이나 어법상 알맞은 낱말을 골라 쓰시오.

➡ (A) _____ (B) _____ (C) _____

05 위 글의 밑줄 친 ⓐTheir가 가리키는 것을 본문에서 찾아 쓰시오.

➡ _____

06 위 글의 밑줄 친 ⓑ2016을 영어로 읽는 법을 쓰시오.

➡ _____

[07~09] 다음 글을 읽고 물음에 답하시오.

> **Q. Could you tell us more about haenyeo? What's so special about them?**
> I can tell you three things. First, haenyeo are a symbol of strong women. Jejudo, which is a volcanic island, is not suitable for farming, so many haenyeo have become the breadwinners for their families. Second, haenyeo form their own communities and

help each other. For example, more-experienced haenyeo train less-experienced haenyeo. Third, because they stay in the water without any breathing devices, haenyeo can't catch a lot of seafood. This is good for the underwater environment. Catching too much ⓐ_____ life at one time in one place can destroy the ocean.

07 주어진 영영풀이를 참고하여 빈칸 ⓐ에 철자 m으로 시작하는 단어를 쓰시오.

> relating to the sea or to the animals and plants that live in the sea

➡ _____

08 Why is the way haenyeo catch seafood good for the underwater environment? Fill in the blanks (A) and (B) with suitable words.

> Because they stay in the water without any (A)_____ _____, haenyeo (B)_____ _____ a lot of seafood.

09 해녀에 대한 특별한 점 3가지를 우리말로 쓰시오.

➡ (1) _____
(2) _____
(3) _____
_____

[10~13] 다음 글을 읽고 물음에 답하시오.

> **Q. Lastly, please tell us ⓐ_____.**
> I once attended an overseas exhibition with a couple of haenyeo to give a talk about their lives. When I finished my talk, ⓑone of the haenyeo held my hand tightly. She

said to me, "Thank you so much. I've never known in my whole life that I was such a special person." She was crying with happiness. Everyone in the audience was deeply ⓒmoved. I can never forget that moment, so I'll continue to take pictures of haenyeo. I want to tell more beautiful stories about them to many more people in the world. <I: Zin Kim>

10 다음 주어진 의문문을 위 글의 빈칸 ⓐ에 알맞은 순서로 배열하여 쓰시오.

> What are you planning to do in the future?

➡ _____

11 위 글의 밑줄 친 ⓑ를 다음과 같이 바꿔 쓸 때 빈칸에 들어갈 알맞은 단어를 쓰시오.

➡ one of the haenyeo held _____ by the hand tightly

12 위 글의 밑줄 친 ⓒmoved와 바꿔 쓸 수 있는 말을 쓰시오.

➡ _____

13 위 글의 내용과 일치하도록 다음 빈칸 (A)와 (B)에 알맞은 단어를 쓰시오.

> Zin Kim will continue to (A)_____ _____ of haenyeo as she can never forget the moment when one of the haenyeo thanked her. She wants to tell (B)_____ _____ _____ about haenyeo to many more people in the world.

Communicate – B Talk and Play

A: I wonder what these are.
간접의문문 어순으로 '의문사+주어+동사'의 순서로 이어진다.
B: They're called songpyeon.

A: Could you explain more about them?
= songpyeon
B: They're traditional Korean rice cakes.

구문해설 • traditional: 전통적인

해석

A: 나는 이것들이 무엇인지 궁금해.

B: 그것들은 송편이라고 불려.

A: 이것에 대해 좀 더 설명해 줄래?

B: 그것들은 전통적인 한국 떡이야.

After You Read A

A Photographer Who Loves Haenyeo

Zin Kim, an underwater photographer, has promoted the culture of Jeju
현재완료(계속적 용법)
haenyeo worldwide. She decided to take pictures of them when she met a
= take their pictures
haenyeo who was enjoying her job. It was not easy taking their pictures at
관계대명사(주격)   가주어   진주어(동명사)
first. However, when she told them that she wanted to show their culture to the
접속사(명사절)
world, the haenyeo finally opened their minds. At an overseas exhibition, she
부사(동사 수식)   → its(×) 주의 haenyeo는 복수(a haenyeo는 단수)
gave a talk about the lives of haenyeo. After her speech, one of the haenyeo
one of the 복수명사+단수동사
was crying with happiness. Zin Kim said that she would continue to take
시제 일치(will과거)
pictures of haenyeo.

구문해설 • underwater: 수중의, 물속의 • promote: 홍보하다, 촉진하다 • overseas: 해외의
• exhibition: 전시회

해녀를 사랑하는 사진작가

수중 사진작가 김진은 전 세계에 제주의 해녀 문화를 홍보해 왔다. 그녀는 자신의 일을 즐기고 있었던 한 해녀를 만났을 때, 그들의 사진을 찍기로 결심했다. 처음에는 그들의 사진을 찍는 것이 쉽지 않았다. 그러나, 그녀가 세상 사람들에게 그들의 문화를 보여주고 싶다고 그들에게 말했을 때, 마침내 해녀들은 마음을 열었다. 한 해외 전시회에서 그녀는 해녀들의 삶에 대해 강연했다. 그녀의 연설이 끝나자 해녀들 중 한 사람은 기쁨의 눈물을 흘렸다. 김진은 앞으로도 해녀들의 사진 찍는 일을 계속할 것이라고 말했다.

Write

Kim Minho is a barista. He makes coffee drinks for a living. He became a
for a living: 밥벌이로, 생계 수단으로
barista after he had found out about his passion for coffee. His favorite part of
바리스타가 되기 전에 발견한 것이므로, 과거완료시제를 사용
his job is decorating coffee with hot milk and watching his customers enjoying
동명사 보어   동명사 보어   지각동사 whatching의
목적격보어로 쓰인 현재분사
it. He is planning to open his own coffee shop.
opening(×)

구문해설 • barista: 바리스타, 커피 내리는 사람 • find out: 발견하다, 찾다 • passion: 열정, 흥미
• decorate: 장식하다, 꾸미다 • customer: 손님

김민호는 바리스타이다. 그의 직업은 커피 음료를 만드는 것이다. 그는 커피에 대한 그의 열정을 발견한 후에 바리스타가 되었다. 그의 직업에서 그가 가장 좋아하는 부분은 뜨거운 우유로 커피를 장식하고 그의 손님들이 그것을 즐기는 것을 보는 것이다. 그는 자신의 커피점을 열 계획이다.

Words & Expressions

01 다음 짝지어진 단어의 관계가 같도록 빈칸에 알맞은 말을 쓰시오.

> dark : darkness = happy : _____

02 다음 영영풀이가 가리키는 것을 고르시오.

> the member of a family who earns the money to support the others

① baker
② breadwinner
③ diver
④ audience
⑤ presenter

03 다음 중 밑줄 친 부분의 뜻풀이가 바르지 <u>않은</u> 것은?

① Could you <u>explain</u> more about it? (설명하다)
② There are a lot of <u>female</u> teachers in Korea. (여성의)
③ I'm planning an <u>overseas</u> trip. (해외의)
④ I have been on a trip for the <u>past</u> few days. (지나간)
⑤ She is walking along the <u>path</u>. (신뢰)

04 다음 우리말에 맞게 빈칸에 알맞은 말을 쓰시오.

(1) 너는 어디로 휴가를 가고 싶니?
➡ Where do you want to _____?
(2) 제가 두 서너 개의 질문을 하겠습니다.
➡ I'm going to ask _____ questions.
(3) 이 음악은 군인들을 격려하기 위해 만들어졌다.
➡ This music was made to _____ soldiers.

(4) 질문이 있다면 제게 전화주세요.
➡ _____ me _____ if you have any questions.

05 다음 문장의 빈칸에 들어갈 말을 〈보기〉에서 골라 쓰시오.

> ┤ 보기 ├
> heritage / greenhouse / device / breathe / overwork

(1) Her _____ and stress caused her to be ill.
(2) In winter, farmers grow vegetables in their _____.
(3) Cotton clothing allows your skin to _____.
(4) They tried to invent a _____ to measure brain activity during sleep.
(5) We should protect our national _____.

Conversation

[06~07] 다음 대화를 읽고 물음에 답하시오.

Jack: Excuse me, I'd like to use a copy machine.
Sue: O.K. You can use this machine.
Jack: Could you explain how to make double-sided copies?
Sue: Sure. Press the button for double-sided copies, and then press the start button.
Jack: Thank you.

06 What does Jack want to make?
➡ _____

07 What will Jack do before pressing the start button?
➡ _____

[08~09] 다음 대화를 읽고 물음에 답하시오.

Tom: Are you going somewhere this summer? (A)

Jane: I'm going to Jejudo to walk along the Jeju Olle Trail. (B)

Tom: The Jeju Olle Trail? (C)

Jane: It's a long hiking path around Jejudo. (D)

Tom: Oh, I see. I hope you enjoy your trip! (E)

08 위 대화의 (A)~(E) 중 주어진 문장이 들어가기에 가장 적절한 곳은?

> Could you explain what that is?

① (A)   ② (B)   ③ (C)   ④ (D)   ⑤ (E)

09 위 대화를 읽고 대답할 수 없는 것은?

① Where is Jane going to visit this summer?

② What is the Jeju Olle Trail?

③ Why does Jane want to visit Jejudo?

④ What does Tom hope for Jane?

⑤ What does Tom want to do in Jejudo?

[10~12] 다음 대화를 읽고 물음에 답하시오.

Jaden: Do you hear that? I wonder where that music is coming from.

Yuri: I think it's coming from over there. Do you want to go and ⓐcheck out it?

Jaden: Yes, I love ⓑthat strong beat. Is it traditional Korean music?

Yuri: Yes, it's ⓒcalled nongak. It's a kind of community band music.

Jaden: Nongak? Could you explain a little bit more about it?

Yuri: It's traditionally used to cheer up farmers and ⓓwish for a good harvest.

Jaden: I see. Look! Some people are dancing to the rhythm.

Yuri: Yes, that's a big part of nongak. Dancing together ⓔcompletes the music.

Jaden: Let's join them.

Yuri: Sure. Why not?

10 위 대화의 밑줄 친 ⓐ~ⓔ 중 어법상 어색한 것을 찾아 바르게 고치시오.

➡ _____

11 위 대화에서 다음 주어진 영영풀이가 가리키는 말을 찾아 쓰시오.

> one of a series of regular movements or hitting actions

➡ _____

12 위 대화의 내용과 일치하지 않는 것은?

① Jaden은 들려오는 음악의 강한 비트가 마음에 든다.

② Jaden과 유리는 농악을 듣고 있다.

③ 농악은 공동체 악단 음악의 한 종류이다.

④ 농악은 전통적으로 농부들의 힘을 북돋아 주고 풍년을 기원하기 위해 사용되었다.

⑤ 리듬은 농악의 큰 부분으로서 음악을 완성한다.

13 다음 대화를 참고하여 주어진 빈칸에 적절한 단어를 쓰시오.

Philip: Sam, have you ever eaten cheese fondue made with Swiss style?

Sam: Yes, two times.

Philip: When did you first eat it?

Sam: Before I graduated from the college.

➡ Sam _____ _____ cheese fondue before he graduated from the college.

[14~15] 다음 중 어법상 <u>어색한</u> 문장을 <u>모두</u> 고르시오.

14 ① The people can't even guess where are the monsters from.
② The participants don't understand why the speaker is interested in.
③ Mom doesn't know whether Jamie and Esther are coming.
④ When do you think the researcher will complete the project?
⑤ There's no one knowing when the car accident happened.

15 ① I wonder why she didn't choose me as her colleague.
② Do you know who made these yummy cookies and drinks?
③ Would you tell me when did he leave the office?
④ Do you think when Tracy will come back for her original position?
⑤ Do you have any idea how long it will take to get to the wedding?

16 다음 그림을 보고 괄호 안의 단어를 배열하여 빈칸을 알맞게 채우시오.

(1)

➡ Junho is _____
_____. (which, go, thinking, should, he, to, about, university)

(2)

➡ Ye-eun is _____
_____. (when, stop, will, the, wondering, rain)

17 다음 괄호 안에서 어법상 알맞은 것을 고르시오.

(1) Sven dropped the carrot that Olaf (had pulled / has pulled) out of the field in the snow.
(2) Last week, we learned that Kennedy (had been killed / was killed) by gunshot in 1963.
(3) The rock band (has already gone / had already gone) to New York before their fans got informed of the news.
(4) Some film lovers around the world said that they (have been / had been) learning Korean to watch *Parasite* without subtitles.
(5) An invitation was sent to the girl after the prince (had seen / has seen) her dancing on the street.
(6) I wonder when the angels (had appeared / appeared / has appeared) to the nuns.

18 다음 쇼핑몰의 안내 페이지와 〈보기〉의 질문을 참고하여 알맞은 내용을 골라 빈칸에 간접의문문을 써 넣으시오.

Fresh Daddy Grocery
• Open Hours: 10a.m. ~ 8p.m.
• Address: 123 Ilsan, Goyang
• Nearby Station: Daewha (line 3)
• Contact: mngr@freshdaddy.co.kr

┤ 보기 ├
• Is there any subway station near the store?
• What time does the store open?
• How can we contact the store manager?
• Where is the store located?

(1) Do you know _____?
→ The store opens at 10 a.m.

(2) Can you tell me _____
_____?
→ By e-mail. mngr@freshdaddy.co.kr.

(3) Tell me _____.
→ Fresh Daddy Grocery is at 123 Ilsan, Goyang.

(4) Do you know _____
_____?
→ Yes, the nearest subway station from the store is Daewha on line 3.

19 다음 각 문장의 밑줄 친 부분이 과거완료시제의 용법 중 어떤 것에 해당하는지 〈보기〉에서 찾아 기호를 쓰시오.

┤ 보기 ├
ⓐ 완료   ⓑ 경험   ⓒ 결과   ⓓ 계속

(1) I had never seen the desert until I went to Sahara last year. (_____)

(2) As soon as she came back to her desk, she felt something had gone from her drawer. (_____)

(3) Before the boss came up, Jessica had finished her report. (_____)

(4) The lady couldn't notice the old man since she had lost her sight. (_____)

(5) By the time the teacher found something strange, Michael had already completed his reading. (_____)

(6) Jacob had lived in Daejeon for 4 years by last year. (_____)

(7) Bong had won several awards before winning the Academy Award. (_____)

(8) The girl had stayed in the dormitory until her parents came to visit her. (_____)

20 다음 그림과 스케줄 표를 보고 과거완료시제를 활용하여, 빈칸에 알맞은 말을 써 넣으시오.

Today's Schedule
• Vanessa – clean the windows and wash the dishes
• Sally – give the dog some food and water the plant
---

(1) When Mom came home, she found
_____
_____.

(2) When Mom came home, she found
_____
_____.

21 다음 우리말에 맞도록 괄호 안에 주어진 어휘를 알맞게 배열하시오.

(1) 수진이는 왜 자신이 다른 나라에 가서 요리법을 배워야 하는지 이해할 수 없었다. (had to, in, how, why, to cook, she, learn, another country)

➡ Sujin couldn't understand _____

_____ .

(2) 비행기에 남은 좌석이 있는지 확인해 주시겠어요? (seats, there, the plane, left, any, on, are, if)

➡ Could you check _____

_____ ?

Reading

[22~24] 다음 글을 읽고 물음에 답하시오.

Q. Could you tell us more about haenyeo? What's so special about them?

I can tell you three things. First, haenyeo are a symbol of strong women. Jejudo, which is a volcanic island, is not suitable ⓐ____ farming, so many haenyeo have become the breadwinners ⓑ____ their families. Second, haenyeo form their own communities and help each other. For example, more-experienced haenyeo train less-experienced haenyeo. Third, because they stay in the water without any breathing devices, haenyeo can't catch a lot of seafood. This is good for the underwater environment. ⓒCatching too much marine life at one time in one place can destroy the ocean.

22 위 글의 빈칸 ⓐ와 ⓑ에 공통으로 들어갈 알맞은 전치사를 고르시오.

① to   ② on   ③ for

④ in   ⑤ at

23 위 글의 밑줄 친 ⓒCatching과 문법적 쓰임이 같은 것을 모두 고르시오.

① Our cat is good at catching mice.

② Do you know the man catching fish?

③ I think I'm catching a cold.

④ My hobby is catching the fish.

⑤ I saw a woman catching a butterfly.

24 According to the passage, which is NOT true?

① Haenyeo are a symbol of strong women.

② Jejudo is a volcanic island.

③ Haenyeo form their own communities.

④ Haenyeo stay in the water with no breathing devices.

⑤ Haenyeo can catch a lot of seafood at one time.

[25~26] 다음 글을 읽고 물음에 답하시오.

Q. Lastly, please tell us what you're planning to do in the future.

I once attended an overseas exhibition with a couple of haenyeo to give a talk about their lives. When I finished my talk, one of the haenyeo held my hand tightly. She said to me, "Thank you so much. I've never known in my whole life that I was such a special person." She was crying with happiness. Everyone in the audience was deeply ⓐmoved. I can never forget that moment, so I'll continue to take pictures of haenyeo. I want to tell more beautiful stories about them to many more people in the world.   <I: Zin Kim>.

25 위 글의 밑줄 친 ⓐmoved와 같은 의미로 쓰인 것을 고르시오.

① He moved towards the window.
② The sight moved me to tears.
③ We moved to the country last week.
④ The ship moved before the wind.
⑤ I moved that a vote should be taken on this.

26 위 글의 주제로 알맞은 것을 고르시오.

① an overseas exhibition Zin Kim attended
② giving a talk about haenyeo's lives
③ Zin Kim's plan in the future
④ the happiness of one of the haenyeo
⑤ beautiful stories about haenyeo

[27~29] 다음 글을 읽고 물음에 답하시오.

A Photographer Who Loves Haenyeo

Zin Kim, an underwater photographer, has promoted the culture of Jeju haenyeo worldwide. She decided to take pictures of them when she met a haenyeo who was enjoying her job.

It was not easy taking their pictures at first. ____ⓐ____, when she told them that she wanted to show their culture to the world, the haenyeo finally opened their minds.

At an overseas exhibition, she gave a talk about the lives of haenyeo. After her speech, one of the haenyeo was crying with happiness. Zin Kim said that she would continue to take pictures of haenyeo.

27 위 글의 빈칸 ⓐ에 들어갈 알맞은 말을 고르시오.

① That is   ② Moreover
③ Thus   ④ For example
⑤ However

28 위 글의 종류로 알맞은 것을 고르시오.

① review   ② book report
③ diary   ④ article
⑤ autobiography

29 Which question CANNOT be answered after reading the passage?

① What does Zin Kim do?
② How did Zin Kim take pictures of haenyeo?
③ When did Zin Kim decide to take pictures of haenyeo?
④ Was it easy to take pictures of haenyeo at first?
⑤ What did Zin Kim want to show to the world?

01 다음 문장의 빈칸에 공통으로 들어갈 말을 고르시오.

> • The manager will _____ a presentation on the new items.
> • Can you _____ me your hand?
> • I usually _____ a call to my grandmother every week.

① give   ② take   ③ keep
④ like   ⑤ check

02 다음 대화가 자연스럽게 이어지도록 순서대로 배열하시오.

> (A) Really? Then, why don't we go somewhere, too?
> (B) O.K.
> (C) Lots of people are going on vacation this weekend.
> (D) Look over there. I wonder why there are so many cars on the road.

➡ _____

[03~04] 다음 대화를 읽고 물음에 답하시오.

Jaden: Do you hear that? I wonder where that music is coming from.

Yuri: (A) I think it's coming from over there. Do you want to go and check it out?

Jaden: Yes, I love that strong beat. Is it traditional Korean music?

Yuri: (B) It's a kind of community band music.

Jaden: Nongak? Could you explain a little bit more about it?

Yuri: (C) It's traditionally used to cheer up farmers and wish for a good harvest.

Jaden: (D)I see. Look! Some people are dancing to the rhythm.

Yuri: Yes, that's a big part of nongak. Dancing together completes the music.

Jaden: (E) Let's join them.

Yuri: Sure. Why not?

03 위 대화의 (A)~(E) 중 주어진 문장이 들어가기에 적절한 곳은?

> Yes, it's called nongak.

① (A)   ② (B)   ③ (C)   ④ (D)   ⑤ (E)

04 위 대화를 읽고 대답할 수 없는 것은?

① Where is the strong beat coming from?
② What is nongak?
③ What are some people doing to the rhythm?
④ What is a big part of nongak?
⑤ What kind of dancing can complete the music?

[05~06] 다음 대화를 읽고 물음에 답하시오.

W: Excuse me, I'd like to borrow an audio guide.

M: Here you are.

W: Could you explain how to use it?

M: Sure. Press this button, and it'll tell you what to do.

05 What does the woman want to do?

➡ _____

06 What should the woman do to use the audio guide?

➡ _____

[07~08] 다음 대화를 읽고 물음에 답하시오.

> Emma: Look over there. (A)도로에 왜 저렇게 차가 많은지 궁금하네요.
>
> Mike: Lots of people are going on vacation this weekend.
>
> Emma: Really? Then, (B)why don't we go somewhere, too? (how)
>
> Mike: O.K.

✏️ 출제율 95%

07 위 대화의 밑줄 친 (A)의 우리말을 〈보기〉에 주어진 단어들을 모두 배열하여 영작하시오.

> ┤ 보기 ├
>
> there / wonder / on / I / the / cars / so / are / road / why /many

➡️ _____

✏️ 출제율 90%

08 위 대화의 밑줄 친 (B)와 의도가 같도록 주어진 단어를 사용하여 다시 쓰시오.

➡️ _____

✏️ 출제율 95%

09 다음 대화가 자연스럽게 이어지도록 순서대로 배열하시오.

> (A) How do you know that?
> (B) That's Gwangandaegyo in Busan.
> (C) I went there with my family last summer.
> (D) Wow, look at the bridge in this ad. I wonder where the photo was taken.

➡️ _____

[10~11] 다음 대화를 읽고 물음에 답하시오.

> Jack: Excuse me, I'd like to use a copy machine.
>
> Sue: O.K. You can use this machine.
>
> Jack: 어떻게 양면 복사를 하는지 설명해 주실 수 있나요?
>
> Sue: Sure. Press the button for double-sided copies, and then press the start button.
>
> Jack: Thank you.

✏️ 출제율 95%

10 위 대화의 밑줄 친 우리말을 〈보기〉에 주어진 단어를 알맞게 배열하여 영작하시오.

> ┤ 보기 ├
>
> how / you / copies / explain / could / make / double-sided / to

➡️ _____

_____

✏️ 출제율 100%

11 위 대화의 내용과 일치하지 않는 것은?

① Jack wants to use a copy machine.
② Jack wants to make double-sided copies.
③ Sue knows how to make double-sided copies.
④ Jack should press the two buttons to make double-sided copies.
⑤ Jack should press the start button at first.

✏️ 출제율 95%

12 다음 우리말을 바르게 영작한 것은?

> 당신은 Paul이 무슨 음악을 듣고 있다고 생각합니까?

① What music do you suppose Paul is listening to?
② What do you suppose music is Paul listening to?
③ Do you suppose what music is Paul listening to?
④ Is what music you suppose Paul listening to?
⑤ What music do you suppose is Paul listening to?

13 〈보기〉와 같이 과거완료시제를 이용하여, 두 문장을 괄호 안에 주어진 접속사로 시작하는 한 문장으로 만드시오.

> ── 보기 ──
>
> All the Korean film fans shouted for joy. Bong won the Academy Awards. (because)
>
> → Because Bong had won the Academy Awards, all the Korean film fans shouted for joy.

(1) Susan promised her teacher not to throw away used batteries. She learned the importance of recycling. (after)

➡ _____
_____
_____

(2) Sunwoo lay in his room all day long. He sprained his ankle during the basketball game. (before)

➡ _____
_____
_____

14 다음 빈칸에 들어가기에 어색한 문장을 모두 골라 번호를 쓰고 알맞게 고쳐 다시 쓰시오.

> Do you know _____?

ⓐ when does the shopping mall close
ⓑ where the nearest subway station is
ⓒ what kind of movie was she watching
ⓓ what does she usually do on Sundays
ⓔ how many toys there are in the room
ⓕ what time does the show begin

➡ _____
_____
_____

15 다음 중 어법상 올바른 문장을 <u>모두</u> 고르면? (정답 2개)

① His family happened to know that Brian has worked hard only to be taken to hospital the day before.

② The first half of the match already started when we had arrived at the stadium.

③ Most Asians felt proud that Director Bong has won the grand prize at the Cannes Film Festival for the film.

④ Marty returned the umbrella which she had borrowed from the restaurant.

⑤ The flower looked much fresher than before because it had rained the day before.

16 다음 그림을 보고, 내용에 맞게 〈보기〉에서 알맞은 단어를 각각 선택하여 어법에 맞게 빈칸에 채워 넣으시오.

> ── 보기 ──
> • already / much / often / how → 1회씩 사용
> • gain / eat / weigh → 1회씩 사용, 어형변화 가능
> • had / he → 2회씩 사용

> The bulldog wanted to know _____ _____ _____ _____. He was surprised to find that _____ _____ _____ _____ weight before he stood on the scale. He regretted that he _____ _____ _____ some snacks before going to bed.

출제율 90%

17 다음 우리말과 그 영작이 바르게 짝지어지지 <u>않은</u> 것은?

① 네가 몇 시에 올 것인지 궁금하다.
→ I wonder what time you will come.

② 누가 그 강아지를 내게 줬는지 말해줘.
→ Tell me who gave me the puppy.

③ 그녀가 무슨 드레스를 입었는지 기억이 안 난다.
→ I can't remember what dress she put on.

④ 그녀가 몇 살이라고 짐작하니?
→ Do you guess how old she is?

⑤ 수민이가 왜 날 싫어하는지 몰라.
→ I don't know why Sumin hates me.

출제율 100%

19 위 글의 주제로 알맞은 것을 고르시오.

① how to take pictures of haenyeo

② the hard lives of haenyeo

③ the reason Zin Kim became interested in taking photos of haenyeo

④ the difficulty of taking pictures of haenyeo

⑤ the most beautiful picture that has ever been taken

출제율 90%

20 Until she happened to take pictures of a haenyeo, what kind of photos of haenyeo had Zin Kim only seen? Answer in English in a full sentence.

➡ _____

_____

[18~20] 다음 글을 읽고 물음에 답하시오.

> **Q. How did you become interested in taking photos of haenyeo?**
>
> One day, I happened to take pictures of a haenyeo. I was surprised to find that she was enjoying her job. Until then, I had only seen black-and-white photos of haenyeo who looked very tired. ___ⓐ___, she kept laughing even after she had been in the water for over five hours. I realized then that I should take pictures of haenyeo. <I: Zin Kim>

출제율 95%

18 위 글의 빈칸 ⓐ에 들어갈 알맞은 말을 고르시오.

① In addition ② For example

③ That is ④ However

⑤ Therefore

[21~22] 다음 글을 읽고 물음에 답하시오.

> **Q. You take beautiful pictures of them, but isn't ⓐit difficult to take pictures of haenyeo?**
>
> At first, they didn't understand why I wanted to take their pictures. They didn't think they looked pretty in their wetsuits. So, I said to them, "You're very special. I want to show your culture to the world." They opened up to me then. Of course, I also promised them that I would make them look beautiful in my pictures. <I: Zin Kim>

출제율 95%

21 위 글의 밑줄 친 ⓐit과 문법적 쓰임이 같은 것을 고르시오.

① I make it a rule to eat breakfast.

② It is 2 miles from here to the airport.

③ It is I that am to blame.

④ Did you see it?

⑤ It is important for you to have a dream.

22 According to the passage, which is NOT true?

① Zin Kim takes beautiful pictures of haenyeo.

② From the beginning, Zin Kim had no difficulty in taking pictures of haenyeo.

③ Haenyeo didn't think they looked pretty in their wetsuits.

④ Zin Kim wanted to show haenyeo's culture to the world.

⑤ Zin Kim promised haenyeo that she would make them look beautiful in her pictures.

[23~25] 다음 글을 읽고 물음에 답하시오.

Q. ⓐLastly, please tell us what you're planning to do in the future.

I once attended an overseas exhibition with a couple of haenyeo ⓑto give a talk about their lives. (①) She said to me, "Thank you so much. (②) I've never known in my whole life that I was such a special person." (③) She was crying with happiness. (④) Everyone in the audience was deeply moved. (⑤) I can never forget that moment, so I'll continue to take pictures of haenyeo. I want to tell more beautiful stories about them to many more people in the world.

23 위 글의 흐름으로 보아, 주어진 문장이 들어가기에 가장 적절한 곳은?

When I finished my talk, one of the haenyeo held my hand tightly.

①   ②   ③   ④   ⑤

24 위 글의 밑줄 친 ⓐLastly와 바꿔 쓸 수 있는 말을 고르시오.

① Eventually   ② Immediately

③ Extremely   ④ Finally

⑤ At last

25 위 글의 밑줄 친 ⓑto give와 to부정사의 용법이 다른 것의 개수를 고르시오.

┌─── 보기 ───
│ ① She went there to give a talk about it.
│ ② It's your turn to give a talk about it.
│ ③ He is wise enough to give a talk about it.
│ ④ I felt proud to give a talk about it.
│ ⑤ It was exciting to give a talk about it.
└───

① 1개   ② 2개   ③ 3개   ④ 4개   ⑤ 5개

[26~28] 다음 글을 읽고 물음에 답하시오.

Kim Minho is a barista. He makes coffee drinks ⓐ a living. He became a barista after he had found out about his passion ⓑ coffee. His favorite part of his job is decorating coffee with hot milk and watching his customers enjoying it. He is planning to open his own coffee shop.

26 위 글의 빈칸 ⓐ와 ⓑ에 공통으로 들어갈 알맞은 전치사를 쓰시오.

➡ _____

27 주어진 영영풀이에 해당하는 단어를 본문에서 찾아 쓰시오.

a person who makes and serves coffee in a coffee bar

➡ _____

28 What's Kim Minho's favorite part of his job? Answer in English beginning with "It's".

➡ _____
_____

[01~03] 다음 대화를 읽고 물음에 답하시오.

Brian: Look over there. I wonder why there are so many people waiting in line.

Sujin: They're waiting to get into the new bakery there.

Brian: Why? Is it famous?

Sujin: Yes. It was on a TV program.

Brian: Really? We should try their bread then.

Sujin: Sure.

01 Why are so many people waiting in line?

➡ _____

02 Why is the new bakery famous? (7 words)

➡ _____

03 What does Brian want to try?

➡ _____

[04~05] 다음 중에서 틀린 문장을 찾아 번호를 쓰고, 바르게 고쳐 문장을 다시 쓰시오.

04 ① The film director had been tired because he spoke in front of so many people.

② The mechanic told her that someone had touched the tires of her car.

③ Emilia found out that she had lost her smartphone.

④ Julie decided to marry Jake as she had liked him for a long time.

⑤ The accounting manager said he had already completed his financial report.

➡ _____

05 ① The president wants to know what his secretary bought a week ago.

② I have no idea why the super hero is blamed for the accident.

③ Could you tell us if the injured soldier will come tomorrow morning?

④ Do you think where the police officer caught the thief?

⑤ Does Michael know how you could escape from the prison?

➡ _____

06 〈보기〉처럼 괄호 안에 주어진 접속사와 과거완료시제를 이용하여 두 문장을 한 문장으로 쓰시오.

┌─ 보기 ─┐

James was too full to eat more. He ate all three meals by himself. (Because로 시작)

→ Because James had eaten all three meals by himself, he was too full to eat more.

(1) Mary fought off a strange man's attack. She learned taekwondo before. (Because로 시작)

➡ _____

(2) Kevin never thought of quitting drinking. He saw a video of himself being a heavy drinker. (Until로 시작)

➡ _____

[07~09] 다음 글을 읽고 물음에 답하시오.

Q. You take beautiful pictures of them, but isn't it difficult to take pictures of haenyeo?

At first, they didn't understand why I wanted to take their pictures. ⓐThey didn't think they looked prettily in their wetsuits. So, I said to them, "You're very special. I want to show your culture to the world." They opened up to me then. Of course, I also promised them that ⓑ내 사진 속에서 그들을 아름답게 보이도록 하겠다. <I: Zin Kim>

07 위 글의 밑줄 친 ⓐ에서 어법상 틀린 부분을 찾아 고치시오.

➡ _____ ➡ _____

08 위 글의 밑줄 친 ⓑ의 우리말에 맞게 주어진 어휘를 알맞게 배열하시오.

> them / pictures / beautiful / make / I / in / would / my / look

➡ _____

09 Why did Zin Kim want to take pictures of haenyeo? Fill in the blanks (A) and (B) with suitable words.

> Because haenyeo are (A)_____ _____ and she wanted to (B)_____ _____ _____ to the world.

[10~12] 다음 글을 읽고 물음에 답하시오.

Q. Could you tell us more about haenyeo? What's so special about them?

I can tell you three things. First, haenyeo are a symbol of strong women. Jejudo, which is a volcanic island, is not suitable for farming, so many haenyeo have become the breadwinners for their families. Second, haenyeo form their own communities and help each other. For example, more-experienced haenyeo train less-experienced haenyeo. Third, because they stay in the water (A)[with / without] any breathing devices, haenyeo can't catch a lot of seafood. This is good (B)[at / for] the underwater environment. Catching too much marine life at one time in one place can (C)[destroy / protect] the ocean.

10 위 글의 괄호 (A)~(C)에서 문맥상 알맞은 낱말을 골라 쓰시오.

➡ (A) _____ (B) _____ (C) _____

11 다음 빈칸 (A)와 (B)에 알맞은 단어를 넣어 해녀들이 그들 자신의 공동체를 조직하고 서로 돕는 한 예를 완성하시오.

> (A)_____ haenyeo are trained by (B)_____ haenyeo.

12 Why is it impossible for haenyeo to catch a lot of seafood at one time? Answer in English beginning with "Because".

➡ _____

01 다음 대화를 읽고 대화의 내용과 일치하도록 Jaden의 일기를 완성하시오.

> Jaden: Do you hear that? I wonder where that music is coming from.
>
> Yuri: I think it's coming from over there. Do you want to go and check it out?
>
> Jaden: Yes, I love that strong beat. Is it traditional Korean music?
>
> Yuri: Yes, it's called nongak. It's a kind of community band music.
>
> Jaden: Nongak? Could you explain a little bit more about it?
>
> Yuri: It's traditionally used to cheer up farmers and wish for a good harvest.
>
> Jaden: I see. Look! Some people are dancing to the rhythm.
>
> Yuri: Yes, that's a big part of nongak. Dancing together completes the music.
>
> Jaden: Let's join them.
>
> Yuri: Sure. Why not?

> Walking down the street, I heard music with a (A)_____. I wanted to know (B)_____. Yuri and I found that it was traditional Korean music, called (C)_____. Yuri explained that it's a kind of (D)_____ and traditionally used to (E)_____. It was impressive for me that some people were dancing to the rhythm because dancing was a big part of nongak. Yuri and I joined them and completed the music together.

02 다음 그림을 보고, 그림의 상황에 맞게 〈보기〉와 같이 간접의문을 사용하여 어법에 맞게 자유롭게 영작하시오.

┌─ 보기 ─
Do you know when you should feed the puppy?
Tell me if you checked our mailbox.

(1) _____

(2) _____

(3) _____

단원별 모의고사

01 다음 영영풀이가 가리키는 것을 고르시오.

> a picture, set of words, or a short film, intended to persuade people to buy

① advertisement ② audio guide
③ jellyfish ④ beat
⑤ sunshine

02 다음 주어진 문장의 밑줄 친 beat와 같은 의미로 쓰인 것은?

> This type of music has a strong beat.

① I like the steady beat of the drums.
② He beat me at chess.
③ Hailstones beat against the window.
④ My mother beat dust out of the carpet.
⑤ I heard the sound of beating the door.

03 다음 우리말에 맞게 주어진 단어를 활용하여 영작하시오.

(1) 나는 사진작가가 되고 싶다. (photo)
➡ _____

(2) 그녀는 가장 적절한 후보였다. (suit)
➡ _____

(3) 그는 내 손을 꽉 잡았다. (hold, tight)
➡ _____

(4) 나는 소설을 빌리고 싶습니다. (like)
➡ _____

[04~05] 다음 대화를 읽고 물음에 답하시오.

G: Wow, look at the bridge in this ad.
_____
B: That's Gwangandaegyo in Busan.
G: How do you know that?
B: I went there with my family last summer.

04 위 대화의 빈칸에 들어갈 말로 적절하지 않은 것은?

① I wonder where the photo was taken.
② Can you tell me where the photo was taken?
③ Can I ask you where the photo was taken?
④ I want to know where the photo was taken.
⑤ I'm sure where the photo was taken.

05 Where did the boy visit last summer?

➡ _____
_____

[06~07] 다음 대화를 읽고 물음에 답하시오.

Brian: Look over there. _____
Sujin: They're waiting to get into the new bakery there.
Brian: Why? Is it famous?
Sujin: Yes. It was on a TV program.
Brian: Really? We should try their bread then.
Sujin: Sure.

06 위 대화의 빈칸에 들어갈 말을 〈보기〉에 주어진 단어들을 배열하여 완성하시오.

> ┤ 보기 ├
> many / in / why / are / wonder / so / I / people / waiting / line / there

➡ _____
_____

07 위 대화를 읽고 대답할 수 없는 것은?

① What is Brian wondering?
② Why are many people waiting in line?
③ Why is the new bakery famous?
④ What does Brian want to try?
⑤ When was the new bakery on the TV program?

08 다음 대화가 자연스럽게 이어지도록 순서대로 배열하시오.

> (A) It's a long hiking path around Jejudo.
> (B) Oh, I see. I hope you enjoy your trip!
> (C) Are you going somewhere this summer?
> (D) I'm going to Jejudo to walk along the Jeju Olle Trail.
> (E) The Jeju Olle Trail? Could you explain what that is?

➡ _____

[09~10] 다음 대화를 읽고 물음에 답하시오.

> Emma: Look over there. I wonder why there are so many cars on the road.
> Mike: Lots of people are going on vacation this weekend.
> Emma: Really? Then, why don't we go somewhere, too?
> Mike: O.K.

09 Why are so many cars on the road?

➡ _____

_____

10 What did Emma suggest to Mike?

➡ _____

11 다음 짝지어진 대화가 <u>어색한</u> 것은?

① A: I'm wondering why he got upset.
　 B: I think he had a fight with his brother.
② A: Can you tell me what they are?
　 B: They're called songpyeon.
③ A: Could you tell me about them?
　 B: They're traditional Korea rice cakes.
④ A: Would you give me more information?
　 B: Sure. Let's take a look at this book together.
⑤ A: I'm curious why she looks so sad.
　 B: I'm not following you.

12 다음 주어진 우리말을 영작한 것으로 옳은 것은?

> 이것이 무엇인지 설명해 주시겠어요?

① Can you explain what is this?
② Could you explain what this is?
③ Could you explain that what this?
④ What could you explain this is?
⑤ What could you explain is this?

13 다음 두 문장을 한 문장으로 만들 때 빈칸에 들어갈 말로 가장 알맞은 것은?

> • He was infected by the virus.
> • He stayed at the center of the disease for 3 months.
> → He was infected by the virus because _____

① he might stay at the center of the disease for 3 months.
② had he stayed at the center of the disease for 3 months.
③ he has stayed at the center of the disease for 3 months.
④ he had stayed at the center of the disease for 3 months.
⑤ he could have stayed at the center of the disease for 3 months.

14 다음 중 밑줄 친 부분의 쓰임이 나머지 넷과 <u>다른</u> 것은?

① Mr. Baker doesn't know <u>where the post office is located</u>.
② Mina asked me <u>what time the bank would close</u>.
③ I wonder <u>when my girlfriend will come to France</u>.
④ The executives of the company don't understand <u>why the facility is required</u>.
⑤ Let everybody know about the man <u>who won the Oscars</u> yesterday.

15 다음 그림을 보고, 주어진 단어들을 알맞게 배열하여 영작하되, 과거완료시제를 반드시 포함하시오. (동사를 변형)

(the woman, put, the fish, really, if)

➡ James wondered _____
_____ in the fish-shaped bun.

16 다음에 등장하는 사람과 직업에 대한 안내문을 읽고 괄호 안에 주어진 어휘를 알맞게 배열하여 빈칸 (A)와 (B)를 채우시오.

Yori became a content creator (A)_____
_____ (gotten, she, after, views, had, 20,000) on her first video clip on WeTube. Her favorite part of her job is (B)_____
_____ (about, what, sharing, special, Korean food, is) with many people around the world.

[17~18] 다음 글을 읽고 물음에 답하시오.

Q. How did you become interested in taking photos of haenyeo?

One day, I happened to take pictures of a haenyeo. I was surprised ⓐto find that she was enjoying her job. Until then, I had only seen black-and-white photos of haenyeo who looked very tired. However, she kept laughing even after she had been in the water for over five hours. I realized then that I should take pictures of haenyeo. <I: Zin Kim>

17 위 글의 밑줄 친 ⓐto find와 to부정사의 용법이 같은 것을 <u>모두</u> 고르시오.

① She was too tired <u>to find</u> it.
② Do you know how <u>to find</u> it?
③ I was eager <u>to find</u> it.
④ Tell me the way <u>to find</u> it.
⑤ Is it difficult <u>to find</u> it?

18 According to the passage, which is NOT true?

① Zin Kim happened to take pictures of a haenyeo.
② The haenyeo was enjoying her job.
③ Before Zin Kim took pictures of a haenyeo, she had seen many colorful photos of haenyeo.
④ The haenyeo Zin Kim took pictures of kept laughing even after she had been in the water for over five hours.
⑤ At that time, Zin Kim realized that she should take pictures of haenyeo.

[19~21] 다음 글을 읽고 물음에 답하시오.

Q. Could you tell us more about haenyeo?
ⓐ
_____

I can tell you three things. First, haenyeo are a symbol of strong women. Jejudo, which is a volcanic island, is not suitable for farming, so ⓑ많은 해녀들이 가족들의 생계비를 버는 가장이 되어 왔어요. (①) Second, haenyeo form their own communities and help each other. (②) For example, more-experienced haenyeo train less-experienced haenyeo. (③) Third, because they stay in the water without any breathing devices, haenyeo can't catch a lot of seafood. (④) Catching too much marine life at one time in one place can destroy the ocean. (⑤)

19 위 글의 빈칸 ⓐ에 들어갈 알맞은 질문을 고르시오.

① What's so special about them?
② How did you become interested in taking photos of them?
③ Isn't it difficult to take their pictures?
④ What's the secret of holding their breath?
⑤ What are you planning to do in the future?

20 위 글의 흐름으로 보아, 주어진 문장이 들어가기에 가장 적절한 곳은?

> This is good for the underwater environment.

①   ②   ③   ④   ⑤

21 위 글의 밑줄 친 ⓑ의 우리말에 맞게 9 단어로 영작하시오.

➡ _____
_____

[22~24] 다음 글을 읽고 물음에 답하시오.

Yori is a content creator about traditional Korean food. She posts her video clips about making and eating Korean food. She became a content creator after she had gotten ⓐ20,000 views on her first video clip on WeTube. Her favorite part of her job is sharing ⓑwhat is special about Korean food with many people around the world. She is planning to write a cookbook on Korean food.

22 위 글의 밑줄 친 ⓐ를 영어로 읽는 법을 쓰시오.

➡ _____

23 위 글의 밑줄 친 ⓑwhat과 바꿔 쓸 수 있는 말을 세 단어로 쓰시오.

➡ _____

24 위 글을 읽고 답할 수 <u>없는</u> 질문을 고르시오.

① What does Yori do?
② How did Yori become a content creator?
③ When did Yori get 20,000 views on her first video clip on WeTube?
④ What is Yori's favorite part of her job?
⑤ What is Yori planning to do in the future?

A Journey into Your Mind

🐦 의사소통 기능

- 걱정하기
  I'm worried about Sports Day.

- 의무 부인하기
  You don't have to clean the classroom.

🐦 언어 형식

- 분사구문
  Feeling nervous, Jisu was carefully studying her notes in her chair.

- not only ~ but also ...
  His rival became **not only** a political supporter **but also** a good friend.

Words & Expressions

교과서

Key Words

- **actually** [ǽktʃuəli] 부 실제로
- **anxious** [ǽŋkʃəs] 형 불안해하는
- **apart** [əpáːrt] 부 (거리·공간·시간상으로) 떨어져
- **behavior** [bihéivjər] 명 행동
- **bored** [bɔːrd] 형 지루해하는
- **carefully** [kɛ́ərfəli] 부 조심스럽게
- **chew** [tʃuː] 동 (음식을) 씹다
- **competition** [kàmpətíʃən] 명 경쟁, 대회
- **confident** [kánfədənt] 형 자신감 있는
- **convenient** [kənvíːnjənt] 형 편리한
- **decide** [disáid] 동 결심하다
- **enemy** [énəmi] 명 적
- **famously** [féiməsli] 부 유명하게
- **graduate** [grǽdʒuət] 동 졸업하다
- **guess** [ges] 동 추측하다
- **helpless** [hélplis] 형 무력한
- **hip** [hip] 명 엉덩이, 허리께
- **instead** [instéd] 부 대신에
- **judge** [dʒʌdʒ] 동 판단하다
- **lend** [lend] 동 빌려주다
- **lucky** [lʌ́ki] 형 행운인, 운이 좋은
- **Mexican** [méksikən] 형 멕시코 출신의, 멕시코의
- **mind** [maind] 명 마음, 정신

- **nervous** [nə́ːrvəs] 형 불안해하는
- **place** [pleis] 동 놓다, 두다
- **political** [pəlítikəl] 형 정치적인
- **practice** [prǽktis] 동 연습하다
- **prepare** [pripɛ́ər] 동 준비하다
- **presentation** [prèzəntéiʃən] 명 발표
- **professional** [prəféʃənl] 형 전문적인
- **psychologist** [saikálədʒist] 명 심리학자
- **psychology** [saikálədʒi] 명 심리학
- **rare** [rɛər] 형 드문, 희귀한
- **relax** [rilǽks] 동 휴식을 취하다
- **relay** [ríːlei] 명 이어달리기
- **relieved** [rilíːvd] 형 안도하는
- **rival** [ráivəl] 명 경쟁자
- **seafood** [síːfud] 명 해산물, 해물
- **solution** [səlúːʃən] 명 해결책
- **Sports Day** 운동회
- **stranger** [stréindʒər] 명 낯선 사람
- **stressful** [strésfəl] 형 스트레스가 많은
- **study** [stʌ́di] 명 과목, 연구
- **supporter** [səpɔ́ːrtər] 명 지원자
- **unique** [juːníːk] 형 독특한

Key Expressions

- **according to** ~에 따르면
- **be good at** ~을 잘하다
- **be worried about** ~을 걱정하다
- **by oneself** 혼자서
- **chances are that** 아마 ~일 것이다
- **clear one's mind** 마음을 가다듬다, 마음을 맑게 하다
- **come over** (장소에) 들르다
- **come up with** (해답 등을) 찾아내다, 내놓다
- **do ~ a favor** ~에게 호의를 베풀다
- **get off** 내리다
- **get up** 일어나다
- **have no idea** 알지 못하다
- **I can't wait!** 너무 기다려져!
- **in front of** ~의 앞에
- **make a presentation** 발표하다

- **make a reservation** 예약하다
- **not ~ anymore** 더 이상 ~가 아닌
- **not ~ at all** 결코 ~가 아닌
- **not only A but also B** A뿐만 아니라 B도 또한
- **put too much pressure on** ~에게 너무 많은 부담을 주다
- **Shall we ~?** ~할까요?
- **stand tall** 당당해 보이다, 우뚝 서다
- **with one's feet apart** 양발을 벌린 채로
- **stop by** ~에 들르다
- **strangely enough** 매우 이상하게도
- **turn A into B** A를 B로 바꾸다
- **What if ~?** ~하면 어쩌지?
- **Why don't you ~?** ~하지 않겠니?
- **Why not?** 좋죠!

Word Power

※ 서로 비슷한 뜻을 가진 어휘

- ☐ **actually** 실제로 : **really** 실제로
- ☐ **carefully** 조심스럽게 : **attentively** 주의 깊게
- ☐ **guess** 추측하다 : **suppose** 추측하다
- ☐ **lucky** 운이 좋은 : **fortunate** 운 좋은

- ☐ **anxious** 불안해하는 : **nervous** 불안해하는
- ☐ **confident** 자신감 있는 : **convinced** 확신하는
- ☐ **helpless** 무력한 : **powerless** 힘없는
- ☐ **place** 놓다, 두다 : **put** 두다

※ 서로 반대되는 뜻을 가진 어휘

- ☐ **carefully** 조심스럽게 ↔ **carelessly** 부주의하게
- ☐ **convenient** 편리한 ↔ **inconvenient** 불편한
- ☐ **lend** 빌려주다 ↔ **borrow** 빌리다
- ☐ **rare** 드문, 희귀한 ↔ **common** 흔한

- ☐ **certain** 확실한 ↔ **uncertain** 불확실한
- ☐ **enemy** 적 ↔ **friend** 친구
- ☐ **lucky** 운이 좋은 ↔ **unlucky** 운이 나쁜

※ 명사 – 형용사

- ☐ **beauty** 아름다움 – **beautiful** 아름다운
- ☐ **care** 보살핌, 조심 – **careful** 조심스러운
- ☐ **thought** 생각 – **thoughtful** 신중한
- ☐ **hope** 희망 – **hopeful** 희망찬
- ☐ **person** 사람 – **personal** 개인적인
- ☐ **nation** 국가 – **national** 국가적인

- ☐ **color** 색 – **colorful** 다채로운
- ☐ **success** 성공 – **successful** 성공적인
- ☐ **power** 힘 – **powerful** 힘 있는
- ☐ **stress** 스트레스 – **stressful** 스트레스가 많은
- ☐ **option** 선택 – **optional** 선택적인
- ☐ **tradition** 전통 – **traditional** 전통적인

※ Word Partner (collocations)

- ☐ **come back** 돌아오다
- ☐ **come over** (장소에) 들르다
- ☐ **come to a decision** 결정을 내리다
- ☐ **come to an end** 끝내다

- ☐ **come first** 최우선이다
- ☐ **come prepared** 준비해 오다
- ☐ **come to an agreement** 합의에 이르다
- ☐ **come up with** 생각해 내다

English Dictionary

- ☐ **bake** 굽다
  → to cook something using dry heat, in an oven
  오븐에서 열을 이용해서 어떤 것을 요리하다

- ☐ **chew** (음식을) 씹다
  → to bite food several times before swallowing it
  삼키기 전에 음식을 몇 번 물다

- ☐ **convenient** 편리한
  → useful to you because it saves you time
  시간을 덜어주기 때문에 쓸모가 있는

- ☐ **enemy** 적
  → someone who hates you and wants to harm you
  당신을 싫어하며 당신에게 해를 끼치고 싶어 하는 사람

- ☐ **graduate** 졸업하다
  → to complete your education at a college, school, etc.
  대학이나 학교 등에서 교육을 끝내다

- ☐ **presentation** 발표
  → an event at which you describe or explain a new product or idea
  새로운 상품이나 생각을 묘사하거나 설명하는 행사

- ☐ **psychology** 심리학
  → the study of the mind and how it influences people's behavior
  사람의 마음과 그것이 행동에 영향을 미치는 방식을 연구하는 학문

01 다음 짝지어진 단어의 관계가 같도록 빈칸에 알맞은 말을 주어진 철자로 시작하여 쓰시오.

> carefully : carelessly = common : r_____

02 다음 영영풀이가 가리키는 것을 고르시오.

> the study of the mind and how it influences people's behavior

① politics   ② psychology
③ psychologist   ④ presentation
⑤ solution

03 다음 중 밑줄 친 부분의 뜻풀이가 바르지 <u>않은</u> 것은?

① He decided to retire because of the <u>political</u> scandals. (정치적인)
② Wild flowers are becoming <u>rare</u>. (드문, 귀한)
③ You should not <u>judge</u> a man by his appearance. (판단하다)
④ She was in a relaxed and <u>confident</u> mood. (편안한)
⑤ The man is responsible for a very <u>professional</u> job. (전문적인)

04 다음 주어진 문장의 밑줄 친 judge와 같은 의미로 쓰인 것은?

> Don't <u>judge</u> a book by its cover.

① Chris was asked to <u>judge</u> the singing competition.
② He was brought before the <u>judge</u>.

③ It's difficult to <u>judge</u> how long the journey will take.
④ Mr. White will <u>judge</u> this case.
⑤ We can't <u>judge</u> whether what you're doing well or not.

05 다음 문장에 공통으로 들어갈 말을 고르시오.

> • When will you _____ back?
> • My twin sister tried to _____ up with a unique idea.
> • We would love to have you _____ over and celebrate with us.

① go   ② get
③ lend   ④ decide
⑤ come

서답형

06 다음 우리말에 맞게 빈칸에 알맞은 말을 쓰시오.

(1) 당신은 그것들을 적어도 1미터는 떨어뜨려 놓아야 합니다.
➡ You should place them at least one meter _____.

(2) 아이들은 그들의 잘한 행동에 대해 사탕을 받았다.
➡ Children were given sweets for their good _____.

(3) Jack은 양 허리께에 손을 대고 서 있다.
➡ Jack is standing with his hands on his _____.

(4) 대부분의 별들은 사람의 시야에 보이지 않는다.
➡ Most stars are _____ to human sight.

01 다음 짝지어진 단어의 관계가 같도록 빈칸에 알맞은 말을 쓰시오.

> person : personal = care : _____

02 다음 우리말에 맞게 빈칸에 알맞은 말을 쓰시오.

(1) 아마 그는 회의에 늦을 것이다.
➡ _____ _____ _____ he will be late for the meeting.

(2) 매우 이상하게도, 나는 전혀 불안하지 않다.
➡ _____ _____, I don't feel nervous at all.

(3) 항상 당당해 보이고 리더가 되어라.
➡ Always _____ _____ and be a leader.

(4) 나는 혼자서 이 모든 것을 할 수 없다.
➡ I can't do it all _____ _____.

03 다음 우리말을 주어진 단어를 이용하여 영작하시오.

(1) 나는 전문적인 심리학자가 되고 싶다. (become)
➡ _____

(2) 아이들은 쉽게 지루해한다. (get, bored)
➡ _____

(3) 내 개는 종종 내 신발을 씹는다. (shoes)
➡ _____

(4) 네 자신을 믿어라, 그리고 자신감을 가져라. (be, in)
➡ _____

04 다음 문장의 빈칸에 들어갈 말을 〈보기〉에서 골라 쓰시오.

> **보기**
> rivals / seat / judge / loudly / law

(1) Do not _____ a book by its cover.

(2) People say it is Murphy's _____ when something goes wrong.

(3) When I am happy, I sing _____.

(4) The two teams have been _____ since the first match.

(5) You don't have to sit in your _____.

05 우리말과 일치하도록 주어진 단어를 모두 배열하여 영작하시오.

(1) 그의 그림 실력은 거의 전문가적이다. (skills / professional / are / his / almost / drawing)
➡ _____
_____

(2) 그녀가 예약하는 걸 잊어버리면 어떡하죠? (she / make / a / if / what / reservation / to / forgets)
➡ _____

(3) 나는 마음을 가다듬기 위해 산책하기로 결심했다. (to / a / to / my / I / take / mind / decided / walk / clear)
➡ _____
_____

(4) 두 발을 벌리고 서서 손바닥은 위로 향하게 하라. (upwards / stand / feet / your / your / facing / apart / hands / with / and)
➡ _____
_____

Conversation

① 걱정하기

> • I'm worried about Sports Day. 난 운동회가 걱정돼.

■ 걱정이 된다는 것을 나타내는 표현은 'I'm worried ∼(나는 ∼가 걱정돼.)' 또는 'I'm concerned ∼(나는 ∼가 걱정돼.)'라고 한다. 걱정을 나타내는 nervous 또는 문제를 나타내는 trouble을 써서 'I'm nervous about ∼', 'I'm in trouble ∼'이라고 할 수도 있다.

■ 걱정이 되는 것이 두려움이나 무서움을 포함하고 있을 때는 scared, frightened, terrified 등을 써서 'I'm scared ∼', 'I'm frightened ∼', 'I'm terrified ∼' 등으로 나타내기도 한다. 이 말에 공감할 때는 'Me, too.(나도 그래.)'라고 한다.

■ 걱정이 되는 내용을 덧붙일 때는 전치사 about나 접속사 that을 써서 'I'm worried about ∼' 또는 'I'm worried that ∼'이라고 한다. about 뒤에는 명사나 동명사를 쓰고 that 뒤에는 주어, 동사가 있는 절을 쓴다.

걱정하기

• I'm worried about 명사 / that 주어+동사 ∼.	나는 ∼가 걱정돼.
• I'm concerned about ∼.	나는 ∼가 걱정이야.
• I'm afraid that ∼ .	나는 ∼가 걱정돼.
• I'm nervous about ∼.	나는 ∼가 불안해.
• I'm anxious about ∼.	나는 ∼가 걱정이야.

핵심 Check

1. 다음 밑줄 친 (A)의 우리말과 일치하도록 주어진 어휘를 포함하여 영어로 쓰시오.

   G: What happened to your shoes? Aren't they new?

   B: Yes, but my dog chewed them. He does it all the time. (A)난 그가 걱정돼. (worried, him)

   G: He was probably bored. Why don't you play with him more often?

   B: O.K, I will. I hope he will stop chewing my shoes.

   ➡ _____

② 의무 부인하기

> • **You don't have to clean the classroom.** 너는 교실을 청소할 필요가 없어.

■ '~해야 한다'는 뜻의 의무를 나타내는 표현은 'You have to+동사원형(~해야 한다)', 'You must+동사원형(~해야 한다)', 'You should/ought to+동사원형(~해야 한다)', 'You need to+동사원형(~할 필요가 있다)' 등이다.

■ 의무를 나타내는 'have to'를 부정하여 'don't/doesn't have to+동사원형'이 되면 의무를 부인하여 '~할 필요가 없다'는 뜻으로 'don't need to+동사원형'과 비슷한 의미가 된다. 'There is no need to+동사원형'도 '~할 필요가 없다.'는 의미로 의무를 부인하는 표현이다. must, should는 긍정 표현일 때는 의무를 나타내지만, 'must not', 'should not'처럼 부정이 되면 '~해서는 안 된다'는 의미의 금지를 나타내는 표현이 된다.

■ 그 외에 의무를 나타내는 표현으로 'be supposed to+동사원형(~해야 한다, ~하기로 되어 있다)'가 있고, 'have to'를 강조하여 'have got to+동사원형(~해야 한다)'이 있다. 'be not supposed to'는 '~해서는 안 된다'는 의미의 금지 표현이다.

의무 부인하기

- You don't have to ~.   ~할 필요가 없다.
- You don't need to ~.   ~할 필요가 없다.
- There's no need to ~.   ~할 필요가 없다.

핵심 Check

2. 다음 대화의 밑줄 친 (A)의 우리말에 해당하는 적절한 표현을 쓰시오.

   A: I'm going to the school library. Do I have to bring my student ID?

   B: (A)아니, 그럴 필요 없어.

   ➡  _____ / _____

3. 다음 대화를 자연스러운 순서로 배열하시오.

   M: Shall we have seafood spaghetti for dinner?

   (A) You don't have to do that. We already have what we need.

   (B) Oh, I see. Then, I'll be back home by 6 to help you cook.

   (C) Sure. I'll stop by the store on the way home.

   ➡  _____

Listen and Speak 1 A-1

G: What happened to your shoes? Aren't ❶they new?

B: Yes, but my dog chewed them. ❷He does it all the time. ❸I'm worried about ❷him.

G: He was probably ❹bored. ❺Why don't you play with him more often?

B: O.K., I will. I hope he will ❻stop chewing my shoes.

G: 신발이 왜 그래? 새것 아니었어?
B: 맞는데, 내 개가 씹어 버렸어. 항상 그렇게 해. 그 개가 걱정돼.
G: 아마 심심했을 거야. 개와 더 자주 놀아 주는 게 어때?
B: 알겠어, 그럴게. 그 개가 내 신발 씹는 걸 그만두면 좋겠네.

❶ they는 your shoes를 가리킨다.　　　❷ He와 him은 my dog을 가리킨다.
❸ 걱정이 된다는 것을 나타내는 표현으로 'I'm concerned about him.' 또는 'I'm anxious about him.'으로 바꾸어 표현할 수 있다.
❹ bored: 지루해하는
❺ 'Why don't you ~?'는 무언가를 제안하는 표현으로 'How about ~?' 또는 'What about ~?' 등으로 바꾸어 표현할 수 있다.
❻ stop+-ing: ~하던 것을 멈추다, stop+to부정사: ~하기 위해 멈추다

Check(√) True or False

(1) The boy's dog chewed his new shoes. ⬜T ⬜F

(2) The boy is going to play with his dog if his dog stops chewing his shoes. ⬜T ⬜F

Communicate A

Yuri: Hi, Jaden. Sports Day is next Friday. ❶I can't wait!

Jaden: Really? I'm actually worried about ❷it.

Yuri: Why? ❸Aren't you good at sports?

Jaden: Yes, I am, but I'm worried about the 800-meter relay.

Yuri: What do you mean?

Jaden: I'm the last runner. ❹What if our team loses because of me?

Yuri: I think you're ❺putting too much pressure on yourself.

Jaden: Really? Don't you think I should practice every day?

Yuri: No, you don't have to do that. It's just a school race. It's not about winning or losing.

Jaden: I guess you're right, Yuri. I'm lucky to have a friend like you.

유리: 안녕, Jaden. 운동회가 다음 주 금요일이야. 너무 기다려져!
Jaden: 정말? 난 사실 걱정돼.
유리: 왜? 너 운동 잘하지 않아?
Jaden: 응, 그렇긴 하지만, 800미터 릴레이가 걱정돼.
유리: 무슨 뜻이니?
Jaden: 내가 마지막 주자거든. 나 때문에 우리 팀이 지면 어쩌지?
유리: 넌 네 스스로에게 너무 많은 압박을 주고 있는 것 같아.
Jaden: 그래? 내가 매일 연습해야 한다고 생각하지 않니?
유리: 아니, 그럴 필요 없어. 그냥 학교 경기일 뿐인걸. 이기고 지고에 관한 게 아냐.
Jaden: 네 말이 맞는 것 같다. 유리야. 너 같은 친구를 둬서 다행이야.

❶ 'I can't wait!'은 '너무 기다려져!'라고 기대감을 나타내는 표현으로 'I'm looking forward to it.' 등으로 바꾸어 표현할 수 있다.
❷ it은 'Sports Day'를 가리킨다.　　　❸ be good at ~: ~을 잘하다
❹ What if ~?: '~하면 어쩌지?'라는 의미를 나타낸다.　　　❺ put too much pressure on: ~에게 너무 많은 부담을 주다

Check(√) True or False

(3) Jaden is going to take part in the 800-meter relay as the last runner. ⬜T ⬜F

(4) Yuri focuses on the importance of winning at the race. ⬜T ⬜F

Listen and Speak 1 A-2

B: You look a bit ❶nervous.

G: I'm worried about my swimming ❷ competition this Saturday.

B: Don't worry. You're ❸such a good swimmer. Just relax and enjoy yourself!

G: Thanks. I feel much better now.

❶ nervous: 긴장된
❷ competition: 대회
❸ such a(n)+형용사+명사

 Listen and Speak 2 A-1

B: Mom, what time are we going to ❶Grandma's place tomorrow morning?

W: About 8 a.m. I'm going to ❷bake cookies for ❸her before we go.

B: Then, should I ❹get up early to help you?

W: ❺You don't have to. Your dad will help me.

B: O.K, then. Good night, Mom!

❶ place: 주택, 집
❷ bake: 굽다
❸ her는 Grandma를 가리킨다.
❹ get up: 일어나다
❺ 의무를 부인하는 표현으로 'You don't need to.'로 바꾸어 표현할 수 있다.

Listen and Speak 2 A-2

W: Shall we try that new Mexican restaurant tomorrow?

M: ❶Why not? I'll call the restaurant to ❷make a reservation for us.

W: You don't have to call them. You can ❸do it online.

M: Oh, I see. How ❹convenient!

❶ 'Why not?'은 '좋죠!'라는 동의의 표현이다.
❷ make a reservation: 예약하다
❸ do it = make a reservation
❹ convenient: 편리한

 Progress Check 1

B: You look ❶a bit nervous.

G: Well, I'm worried about my ❷presentation in history class.

B: Don't worry. ❸You've prepared ❹a lot. You'll ❺do a great job.

G: Thanks. I feel much better now.

❶ a bit: 조금
❷ presentation: 발표
❸ have p.p. 형태로 현재완료 시제를 나타낸다. prepare: 준비하다
❹ a lot: 많이
❺ do a great job: 잘하다

 Progress Check 2

M: ❶Shall we have ❷seafood spaghetti for dinner?

W: Sure. I'll ❸stop by the store ❹on the way home.

M: You don't have to ❺do that. We already have what we need.

W: Oh, I see. Then, I'll ❻be back home by 6 to help you cook.

❶ Shall we ~?: 우리 ~할까요?
❷ seafood: 해산물
❸ stop by: ~에 들르다 (= drop by)
❹ on the way home: 집에 가는 길에
❺ do that = stop by the store
❻ be back home: 집에 돌아오다

● 다음 우리말과 일치하도록 빈칸에 알맞은 말을 쓰시오.

Listen & Speak 1 A-1

G: What _____ _____ your shoes? Aren't they new?

B: Yes, but my dog _____ them. He does it _____ _____ _____. I'm _____ _____ him.

G: He was probably _____. _____ _____ _____ play with him more often?

B: O.K., I will. I _____ he will stop _____ my shoes.

G: 신발이 왜 그래? 새것 아니었어?

B: 맞는데, 내 개가 씹어 버렸어. 항상 그렇게 해. 그 개가 걱정돼.

G: 아마 심심했었을 거야. 개와 더 자주 놀아 주는 게 어때?

B: 알겠어, 그렇게. 그 개가 내 신발 씹는 걸 그만두면 좋겠네.

Listen & Speak 1 A-2

B: You look a bit _____.

G: I'm worried about my _____ _____ this Saturday.

B: Don't _____. You're such a good swimmer. Just _____ and _____ yourself!

G: Thanks. I feel much _____ now.

B: 너 좀 긴장한 것 같아 보이는데.

G: 이번 토요일에 있는 수영 대회가 걱정돼.

B: 걱정 마. 너는 수영을 아주 잘 하잖아. 그냥 긴장을 풀고 즐겨!

G: 고마워. 기분이 훨씬 괜찮아졌어.

Listen & Speak 2 A-1

B: Mom, _____ _____ are we going to Grandma's place tomorrow morning?

W: About 8 a.m. I'm going to _____ _____ for her before we go.

B: Then, should I _____ _____ early to help you?

W: You _____ _____ _____. Your dad will help me.

B: O.K, then. Good night, Mom!

B: 엄마, 우리 내일 아침 몇 시에 할머니 댁에 가나요?

W: 8시쯤에. 가기 전에 할머니를 위해 쿠키를 구울 거란다.

B: 그럼, 제가 일찍 일어나서 도와드릴까요?

W: 그럴 필요 없단다. 아빠가 도와주실 거야.

B: 알겠어요, 그럼. 안녕히 주무세요, 엄마!

Listen & Speak 2 A-2

W: _____ _____ _____ that new Mexican restaurant tomorrow?

M: _____ not? I'll call the restaurant to _____ _____ _____ for us.

W: You _____ _____ _____ call them. You can do it _____.

M: Oh, I see. How _____!

W: 우리 내일 새로 생긴 멕시코 레스토랑에 가 볼까요?

M: 좋죠! 레스토랑에 전화해서 예약해 둘게요.

W: 전화할 필요 없어요. 온라인으로 할 수 있거든요.

M: 오, 그렇군요. 정말 편리하네요!

Communicate A

Yuri: Hi, Jaden. Sports Day is next Friday. I can't _____!

Jaden: Really? I'm actually _____ about it.

Yuri: Why? Aren't you _____ _____ sports?

Jaden: Yes, I am, but I'm worried about the 800-meter _____.

Yuri: _____ do you _____?

Jaden: I'm the _____ _____. _____ _____ our team loses because of me?

Yuri: I think you're _____ _____ _____ _____ _____ yourself.

Jaden: Really? Don't you think I should _____ every day?

Yuri: No, you _____ _____ _____ _____ that. It's just a school race. It's not about _____ or _____.

Jaden: I guess you're _____, Yuri. I'm _____ to have a friend like you.

Progress Check 1

B: You look a bit _____.

G: Well, I'm worried about my _____ in _____ class.

B: Don't worry. You've _____ a lot. You'll _____ a great _____.

G: Thanks. I _____ _____ _____ now.

Progress Check 2

M: Shall we have _____ _____ for dinner?

W: Sure. I'll _____ _____ the store _____ _____ home.

M: _____ _____ _____ _____ do that. We already have _____ we need.

W: Oh, I see. Then, I'll be _____ home by 6 to _____ you _____.

해석

유리: 안녕, Jaden. 운동회가 다음 주 금요일이야. 너무 기다려져!
Jaden: 정말? 난 사실 걱정돼.
유리: 왜? 너 운동 잘하지 않아?
Jaden: 응, 그렇긴 하지만, 800미터 릴레이가 걱정돼.
유리: 무슨 뜻이니?
Jaden: 내가 마지막 주자거든. 나 때문에 우리 팀이 지면 어쩌지?
유리: 넌 네 스스로에게 너무 많은 압박을 주고 있는 것 같아.
Jaden: 그래? 내가 매일 연습해야 한다고 생각하지 않니?
유리: 아니, 그럴 필요 없어. 그냥 학교 경기일 뿐인걸. 이기고 지고에 관한 게 아냐.
Jaden: 네 말이 맞는 것 같다, 유리야. 너 같은 친구를 둬서 다행이야.

B: 너 좀 긴장한 것 같다.
G: 그게, 역사 수업 시간에 내가 할 발표가 걱정돼.
B: 걱정 마. 많이 준비했잖아. 잘할 거야.
G: 고마워. 기분이 훨씬 나아졌어.

M: 우리 저녁으로 해물 스파게티를 먹을까요?
W: 좋아요. 집에 오는 길에 가게에 들를게요.
M: 그럴 필요 없어요. 필요한 건 이미 가지고 있거든요.
W: 오, 그렇군요. 그럼, 6시까지 돌아와서 요리하는 걸 도울게요.

Conversation 시험대비 기본평가

[01~02] 다음 대화를 읽고 물음에 답하시오.

Jane: What ⓐhappened to your shoes? Aren't they new?

Brian: Yes, but my dog ⓑchewed them. He does it all the time. I'm ⓒ worried about him.

Jane: He was probably ⓓbored. Why don't you play with him more often?

Brian: O.K., I will. I hope he will stop ⓔto chew my shoes

01 위 대화의 ⓐ~ⓔ중 어색한 것을 찾아 바르게 고치시오.

➡ _____

02 위 대화의 내용과 일치하지 않는 것은?

① Brian의 새 신발이 망가졌다.

② Brian의 개가 Brian의 신발을 처음으로 씹었다.

③ Brian은 그의 개가 걱정이 된다.

④ Jane은 Brian에게 개와 더 자주 놀아줄 것을 제안했다.

⑤ Brian은 그의 개가 신발을 씹는 걸 그만 두길 바란다.

[03~04] 다음 대화를 읽고 물음에 답하시오.

B: You look a bit nervous.

G: I'm worried about my swimming competition this Saturday.

B: Don't worry. You're such a good swimmer. Just relax and enjoy yourself!

G: Thanks. I feel much better now.

03 What's the matter with the girl?

➡ _____

04 What does the boy advise the girl to do?

➡ _____

[01~03] 다음 대화를 읽고 물음에 답하시오.

Jane: What happened to your shoes? Aren't they new?

Brian: Yes, but my dog chewed them. He does it all the time. (A)I'm worried about him.

Jane: He was probably bored. (B)Why don't you play with him more often? (about, how)

Brian: O.K., I will. I hope he will stop chewing my shoes.

01 위 대화의 밑줄 친 (A)와 바꾸어 쓸 수 있는 것을 모두 고르시오.

① I'm anxious about him.

② I'm fond of him.

③ I'm concerned about him.

④ I'm tired of him.

⑤ I'm glad to see him.

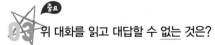

02 위 대화의 밑줄 친 (B)와 의미가 같도록 주어진 단어를 사용하여 다시 쓰시오.

➡ _____

03 위 대화를 읽고 대답할 수 없는 것은?

① What's the problem with Brian's shoes?

② Who chewed Brian's shoes?

③ What is Brian worried about?

④ What does Jane suggest to Brian?

⑤ When did Brian buy his shoes?

[04~05] 다음 대화를 읽고 물음에 답하시오.

B: You look a bit ___(A)___.

G: I'm worried about my swimming competition this Saturday.

B: Don't worry. You're such a good swimmer. Just relax and enjoy yourself!

G: Thanks. I feel much better now.

04 위 대화의 빈칸 (A)에 들어갈 말로 적절한 것은?

① satisfied ② excited

③ happy ④ pleased

⑤ nervous

05 위 대화에 나타난 여자의 심경 변화로 적절한 것은?

① worried → relieved

② nervous → disappointed

③ worried → lonely

④ nervous → lonely

⑤ disappointed → worried

06 다음 대화가 자연스럽게 이어지도록 순서대로 배열하시오.

(A) O.K, then. Good night, Mom!

(B) Then, should I get up early to help you?

(C) About 8 a.m. I'm going to bake cookies for her before we go.

(D) You don't have to. Your dad will help me.

(E) Mom, what time are we going to Grandma's place tomorrow morning?

➡ _____

[07~08] 다음 대화를 읽고 물음에 답하시오.

> Emily: Shall we try that new Mexican restaurant tomorrow?
>
> Tom: Why not? I'll call the restaurant to make a reservation for us.
>
> Emily: You don't have to call them. You can do it online.
>
> Tom: Oh, I see. How convenient!

서답형

07 What does Emily suggest doing?

➡ _____

➡ _____

서답형

08 Why doesn't Tom need to call the restaurant to make a reservation? (6 words)

➡ _____

[09~10] 다음 대화를 읽고 물음에 답하시오.

> Yuri: Hi, Jaden. Sports Day is next Friday. I can't wait!
>
> Jaden: Really? I'm actually worried about it.
>
> Yuri: Why? Aren't you good at sports?
>
> Jaden: Yes, I am, but I'm (A)[concerned / concerning] about the 800-meter relay.
>
> Yuri: What do you mean?
>
> Jaden: I'm the last runner. What if our team loses (B)[because / because of] me?
>
> Yuri: I think you're putting too much pressure on (C)[you / yourself].
>
> Jaden: Really? Don't you think I should practice every day?
>
> Yuri: No, you don't have to do that. It's just a school race. It's not about winning or losing.
>
> Jaden: I guess you're right, Yuri. I'm lucky to have a friend like you.

09 위 대화의 (A)~(C)에 들어갈 말이 바르게 짝지어진 것은?

	(A)	(B)	(C)
①	concerned	because	you
②	concerned	because of	yourself
③	concerned	because of	you
④	concerning	because of	yourself
⑤	concerning	because	you

중요

10 위 대화를 읽고 대답할 수 <u>없는</u> 것은?

① When is Sports Day?

② What is Jaden worried about?

③ How has Jaden's feeling changed?

④ Should Jaden practice for the 800-meter relay every day?

⑤ Who is the first runner of the 800-meter relay?

11 다음 짝지어진 대화가 <u>어색한</u> 것은?

① A: I'm worried about Sports Day. I'm not good at sports.
   B: I know how you feel, but try to enjoy it.

② A: I'm concerned about my brother. He gets angry so often these days.
   B: How about trying to calm him down?

③ A: I'm worried about my English speaking test.
   B: Don't worry. You've prepared a lot. You can make it.

④ A: I'm anxious about my future.
   B: You're such a good student! Everything will be fine.

⑤ A: I'm nervous about my presentation in English class.
   B: I feel much better now. Thanks a lot.

01 다음 대화가 자연스럽게 이어지도록 순서대로 배열하시오.

> (A) Thanks. I feel much better now.
> (B) You look a bit nervous.
> (C) Don't worry. You've prepared a lot. You'll do a great job.
> (D) Well, I'm worried about my presentation in history class.

➡ _____

[02~04] 다음 대화를 읽고 물음에 답하시오.

> Jack: Mom, what time are we going to Grandma's place tomorrow morning?
> Mom: About 8 a.m. I'm going to bake cookies for her before we go.
> Jack: Then, should I get up early to help you?
> Mom: You don't have to. Your dad will help me.
> Jack: O.K, then. Good night, Mom!

02 What is Jack going to do tomorrow?

➡ _____

03 What is Jack's mom going to do before she visits Jack's grandma's place?

➡ _____

04 Why doesn't Jack's mom need his help tomorrow morning?

➡ _____
_____

05 다음 대화의 내용과 일치하도록 Jaden의 일기를 완성하시오.

> Yuri: Hi, Jaden. Sports Day is next Friday. I can't wait!
> Jaden: Really? I'm actually worried about it.
> Yuri: Why? Aren't you good at sports?
> Jaden: Yes, I am, but I'm worried about the 800-meter relay.
> Yuri: What do you mean?
> Jaden: I'm the last runner. What if our team loses because of me?
> Yuri: I think you're putting too much pressure on yourself.
> Jaden: Really? Don't you think I should practice every day?
> Yuri: No, you don't have to do that. It's just a school race. It's not about winning or losing.
> Jaden: I guess you're right, Yuri. I'm lucky to have a friend like you.

> Mon, June 15th, 2020
> Today, I was so concerned about Sports Day. I was chosen as the (A)_____ of the 800-meter relay. All my classmates believed that I can do it very well. But I felt so burdened. I was worried that (B)_____. I talked about it to Yuri and she said that I was putting too (C)_____ on myself. Actually, I was thinking whether (D)_____ every day or not. Yuri advised me not to do so, because it's just a school race, not about (E)_____. I was encouraged by her a lot. I really appreciated her today.

Grammar

① 분사구문

> • **Feeling** nervous, Jisu was carefully studying her notes in her chair.
> 지수는 긴장이 되어, 의자에 앉아 자신의 필기를 열심히 들여다보고 있었다.

■ 종속접속사가 이끄는 부사절을 분사를 이용하여 간략한 부사구로 바꾼 것이다.

• **While I was walking** on the street, I saw my teacher.

= **Walking** on the street, I saw my teacher. 거리를 걷고 있었을 때, 나는 선생님을 봤다.

■ 부사구와 주절의 관계에 따라 양보, 동시동작, 이유, 시간, 조건 등의 의미로 쓰인다.

(1) 양보: **Although he is** over 90, the businessman runs faster than the young.

= **Being** over 90, the businessman runs faster than the young.
비록 그 사업가는 90세가 넘었지만, 젊은 사람들보다 빨리 뛴다.

(2) 동시동작(부대상황): **While she sat** on the bed, she watched TV.

= **Sitting** on the bed, she watched TV. 침대에 앉아서 그녀는 TV를 시청했다.

(3) 이유: **As he was** tired, Harry went to bed early.

= **Being tired**, Harry went to bed early. 피곤했기 때문에, Harry는 일찍 잠자리에 들었다.

(4) 시간: **When she doesn't work**, she enjoys the board games.

= **Not working**, she enjoys the board games. 일하지 않을 때, 그녀는 보드게임을 즐긴다.

(5) 조건: **If you take** a taxi, you'll get to the party on time.

= **Taking** a taxi, you'll get to the party on time. 택시를 타면, 파티에 제 시간에 도착할 거야.

■ 종속절의 시제가 주절보다 앞선 경우, 완료분사구문을 사용한다.

• **As she had done** it before, Susan knew how to fix the copy machine.

= **Having done** it before, Susan knew how to fix the copy machine.

■ 주절과 종속절의 주어가 다를 경우, 분사구문의 주어를 남겨 두는 것을 독립분사구문이라고 하며, 일반인이 주어일 경우에는 생략 가능하다. (비인칭 독립분사구문)

(1) 독립분사구문: **As it was** cloudy, we couldn't go on a field trip.

= **It being** cloudy, we couldn't go on a field trip. 날이 흐려서, 소풍을 갈 수 없었다.

(2) 비인칭 독립분사구문: **generally speaking**(일반적으로 말해), **considering**(~를 고려하면)

(3) with+목적어+분사: Mom fell asleep **with the TV turned on**. (TV를 켠 채로)

핵심 Check

1. 다음 괄호 안에서 알맞은 말을 고르시오.

(1) (Feeling / Felt) worried, Jake drove to the subway station to pick her up.

(2) With night (come / coming) on, it got colder and colder.

② 상관접속사 not only ~ but also ...

• His rival became **not only** a political supporter **but also** a good friend.
그의 경쟁자는 정치적 지원자 뿐만 아니라 좋은 친구가 되었다.

■ 상관접속사 'not only A but also B'는 'A뿐만 아니라 B도 또한'이라는 뜻이며, 'B as well as A'로 바꿀 수 있다. 접속사이므로 A와 B 자리에 명사뿐만 아니라 동사, 형용사, 준동사 등 어떤 것이든 올 수 있으며, A에 동사가 오면 B에도 동사가 와야 한다.

• My mom is **not only** a good cook **but also** a great painter.

= My mom is a great painter as well as a good cook. 우리 어머니는 훌륭한 요리사일 뿐만 아니라 대단한 화가이기도 하다.

■ 상관접속사의 종류와 주어로 쓰일 때의 수 일치

(1) Not only A but also B(= B as well as A): A뿐만 아니라 B도 또한 (B에 일치)

• **Not only** they **but also** she wants the job. 그들뿐만 아니라 그녀도 그 일을 원한다.

= She **as well as** they **wants** the job.

(2) Not A but B: A가 아니라 B (B에 일치)

• **Not** they **but** she **wants** the job. 그들이 아니라 그녀가 그 일을 원한다.

(3) Both A and B: A와 B 둘 다 (복수 주어)

• **Both** they **and** she **want** the job. 그들과 그녀 모두 다 그 일을 원한다.

(4) Either A or B: A 또는 B 둘 중 하나 (동사와 가까운 주어에 일치)

• **Either** they **or** she **wants** the job. 그들 또는 그녀 둘 중 하나는 그 일을 원한다.

(5) Neither A nor B: A도 B도 아닌 (동사와 가까운 주어에 일치)

• **Neither** they **nor** she **wants** the job. 그들도 그녀도 그 일을 원하지 않는다.

■ Not only가 주어가 아닌 동사를 받을 경우 문두에 오면 도치가 일어난다.

• **Not only** is he wise, **but also** he is kind. 그는 현명할 뿐만 아니라 친절하다.

• **Not only** could she read the book, **but also** she could memorize it.
그녀는 그 책을 읽을 수 있었을 뿐만 아니라 그 책을 외울 수도 있었다.

■ not only ~ but also에서 only 대신 just, simply 등을 쓸 수 있고, also는 생략해서 쓰기도 한다.

• The fairy was **not just** wise **but** beautiful. 그 요정은 지혜로울 뿐만 아니라 아름다웠다.

핵심 Check

2. 다음 문장에서 어법상 틀린 부분을 찾아 바르게 고쳐 쓰시오.

(1) Andy not only plays but also teach the guitar. ➡ _____

(2) Not only you but also he are responsible for the problem. ➡ _____

01 다음 빈칸에 들어갈 말로 알맞은 것은?

> Mina is not only a good listener but also _____.

① sings well   ② beautiful   ③ has a sense of humor
④ poor at hearing   ⑤ a great leader

02 다음 부사절을 분사구문으로 바꿔 쓸 때, 빈칸에 들어갈 말로 가장 적절한 것은?

> As he wanted to make his dad feel better, Harry smiled brightly at him.
> → _____ to make his dad feel better, Harry smiled brightly at him.

① He wanting   ② As he wanting   ③ Wanting
④ Having wanted   ⑤ Being wanting

03 다음 중 어법상 옳지 <u>않은</u> 것을 고르시오.

① She is both generous and intelligent.
② Frank's friends not only sing well but also paint well.
③ He is interested either in soccer or in hockey.
④ Kevin not only writes well but also dancing well.
⑤ Nora has not only the dolls but also their house.

04 다음 분사구문을 접속사가 이끄는 부사절로 만들 때, 빈칸에 알맞은 말을 써 넣으시오.

(1) Listening to music, John cleaned his room.
➡ While _____ _____ _____ _____, John cleaned his room.

(2) Feeling lonely, she called her mother in New York.
➡ As _____ _____ _____, she called her mother in New York.

(3) Being small and weak, Ron has enough courage to complete the difficult mission before him.
➡ _____ _____ _____ _____ _____, Ron has enough courage to complete the difficult mission before him.

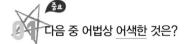

01 다음 중 어법상 어색한 것은?

① Not only your friends but also my uncle have those problems.
② The violinist not only played a beautiful song but also gave a great influence on young kids.
③ Lucy has lived not only in France but also in Egypt.
④ Not only the professor but also the student is working on the project.
⑤ Caroline ate not only the cookies but also the jams that her mother made.

[02~03] 다음 우리말을 알맞게 영작한 것을 고르시오.

02
> 그는 눈을 감은 채로 걷고 있었다.

① He was walking his eyes closing.
② He was closing his eyes and walking.
③ He walked and closed his eyes.
④ He was walking closed his eyes with.
⑤ He was walking with his eyes closed.

03
> 많은 사람들을 괴롭혔는데도 불구하고, Tom은 부자로 잘 살았다.

① Even though he having bullied many people, Tom lived well off.
② Although he bullying many people, Tom lived well off.
③ Having bullied many people, Tom living well off.
④ Though having bullied many people, Tom lived well off.
⑤ He had bullied many people, though Tom lived well off.

[04~05] 다음 중 어법상 옳은 것을 고르시오.

04 ① Both Jinsu and his sister is reading the article about the history of Jeju.
② Not only William but also Bentley have lived in New York since last year.
③ Kevin bought Minsu not only the laptop but also a bag.
④ I don't have neither a pen nor a pencil.
⑤ Not only I am hungry but also can't move a little.

05 ① Not only Mary but also Chris speak Spanish well.
② Not only the students but also the teacher know who the girl is.
③ Not only he but also you is wrong.
④ Tell me not only what you like but also she likes to go.
⑤ Elizabeth not only teaches swimming but also sells a lot of swim suits.

06 다음 문장에서 어법상 어색한 단어 한 개를 찾아서 고치시오.

> Exhausting after the hard work, Paula laid herself down on the bed on coming home.

_____ ➡ _____

07 다음 두 문장을 의미가 같도록 한 문장으로 바꿔 쓸 때 적절하지 않은 것은?

① Tom likes the book. + Jimmy likes the book, too.
→ Not only Tom but also Jimmy likes the book.

② Cory listens to the radio program. + Sean listens to the radio program, too.
→ Both Cory and Sean listens to the radio program.

③ One of the two students, Martha or Sue, may have the answer sheet.
→ Either Martha or Sue may have the answer sheet.

④ Kim doesn't know the way home. Her cousins don't know the way home, either.
→ Neither Kim nor her cousins know the way home.

⑤ Sharon could solve the quiz. + Sharon could pass the exam as well.
→ Sharon could not only solve the quiz but also pass the exam.

08 다음 중 밑줄 친 분사구문의 용법이 〈보기〉와 같은 것은?

┤ 보기 ├
<u>Born</u> in America, Sam isn't good at speaking English.

① <u>Living</u> in Busan for over 10 years, Rena can't understand the conversation between Busan citizens.

② <u>Finishing</u> her homework, Anna went outside to meet her boyfriend.

③ <u>Having</u> nothing special to do, I just called Robert.

④ <u>Not knowing</u> how long she waited for me, I was surprised at her cold hands.

⑤ <u>Turning</u> left at first corner, you can find the post office.

09 다음 〈보기〉의 문장과 가장 가까운 뜻을 가진 문장을 고르시오.

┤ 보기 ├
Not only Josh but also Mina doesn't like smoking as well as drinking.

① Both Josh and Mina don't like smoking but drinking.

② Neither Josh nor Mina likes both smoking and drinking.

③ Either Josh or Mina doesn't like smoking nor drinking.

④ Neither Josh nor Mina doesn't like smoking but also drinking.

⑤ Both Josh and Mina hate not smoking but drinking.

10 다음 주어진 분사구문을 접속사를 이용한 부사절로 만들 때 가장 적절한 것은?

The disease having come from China, Chinese government blames Korea.

① Since the disease comes from China, Chinese government blames Korea.

② Although the disease comes from China, Chinese government blames Korea.

③ If the disease came from China, Chinese government blames Korea.

④ Though the disease came from China, Chinese government blames Korea.

⑤ While the disease comes from China, Chinese government blames Korea.

[11~12] 다음 중 어법상 옳은 문장은?

11
① Cecilia had lost not only the necklace and also the rings.
② You can not only see the snowman but also likes the colder weather in winter.
③ My uncle not only arrived earlier but also prepared our dinner.
④ Not only the passengers were surprised but also irritated.
⑤ William likes only the pen but also the notebooks.

중요
12
① Both Clara or her husband watched the movie *Parasite*.
② Can either you nor the doctor please explain us what worsens the situation?
③ Not only I but also David wonder whether the speaker is telling the truth.
④ I think either you or your mom know how the problem was solved.
⑤ Eliza loves not only Raynold but also me.

서답형
[13~14] 우리말과 일치하도록 괄호 안에 주어진 단어들을 바르게 배열하시오.

13
아주 오래 전에 나무와 마른 풀로 지어졌기 때문에, 그 집은 항상 화재의 위험에 노출되어 있다.
→ (wood, grass, having, and, built, of, been, dry) so long ago, the house is always exposed to the danger of fire.

➡ _____

14
또 다시 회의에 늦고 싶지 않았기 때문에, 그녀는 지하철역으로 최대한 빨리 뛰었다.
(be, for, not, the meeting, to, wanting, late) again, she ran to the subway station as fast as she could.

➡ _____

서답형
15 다음 그림을 보고 자연스러운 문장이 되도록 괄호 안에 주어진 단어를 바르게 배열하여 빈칸을 완성하시오.

(1)

➡ After _____
_____, (tall, Wonder Woman, for, a few, standing, minutes, like), Jisu didn't feel nervous anymore.

(2)

➡ Jenny was _____
_____ a splash on the street. (for, by, school, only, not, but, late, hit, also)

01 다음 우리말과 일치하도록 괄호 안에 주어진 단어들을 바르게 배열하여 문장을 완성하시오.

(1) 마음을 정리하고 싶기 때문에, Kobe는 혼자 하루 여행을 떠나기로 결정했다. (his, to, wanting, mind, clear)

➡ _____, Kobe decided to take a day trip by himself.

(2) 당신은 자신에 대한 확신이 생길 뿐만 아니라, 다른 사람이 보기에도 자신감에 차 보일 것이다. (look, feel, only, about, confident, sure, not, also, yourself, but)

➡ You will _____
_____ to other people.

(3) 경쟁자를 친구로 만들고 싶다면, 경쟁자에게 부탁을 하라. (into, a rival, turn, wanting, a friend, to)

➡ _____,
ask your rival to do you a favor.

02 다음 〈보기〉에 있는 접속사를 한 번씩만 사용하여, 각 밑줄 친 분사구문을 부사절로 바꾸시오. (단, 진행형 표현은 쓸 수 없다.)

┌─── 보기 ───┐
while   because   when   if   though
└──────────────┘

(1) Graduating from high school next year, Tammy wants to become a professional farmer.

➡ _____
_____

(2) Being sick all day long, I could complete the difficult project.

➡ _____
_____

(3) Having a problem that you cannot share with your family or friends, try talking to a stranger.

➡ _____
_____

(4) Listening to the radio, Henry cleaned his guitars.

➡ _____

(5) Not having to worry about being judged, we often tell strangers about our problems.

➡ _____
_____

03 다음 글을 읽고, 질문에 답하시오.

The hardest time in my life was my first grade in middle school. When my family moved to another city, I had to go to a new school. (A)As I didn't have any friends at school, I felt sad and lonely. One day, I asked one of my classmates to show me her notes. (B)(she, help, become, good friend) From this experience, I have learned that asking for help is a good way to make friends.

(1) 밑줄 친 (A)를 접속사가 없는 분사구문으로 바꾸되 'no'를 사용하시오.

➡ _____

(2) (B)의 괄호 속에 밑줄 친 단어들과 not only ~ but also를 활용해, 문맥에 맞게 영작하시오. (시제에 주의할 것)

➡ _____

_____

(3) 위에 나온 단어들을 활용하여, 다음 우리말을 7 단어의 분사구문으로 영작하시오.

'도움을 청하면, 당신은 친구를 사귈 수 있다.'

➡ _____

04 주어진 어구를 이용하여 〈조건〉에 맞게 영작하시오.

┌─ 조건 ─┐
1. 'not only A but also B'를 사용할 것.
2. 주어진 단어를 활용하되, 괄호 안의 글자 수 조건에 맞출 것.

(1) Minju's mom, good doctor, great cook (13 단어)

➡ _____

_____

(2) Harry, speak Spanish, dance well (9 단어)

➡ _____

(3) Seohyun, beautiful, very kind (9 단어)

➡ _____

(4) Frank, his parents, nice (9 단어)

➡ _____

_____

05 다음 문장에서 어법상 어색한 단어를 하나씩만 찾아 바르게 고치시오.

(1) Not only does she believe that she has to get a perfect score on every test but also she study without sleeping.

_____ ➡ _____

(2) Both my cat and your puppy is sick now.

_____ ➡ _____

(3) Either Ms. Brown or her sons is responsible for the problem.

_____ ➡ _____

(4) The new job she got lately was not only difficult but also too stress.

_____ ➡ _____

(5) I wonder why not only Jejudo but also the islands in the south coast is crowded with visitors these days.

_____ ➡ _____

06 다음 그림을 보고 괄호 안의 단어를 배열하여 빈칸을 알맞게 채우시오.

(1)

➡ The reason I recommend this restaurant is

_____

_____. (food, only, healthy, its, not, that, also, is, but, delicious)

(2)

➡ _____

to the local governor. (the farmer, donated, picked, huge, carrot, having, it, a)

Psychology Answers Your Questions

Do you think you have a unique problem? Chances are that many
아마 ~일 것이다. ~할 가능성이 충분하다
other people have the same problem. Psychology is the study of the

human mind and behavior, so it can help you find a solution to your
= psychology   ~가 …하는 것을 도와주다   ~에 대한

problem.

How do I become less nervous?

It was five minutes before Jisu's big presentation in front of the

whole class. Feeling nervous, Jisu was carefully studying her notes in
분사구문(= Because she was feeling)
her chair. Then, her teacher came over and told her to stand tall like
~에 오다, (집에) 들르다   told의 목적격보어
Wonder Woman. After standing tall for a few minutes, Jisu did not feel

nervous anymore. In fact, she was confident that she would make a
앞 문장에 나온 내용에 대해서 자세한 내용을 덧붙이거나 내용을 강조할 때 사용
great presentation. According to Amy Cuddy, a famous psychologist,
according to+명사(구): ~에 따르면   Amy Cuddy와 동격
we can become more confident just by standing tall for two minutes
by+동명사: ~함으로써
before stressful events. Our bodies change our minds, and our minds

can change our behavior. Do you want to feel confident? Stand

with your feet apart, and place your hands on your hips. You will
양발을 벌리고
not only feel sure about yourself but also look confident to other people.
not only A but also: A뿐만 아니라 B도(A와 B에는 문법적으로 동등한 형태의 표현을 쓰며, B를 강조함)

psychology 심리학

unique 유일무이한, 독특한

chances are that 아마 ~일 것이다

mind 마음, 정신

behavior 행동

solution 해법, 해결책

stand tall 당당해 보이다. 우뚝 서다

confident 자신감 있는

apart (거리 · 공간 · 시간상으로) 떨어져

hip 엉덩이, 허리께

확인문제

● 다음 문장이 본문의 내용과 일치하면 T, 일치하지 않으면 F를 쓰시오.

1 Only you have a unique problem. ☐

2 Psychology is the study of the human mind and behavior. ☐

3 After standing tall like Wonder Woman, Jisu felt confident. ☐

4 Our minds can't change our behavior. ☐

Who can help me feel better?

When he graduates from high school next year, Taeho wants to become a professional farmer. However, he has never told anyone about it. He is worried that his parents or his friends will not understand. Wanting to clear his mind, Taeho decided to take a day trip on a train by himself. On the train, he told a complete stranger sitting beside him about his problem. He had no idea why he did it. However, he felt much better when he got off the train. Strangely enough, we often tell strangers about our problems just like Taeho. That is because we do not have to worry about being judged or seeing them again. If you have a problem that you cannot share with your family or friends, try talking to a stranger. You will feel much better.

How do I turn a rival into a friend?

Benjamin Franklin once had a political rival who did not like him at all. Franklin wanted to become friends with him, so he came up with a plan. His rival had a rare book. Franklin asked his rival to lend him the book for a few days. When Franklin returned the book, he thanked him deeply. Since that day, his rival became not only a political supporter but also a good friend. Franklin famously said, "Enemies who do you one favor will want to do more." If you want to turn a rival into a friend, don't do your rival a favor. Instead, ask your rival to do you a favor.

---

graduate 졸업하다

professional 전문적인, 직업의

clear one's mind 마음을 가다듬다. 마음을 맑게 하다

by oneself 혼자

judge 판단하다

political 정치와 관련된, 정치적인

rival 경쟁자, 경쟁 상대

come up with (해답 등을) 찾아내다. 내놓다

rare 드문, 희귀한, 살짝 익힌

do ~ a favor ~에게 호의를 베풀다

확인문제

● 다음 문장이 본문의 내용과 일치하면 T, 일치하지 않으면 F를 쓰시오.

1 Taeho has never told anyone about what he wants to be. ☐

2 Taeho told his friends about his future hope. ☐

3 Franklin borrowed a rare book from his rival. ☐

4 Franklin's rival remained his political rival. ☐

● 우리말을 참고하여 빈칸에 알맞은 말을 쓰시오.

1 _____ Answers Your Questions

2 Do you think you have a _____ problem?

3 _____ _____ that many other people have the same problem.

4 Psychology is the study of the _____ _____ and _____, _____ it can help you _____ a solution _____ your problem.

5 How do I _____ _____ nervous?

6 It was five minutes before Jisu's _____ _____ in front of the _____ _____.

7 _____ nervous, Jisu was _____ _____ her notes in her chair.

8 Then, her teacher _____ _____ and told her _____ _____ like Wonder Woman.

9 After _____ _____ for a few minutes, Jisu did _____ feel nervous _____.

10 _____ _____, she was _____ _____ she would _____ a great presentation.

11 According to Amy Cuddy, a famous psychologist, we can _____ more confident just _____ _____ _____ for two minutes before _____ _____.

12 Our _____ change our _____, and our _____ can change our _____.

13 Do you want to _____ _____?

14 Stand with your feet _____, and _____ your hands _____ your hips.

15 You will _____ _____ _____ _____ about yourself _____ _____ _____ to other people.

16 Who can help me _____ better?

17 When he _____ high school next year, Taeho wants to become a _____ farmer.

18 _____, he _____ _____ _____ anyone about it.

1 심리학이 당신의 물음에 답하다

2 여러분은 당신만의 유일무이한 고민을 가지고 있다고 생각하는가?

3 아마 많은 다른 사람들이 여러분과 똑같은 고민을 가지고 있을 것이다.

4 심리학은 인간의 마음과 행동에 관한 연구이며, 따라서 여러분이 문제에 대한 해결책을 찾는 데 도움을 줄 수 있다.

5 어떻게 하면 긴장을 덜 할 수 있나요?

6 지수가 반 전체 앞에서 발표를 하기 5분 전이었다.

7 지수는 긴장이 되어, 의자에 앉아 자신의 필기를 열심히 들여다보고 있었다.

8 그때 선생님이 다가와서는 원더 우먼처럼 꼿꼿이 서 있어 보라고 말했다.

9 그렇게 몇 분을 우뚝 선 후에, 지수는 더 이상 긴장되지 않았다.

10 사실, 그녀는 발표를 멋있게 할 수 있을 것이라는 자신감이 생겼다.

11 유명한 심리학자인 Amy Cuddy에 의하면, 우리는 스트레스를 받는 상황 이전에 2분 정도 꼿꼿이 서 있는 것만으로도 자신감이 더 생길 수 있다고 한다.

12 우리의 몸은 마음을 바꾸고, 마음은 우리의 행동을 바꿀 수 있다.

13 자신감이 생기기를 원하는가?

14 양발을 벌리고, 허리께에 손을 올려 보아라.

15 자신에 대한 확신이 생길 뿐만 아니라 다른 사람이 보기에도 자신감이 차 보인다.

16 누가 내 기분을 낮게 해 줄 수 있나요?

17 내년에 고등학교를 졸업한 이후에 태호는 전문적인 농부가 되고 싶어 한다.

18 하지만, 누구에게도 그것에 대해 한 번도 말하지 않았다.

19 He is _____ _____ his parents or his friends _____ _____ _____.

20 _____ to _____ _____ _____, Taeho decided _____ _____ a day trip on a train _____ _____.

21 On the train, he told a _____ stranger _____ beside him about his problem.

22 He had no idea _____ _____ _____ _____.

23 _____, he _____ _____ _____ when he got off the train.

24 _____ _____, we often tell strangers about our problems just like Taeho.

25 That is _____ we do not have to worry about _____ _____ or _____ them again.

26 If you have a problem _____ you cannot _____ your family or friends, try _____ to a stranger.

27 You will _____ _____ better.

28 How do I _____ a _____ _____ a friend?

29 Benjamin Franklin once had a political rival _____ did _____ like him _____ _____.

30 Franklin wanted to _____ _____ _____ him, so he _____ _____ _____ a plan.

31 His rival had a _____ book.

32 Franklin asked his rival _____ _____ him the book for _____ _____ _____.

33 When Franklin returned the book, he thanked him _____.

34 _____ that day, his rival became _____ _____ a political supporter _____ _____ a good friend.

35 Franklin famously said, "Enemies _____ _____ _____ _____ _____ will want to do more."

36 If you want to _____ a rival _____ a friend, don't _____ _____ _____ _____ _____.

37 _____, ask your rival _____ _____ you a favor.

19 그는 부모님이나 친구들이 이해하지 못할까 걱정이 된다.

20 마음을 정리하기 위해서, 태호는 혼자 하루 기차 여행을 떠나기로 결심했다.

21 기차에서, 그는 옆에 앉은 전혀 모르는 사람에게 자신의 고민에 대해서 말했다.

22 그는 자신이 왜 그랬는지 알 수 없었다.

23 그러나, 기차에서 내릴 때 기분이 훨씬 좋아졌다.

24 정말 이상하게도, 우리는 태호처럼 우리의 문제에 대해 낯선 사람에게 말할 때가 있다.

25 그것은 우리가 평가받거나 그 사람을 다시 볼 것이라는 걱정을 할 필요가 없기 때문이다.

26 만약 가족이나 친구들과도 나눌 수 없는 고민이 있다면, 낯선 이에게 말해 보아라.

27 기분이 훨씬 나아질 것이다.

28 라이벌을 어떻게 친구로 만들 수 있을까요?

29 Benjamin Franklin에게는 한때 그를 전혀 좋아하지 않는 정치적 경쟁자가 있었다.

30 Franklin은 그와 친구가 되고 싶어서, 계획을 세웠다.

31 그의 경쟁자는 희귀한 책을 가지고 있었다.

32 Franklin은 그의 정적에게 그 책을 며칠 동안 빌려달라고 부탁했다.

33 Franklin이 그 책을 돌려줄 때, 그는 그에게 진심으로 감사를 표했다.

34 그날 이후로, 그의 경쟁자는 정치적인 후원자뿐만 아니라 좋은 친구가 되었다.

35 Franklin은 "당신을 한 번 도운 적은 더 돕고 싶어 하게 된다."라는 유명한 말을 했다.

36 여러분이 경쟁자를 친구로 만들고 싶다면, 경쟁자의 부탁을 들어주지 마라.

37 대신, 경쟁자에게 부탁을 해 보아라.

우리말을 참고하여 본문을 영작하시오.

1 심리학이 당신의 물음에 답하다
➡ _____

2 여러분은 당신만의 유일무이한 고민을 가지고 있다고 생각하는가?
➡ _____

3 아마 많은 다른 사람들이 여러분과 똑같은 고민을 가지고 있을 것이다.
➡ _____

4 심리학은 인간의 마음과 행동에 관한 연구이며, 따라서 여러분이 문제에 대한 해결책을 찾는 데 도움을 줄 수 있다.
➡ _____
_____

5 어떻게 하면 긴장을 덜 할 수 있나요?
➡ _____

6 지수가 반 전체 앞에서 발표를 하기 5분 전이었다.
➡ _____

7 지수는 긴장이 되어, 의자에 앉아 자신의 필기를 열심히 들여다보고 있었다.
➡ _____

8 그때 선생님이 다가와서는 원더우먼처럼 꼿꼿이 서 있어 보라고 말했다.
➡ _____

9 그렇게 몇 분을 우뚝 선 후에, 지수는 더 이상 긴장되지 않았다.
➡ _____

10 사실, 그녀는 발표를 멋있게 할 수 있을 것이라는 자신감이 생겼다.
➡ _____

11 유명한 심리학자인 Amy Cuddy에 의하면, 우리는 스트레스를 받는 상황 이전에 2분 정도 꼿꼿이 서 있는 것만으로도 자신감이 더 생길 수 있다고 한다.
➡ _____
_____

12 우리의 몸은 마음을 바꾸고, 마음은 우리의 행동을 바꿀 수 있다.
➡ _____

13 자신감이 생기기를 원하는가?
➡ _____

14 양발을 벌리고, 허리께에 손을 올려 보아라.
➡ _____

15 자신에 대한 확신이 생길 뿐만 아니라 다른 사람이 보기에도 자신감에 차 보인다.
➡ _____

16 누가 내 기분을 낮게 해 줄 수 있나요?
➡ _____

17 내년에 고등학교를 졸업한 이후에 태호는 전문적인 농부가 되고 싶어 한다.
➡ _____

18 ▶ 하지만, 누구에게도 그것에 대해 한 번도 말하지 않았다.

➡ _____

19 ▶ 그는 부모님이나 친구들이 이해하지 못할까 걱정이 된다.

➡ _____

20 ▶ 마음을 정리하기 위해서, 태호는 혼자 하루 기차 여행을 떠나기로 결심했다.

➡ _____

21 ▶ 기차에서, 그는 옆에 앉은 전혀 모르는 사람에게 자신의 고민에 대해서 말했다.

➡ _____

22 ▶ 그는 자신이 왜 그랬는지 알 수 없었다.

➡ _____

23 ▶ 그러나, 기차에서 내릴 때 기분이 훨씬 좋아졌다.

➡ _____

24 ▶ 정말 이상하게도, 우리는 태호처럼 우리의 문제에 대해 낯선 사람에게 말할 때가 있다.

➡ _____

25 ▶ 그것은 우리가 평가받거나 그 사람을 다시 볼 것이라는 걱정을 할 필요가 없기 때문이다.

➡ _____

26 ▶ 만약 가족이나 친구들과도 나눌 수 없는 고민이 있다면, 낯선 이에게 말해 보아라.

➡ _____

27 ▶ 기분이 훨씬 나아질 것이다.

➡ _____

28 ▶ 라이벌을 어떻게 친구로 만들 수 있을까요?

➡ _____

29 ▶ Benjamin Franklin에게는 한때 그를 전혀 좋아하지 않는 정치적 경쟁자가 있었다.

➡ _____

30 ▶ Franklin은 그와 친구가 되고 싶어서, 계획을 세웠다.

➡ _____

31 ▶ 그의 경쟁자는 희귀한 책을 가지고 있었다.

➡ _____

32 ▶ Franklin은 그의 정적에게 그 책을 며칠 동안 빌려달라고 부탁했다.

➡ _____

33 ▶ Franklin이 그 책을 돌려줄 때, 그는 그에게 진심으로 감사를 표했다.

➡ _____

34 ▶ 그날 이후로, 그의 경쟁자는 정치적인 후원자뿐만 아니라 좋은 친구가 되었다.

➡ _____

35 ▶ Franklin은 "당신을 한 번 도운 적은 더 돕고 싶어 하게 된다."라는 유명한 말을 했다.

➡ _____

36 ▶ 여러분이 경쟁자를 친구로 만들고 싶다면, 경쟁자의 부탁을 들어주지 마라.

➡ _____

37 ▶ 대신, 경쟁자에게 부탁을 해 보아라.

➡ _____

[01~03] 다음 글을 읽고 물음에 답하시오.

Do you think you have a ⓐunique problem? Chances are that many other people have the same problem. Psychology is the study of the human mind and behavior, so it can help you find a solution to your problem.

(A)

It was five minutes before Jisu's big presentation in front of the whole class. Feeling ⓑnervous, Jisu was carefully studying her notes in her chair. Then, her teacher came over and told her to stand tall like Wonder Woman. After standing tall for a few minutes, Jisu did not feel nervous anymore. In fact, she was confident that she would make a great presentation. According to Amy Cuddy, a famous ⓒpsychology, we can become more confident just by standing tall for two minutes before stressful events. Our bodies change our minds, and our minds can change our behavior. Do you want to feel confident? Stand with your feet ⓓapart, and place your hands on your hips. You will not only feel sure about yourself but also look ⓔconfident to other people.

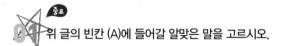

01 위 글의 빈칸 (A)에 들어갈 알맞은 말을 고르시오.

① Why do we become nervous?

② How do I become less nervous?

③ How do I turn a rival into a friend?

④ How do we feel better?

⑤ Who can help me feel better?

02 위 글의 밑줄 친 ⓐ~ⓔ 중 잘못 쓰인 것을 고르시오.

① ⓐ   ② ⓑ   ③ ⓒ   ④ ⓓ   ⑤ ⓔ

03 According to the passage, which is NOT true?

① Many people probably have the same problem as we do.

② Psychology can help us find a solution to our problem.

③ Jisu was going to make a big presentation in front of the whole class.

④ Jisu's teacher asked her to stand still for a few minutes.

⑤ Our bodies change our minds, and our minds can change our behavior.

[04~06] 다음 글을 읽고 물음에 답하시오.

How do I turn a rival into a friend?

Benjamin Franklin once had a political rival who did not like ①him at all. Franklin wanted to become friends with ②him, so ③ he came up with a plan. His rival had a rare book. Franklin asked his rival to lend ④ him the book for a few days. When Franklin returned the book, he thanked him deeply. Since that day, ⑤his rival became not only a political supporter but also a good friend. Franklin famously said, "Enemies ⓐ do you one favor will want to do more." If you want to turn a rival into a friend, don't do your rival a favor. Instead, ask your rival ⓑ you a favor.

04 위 글의 빈칸 ⓐ에 들어갈 알맞은 말을 모두 고르시오.

① that   ② what   ③ which

④ whose   ⑤ who

서답형

05 빈칸 ⓑ에 do를 알맞은 형태로 쓰시오.

➡ _____

06 위 글의 밑줄 친 ①~⑤ 중에서 가리키는 대상이 <u>다른</u> 것을 고르시오.

①   ②   ③   ④   ⑤

[07~09] 다음 글을 읽고 물음에 답하시오.

Who can help me feel better?

When he graduates from high school next year, Taeho wants to become a professional farmer. (①) He is worried that his parents or his friends will not understand. (②) Wanting to clear his mind, Taeho decided to take a day trip on a train ___ⓐ___ . (③) On the train, he told a complete stranger sitting beside him about his problem. (④) He had no idea why he did it. (⑤) However, he felt much better when he got off the train. Strangely enough, we often tell strangers about our problems just like Taeho. ⓑThat is why we do not have to worry about being judged or seeing them again. If you have a problem that you cannot share with your family or friends, try talking to a stranger. You will feel much better.

07 위 글의 흐름으로 보아, 주어진 문장이 들어가기에 가장 적절한 곳은?

> However, he has never told anyone about it.

①   ②   ③   ④   ⑤

서답형

08 위 글의 빈칸 ⓐ에 'alone'과 같은 뜻의 말을 두 단어로 어법에 맞게 쓰시오.

➡ _____

서답형

09 위 글의 밑줄 친 ⓑ에서 어색한 것을 찾아 바르게 고쳐 쓰시오.

_____ ➡ _____

[10~13] 다음 글을 읽고 물음에 답하시오.

Do you think you have a unique problem? ___ⓐ___ are that many other people have the same problem. Psychology is the study of the human mind and behavior, so it can help you find a solution to your problem.

How do I become (A)[less / more] nervous?

It was five minutes before Jisu's big presentation in front of the whole class. ⓑ<u>Feeling</u> nervous, Jisu was carefully studying her notes in her chair. Then, her teacher came over and told her to stand tall like Wonder Woman. After standing tall for a few minutes, Jisu did not feel nervous anymore. In fact, she was confident that she would make a great presentation. According to Amy Cuddy, a famous psychologist, we can become more (B)[nervous / confident] just by standing tall for two minutes before stressful events. Our bodies change our minds, and our minds can change our behavior. Do you want to feel confident? Stand with your feet (C)[apart / together], and place your hands on your hips. You will not only feel sure about yourself but also look confident to other people.

10 위 글의 괄호 (A)~(C)에서 문맥이나 어법상 알맞은 낱말을 골라 쓰시오.

➡ (A) _____ (B) _____ (C) _____

11 위 글의 빈칸 ⓐ에 알맞은 말을 쓰시오.

➡ _____

12 위 글의 밑줄 친 ⓑFeeling과 쓰임이 같은 것을 고르시오.

① I watched Kate singing on the stage.

② He was enjoying himself at the camp.

③ When young, Lindsey was good at playing the piano.

④ Drinking water is good for your health.

⑤ Returning the book, Franklin thanked him deeply.

13 Which question CANNOT be answered after reading the passage?

① What is Amy Cuddy?

② How can we become less nervous?

③ What is the advice of Jisu's teacher?

④ Why do our bodies change our minds?

⑤ How long did Jisu stand tall?

[14~16] 다음 글을 읽고 물음에 답하시오.

(A)
Benjamin Franklin once had a political rival who did not like him at all. Franklin wanted to become friends with him, so he came up with a plan. His rival had a rare book. Franklin asked his rival to lend him the book for ⓐ days. When Franklin returned the book, he thanked him deeply. Since that day, ⓑhis rival became not only a political supporter but also a good friend. Franklin famously said, "Enemies who do you one favor will want to do more." If you want to turn a rival into a friend, don't do your rival a favor. Instead, ask your rival to do you a favor.

14 위 글의 빈칸 (A)에 들어갈 말로 적절한 것은?

① How did Benjamin approach his political rival?

② How do I turn a rival into a friend?

③ Why do we need to turn a rival into a friend?

④ Don't ask your rival to do you a favor.

⑤ Why did Benjamin need to borrow the book?

15 위 글의 빈칸 ⓐ에 들어갈 말로 알맞은 것은?

① little   ② a little   ③ a lot

④ few   ⑤ a few

서답형

16 위 글의 밑줄 친 ⓑ를 'as well as'를 이용하여 바꿔 쓰시오.

➡ _____

_____

[17~20] 다음 글을 읽고 물음에 답하시오.

Who can help me feel better?
When he graduates from high school next year, Taeho wants to become a ⓐ farmer. However, he has never told anyone about it. He is worried that his parents or his friends will not understand. Wanting to clear his mind, Taeho decided to take a day trip on a train by himself. On the train, he told a complete stranger sitting beside him about his problem. He had no idea why he did it. ⓑ , he felt much better when he got off the train. Strangely enough, we often tell strangers about our problems just like Taeho. That is because we do not have to worry about being judged or seeing them again. If you have a problem that you cannot share with your family or friends, try talking to a stranger. You will feel (A)much better.

서답형

17 주어진 영영풀이의 빈칸에 해당하는 말을 빈칸 ⓐ에 철자 p 로 시작하여 쓰시오.

> _____ people have jobs that require advanced education or training

➡ _____

18 빈칸 ⓑ에 들어갈 알맞은 말을 고르시오.

① Moreover ② For example
③ Therefore ④ However
⑤ In addition

19 위 글의 밑줄 친 (A)much와 바꿔 쓸 수 없는 말을 고르시오.

① very ② a lot
③ even ④ still
⑤ far

중요

20 Which question CANNOT be answered after reading the passage?

① What does Taeho want to become when he graduates from high school next year?
② To whom has Taeho told about his wish?
③ Why did Taeho tell a complete stranger sitting beside him about his problem?
④ Why did Taeho decide to take a day trip on a train by himself?
⑤ How can we feel better when we have a problem?

[21~23] 다음 글을 읽고 물음에 답하시오.

How do I become ⓐ _____ nervous?
 It was five minutes before Jisu's big presentation in front of the whole class. Feeling nervous, Jisu was carefully studying her notes in her chair. Then, her teacher came over and told her to stand tall like Wonder Woman. (A)After standing tall for a few minutes, Jisu did not feel nervous no more. In fact, she was confident that she would make a great presentation. According to Amy Cuddy, a famous psychologist, we can become more confident just by (B)standing tall for two minutes before stressful events. Our bodies change our minds, and our minds can change our behavior. Do you want to feel confident? Stand with your feet apart, and place your hands on your hips. You will not only feel sure about yourself but also look confident to other people.

21 위 글의 빈칸 ⓐ에 들어갈 알맞은 말을 고르시오.

① few ② little ③ less
④ more ⑤ very

서답형

22 위 글의 밑줄 친 (A)에서 흐름상 어색한 부분을 찾아 고치시오.

_____ ➡ _____

23 위 글의 밑줄 친 (B)standing과 문법적 쓰임이 다른 것을 모두 고르시오.

① He was standing by the gate.
② Standing on my hands was difficult.
③ Her punishment was standing silently.
④ She looked so miserable, standing there in the rain.
⑤ Standing under the sun was terrible.

[01~03] 다음 글을 읽고 물음에 답하시오.

(A)Who can help me feel better?

When he graduates from high school next year, Taeho wants to become a professional farmer. However, he has never told anyone about it. He is worried that his parents or his friends will not understand. Wanting to clear his mind, Taeho decided to take a day trip on a train by himself. On the train, he told a complete stranger sitting beside him about his problem. He had no idea why he did it. However, he felt much better when he got off the train. ⓐ정말 이상하게도, we often tell strangers about our problems just like Taeho. (B)That is because we do not have to worry about being judged or seeing them again. If you have a problem that you cannot share with your family or friends, try talking to a stranger. You will feel much better.

01 위 글의 밑줄 친 (A)의 답이 될 수 있는 것을 본문에서 찾아 세 단어를 쓰시오.

➡ _____

02 밑줄 친 ⓐ의 우리말에 맞게 enough를 이용하여 두 단어를 쓰시오.

➡ _____

03 위 글의 밑줄 친 (B)That이 가리키는 것을 본문에서 찾아 쓰시오.

➡ _____

[04~06] 다음 글을 읽고 물음에 답하시오.

Do you think you have a unique problem? Chances are that many other people have the same problem. Psychology is the study of the human mind and behavior, so it can help you find a solution to your problem.

How do I become less nervous?

It was five minutes before Jisu's big presentation in front of the whole class. ⓐ Feeling nervous, Jisu was carefully studying her notes in her chair. Then, her teacher came over and told her to stand tall like Wonder Woman. After standing tall for a few minutes, Jisu did not feel nervous anymore. In fact, she was confident that she would make a great presentation. According to Amy Cuddy, a famous psychologist, we can become more confident just by standing tall for two minutes before stressful events. Our bodies change our minds, and our minds can change our behavior. Do you want to feel confident? Stand with your feet apart, and place your hands on your hips. You will not only feel sure about yourself but also look confident to other people.

04 Why can psychology help us find a solution to our problem?

➡ _____
_____

05 How can we get to be more confident?

➡ _____
_____

06 위 글의 밑줄 친 ⓐFeeling을 부사절로 고쳐 쓰시오.

➡ _____

[07~09] 다음 글을 읽고 물음에 답하시오.

How do I turn a rival into a friend?

Benjamin Franklin once had a political rival who did not like him at all. Franklin wanted to become friends ⓐ_____ him, so he came up ⓐ_____ a plan. His rival had a rare book. Franklin asked his rival to lend him the book for a few days. ⓑWhen Franklin returned the book, he thanked him deep. Since that day, ⓒhis rival became not only a political supporter but also a good friend. Franklin famously said, "Enemies who do you one favor will want to do more." If you want to turn a rival into a friend, don't do your rival a favor. Instead, ask your rival to do you a favor.

07 위 글의 빈칸 ⓐ에 공통으로 들어갈 전치사를 쓰시오.

➡ _____

중요

08 위 글의 밑줄 친 ⓑ에서 어색한 부분을 찾아 고치시오.

_____ ➡ _____

09 위 글의 밑줄 친 ⓒ를 'as well as'를 이용하여 바꿔 쓰시오.

➡ _____

_____

[10~13] 다음 글을 읽고 물음에 답하시오.

Who can help me feel better?

When he graduates from high school next year, Taeho wants to become a professional farmer. However, he has never told anyone about ⓐit. He is worried that his parents or his friends will not understand. (A)[Wanting / Wanted] to clear his mind, Taeho decided to take a day trip on a train by himself. On the train, he told a complete stranger (B)[sat / sitting] beside him about his problem. ⓑ그는 자신이 왜 그랬는지 알 수 없었다. However, he felt much better when he got off the train. Strangely enough, we often tell strangers about our problems just like Taeho. That is because we do not have to worry about (C)[being judged / judging] or seeing them again. If you have a problem that you cannot share with your family or friends, try talking to a stranger. You will feel much better.

중요

10 위 글의 괄호 (A)~(C)에서 문맥이나 어법상 알맞은 낱말을 고르시오.

➡ (A) _____ (B) _____ (C) _____

11 위 글의 밑줄 친 ⓐit이 가리키는 것을 본문에서 찾아 쓰시오.

➡ _____

12 위 글의 밑줄 친 ⓑ의 우리말을 주어진 어휘를 이용하여 영작하시오. (no, idea, it)

➡ _____

고난이도

13 위 글의 내용과 일치하도록 다음 빈칸 (A)와 (B)에 알맞은 단어를 쓰시오.

Taeho wants to become a professional farmer, but he is worried that his parents or his friends will not understand. While taking a day trip on a train by himself, he told (A)_____ _____ _____ about his problem. He didn't know why he did it. But he felt (B)_____ _____ when he got off the train.

Listen & Speak 2 – B Think and Talk

A: What don't I have to do on Stress-Free Day?

B: You don't have to clean the classroom.
　　= You don't need to

C: You don't have to come to school by 8:30.

구문해설　• stress-free: 스트레스가 없는

해석

A: 스트레스가 없는 날에 무엇을 할 필요가 없을까?

B: 너는 교실 청소를 할 필요가 없어.

C: 너는 8:30분까지 학교에 올 필요가 없어.

Link

How confident do you feel about yourself? Wanting to find the answer
　　　　　　　　　　　　　　　　　　分사구문(= As[Because] we wanted)
to this question, we created a test about confidence. Thirty students took the
[행위·동작·작용의 대상] ~에 대하여　　　　　　　　　　　　시험[검사]을 치르다
test. The average score was nine. Eighteen students scored above the average
　　　　　　　　　　　　　　　　　　　　　　　　[초과] ~ 이상인[으로]
score. Thus, sixty percent of the students felt quite confident about themselves.
결과를 이끄는 연결어　　　　　　　　　　　　　　　　　　　them(×)

구문해설　• confident: 자신감이 있는　• confidence: 자신감　• average: 평균; 평균의

당신은 스스로에 대해 얼마나 확신이 있나요? 질문에 대한 답을 찾고 싶어, 우리는 자신감에 대한 검사지를 만들었습니다. 30명의 학생들이 검사를 했습니다. 평균적인 점수는 9점이었습니다. 18명의 학생들이 평균 점수를 넘었습니다. 따라서, 학생들의 60%가 그들 스스로에 대해 꽤 자신감을 갖고 있습니다.

Write

The hardest time in my life

The hardest time in my life was when my grandmother passed away five years
　　　최상급　　　　　　　　　　the time when: ~할 때
ago. When I was younger, she took care of me most of the time. Not having
　　　　　　　비교 대상 없는 비교급(자기 자신)　　　　= As[Because] I didn't have her around의 분사구문
her around, I felt sad and lonely. One day, I found my grandmother's diary.
　　　　　　　지각동사+형용사
She not only wrote a lot about her memories but also wished that I would lead
(= Not only did she write ~, but also she wished)　　　　　　　병렬 구조　　　will의 과거형(시제 일치)
a happy life. From this experience, I have learned that I should try to be happy
　　　　　　　　　　　　　　부사구　　　　　　　현재완료
just as she wished.
be 형용사 just as(접속사) S+wished: S가 원했던 것처럼 ~하다

구문해설　• pass away: 죽다　• have ~ around: ~가 곁에 있다　• just as: ~가 …한 것과 같이

내 삶에서 가장 힘들었던 순간

내 삶에서 가장 힘들었던 순간은 5년 전 할머니께서 돌아가셨을 때였다. 내가 더 어렸을 때, 그녀는 대부분의 시간 동안 나를 돌봐주셨다. 그녀가 곁에 없어서, 나는 슬프고 외로웠다. 어느 날, 나는 할머니의 일기장을 발견했다. 그녀는 그녀의 기억에 대해 많이 적었을 뿐만 아니라, 내가 행복한 삶을 살기를 바랐다. 이 경험을 통해, 나는 그녀가 원했던 것처럼 행복해지려고 노력해야 한다는 것을 배웠다.

영역별 핵심문제

Words & Expressions

01 다음 짝지어진 단어의 관계가 같도록 빈칸에 알맞은 말을 쓰시오.

> tradition : traditional = success : _____

02 다음 영영풀이가 가리키는 것을 고르시오.

> to complete your education at a college, school, etc.

① graduate   ② judge
③ guess   ④ decide
⑤ prepare

03 다음 중 밑줄 친 부분의 뜻풀이가 바르지 <u>않은</u> 것은?

① I want to be a specialist in child <u>psychology</u>. (심리학)
② We blamed his bad <u>behavior</u>. (행동)
③ Do you have a better <u>solution</u>? (해결책)
④ He drew a <u>unique</u> picture on the wall. (독특한)
⑤ The two houses stand 500 meters <u>apart</u>. (가까이)

04 다음 우리말에 맞게 빈칸에 알맞은 말을 쓰시오. (철자가 주어진 것은 그 철자로 시작할 것.)

(1) 그녀는 아마 며칠 후에 떠날 것이다.
➡ She will p_____ leave in a few days.

(2) 너는 그 문제에 대해 좀 전문적인 조언을 얻을 필요가 있다.
➡ You need to get some _____ advice about that problem.

(3) 나는 사람의 마음에 관심이 있어서, 대학에서 심리학을 공부할 것이다.
➡ I am interested in the human mind, so I will study _____ in college.

(4) 그녀는 희귀한 병을 가졌다.
➡ She has a r_____ disease.

05 다음 문장의 빈칸에 들어갈 말을 〈보기〉에서 골라 쓰시오.

> ┤ 보기 ├
> chances are that / get off / stop by / stand tall / make a presentation

(1) Are you going to _____ at the meeting?
(2) Could you _____ the store for some bread on the way home?
(3) Go out into the real world and _____, my students!
(4) _____ our team will win the championship.
(5) We need to _____ at the next station.

06 다음 문장에 공통으로 들어갈 말을 고르시오.

> • I can't handle this project _____ myself.
> • Would you stop _____ my office and do me a favor?
> • I'll be back home _____ 6 to help you.

① by   ② with
③ from   ④ to
⑤ of

Conversation

[07~09] 다음 대화를 읽고 물음에 답하시오.

Minsu: Shall we have seafood spaghetti ⓐfor dinner?

Emma: Sure. I'll (A)stop by the store ⓑon the way home.

Minsu: You don't have ⓒto do that. We already have ⓓwhat we need.

Emma: Oh, I see. Then, I'll be back home by 6 to ⓔhelp you cooking.

07 위 대화의 밑줄 친 ⓐ~ⓔ 중 어법상 틀린 것을 찾아 바르게 고치시오.

➡ _____ ➡ _____

08 위 대화의 밑줄 친 (A)와 바꾸어 쓸 수 있는 것은?

① drop
② chew
③ get
④ decide
⑤ judge

09 위 대화의 내용과 일치하지 않는 것은?

① 민수는 Emma에게 저녁에 해산물 스파게티 먹을 것을 제안했다.
② Emma는 집에 오는 길에 가게에 들를 것이다.
③ 민수는 이미 스파게티에 필요한 것을 갖고 있다.
④ Emma는 6시까지 집에 돌아올 것이다.
⑤ Emma는 민수가 요리하는 것을 도울 것이다.

[10~11] 다음 대화를 읽고 물음에 답하시오.

B: You look a bit nervous.

G: Well, _____(A)

B: Don't worry. You've prepared a lot. You'll do a great job.

G: Thanks. I feel much better now.

10 위 대화의 빈칸 (A)에 들어갈 말을 주어진 단어를 모두 배열하여 영작하시오.

┌─ 보기 ┐
history class / about / in / presentation / worried / I'm / my
└─────┘

➡ _____

11 위 대화의 내용과 일치하지 <u>않는</u> 것은?

① 소녀는 약간 긴장되어 보인다.
② 소녀는 역사 시간에 할 발표를 걱정한다.
③ 소녀는 발표 준비를 많이 했다.
④ 소녀는 소년 덕분에 기분이 훨씬 나아졌다.
⑤ 소년은 소녀의 발표를 칭찬하였다.

12 다음 대화가 자연스럽게 이어지도록 순서대로 배열하시오.

(A) Oh, I see. How convenient!
(B) You don't have to call them. You can do it online.
(C) Shall we try that new Mexican restaurant tomorrow?
(D) Why not? I'll call the restaurant to make a reservation for us.

➡ _____

[13~14] 다음 대화를 읽고 물음에 답하시오.

Jane: What happened to your shoes? Aren't they new?

Brian: Yes, but my dog chewed them. He does it all the time. I'm worried about him.

Jane: He was probably bored. Why don't you play with him more often?

Brian: O.K., I will. I hope he will stop chewing my shoes.

13 What happened to Brian's shoes?

➡ _____

14 What does Jane advise Brian to do?

➡ _____

(2)

➡ Jiho has decided _____

_____. (to go, nor, to get, college, neither, to, a job)

Grammar

15 다음 문장의 밑줄 친 분사구문을 부사절로 바르게 바꾼 것은?

> <u>Living alone in this big apartment,</u> I rarely feel lonely.

① Because I live in this big apartment,
② While I'm living in this big apartment,
③ If I live in this big apartment,
④ Though I live in this big apartment,
⑤ Unless I live in this big apartment,

16 다음 그림을 보고 괄호 안의 단어를 배열하여 빈칸을 알맞게 채우시오. (단, 단어 배열은 그림의 왼쪽에서 오른쪽임.)

(1)

➡ _____

on the spider web. (in, the honeybee, are, the ladybug, both, and, trouble)

---

17 다음 중 어법상 어색한 문장을 모두 고르시오.

① Not only can people guess the story but they also know the ending.
② Both the participants or the researchers were satisfied with the result.
③ Either Jamie and Esther is coming today.
④ I can't even imagine not only when but also where the event will happen.
⑤ Neither Thomas nor his team members were present at the meeting.

18 다음 괄호 안에서 어법상 알맞은 것을 고르시오.

(1) Not only Sammy but also Olga (like / likes) the soup so much.
(2) Maria required that the dance teams should practice not only singing but also (to dance / dancing).
(3) Either Kennedy (or / nor) Jason should complete the assignment by tomorrow.
(4) Either the recording engineers or the music director (is / are) going to direct the song production.
(5) Not the angels but the devil (appear / appears) before the sad soul.

19 다음 문장의 밑줄 친 부사절을 분사구문으로 알맞게 바꾼 것을 고르시오.

> As she doesn't have anyone around to encourage her, Joanne felt even more lonely.

① As she having not anyone around to encourage her,

② There being someone around to encourage her,

③ Having not anyone around to encourage her,

④ As having not anyone around to encourage her,

⑤ Not having anyone around to encourage her,

20 다음 밑줄 친 부분 중 어법상 어색한 것을 고르시오.

① Not having money, Robert couldn't buy the birthday present for his wife.

② Raining all day, the club members stayed at home and watched their video clips.

③ Being tired, Sonya went to bed early.

④ Finding the book he had lost, I called him to come over to my place.

⑤ Frankly speaking, the prime minster of Japan seemed like an idiot.

Reading

[21~22] 다음 글을 읽고 물음에 답하시오.

Do you think you have a unique problem? Chances are that many other people have the same problem. Psychology is the study of the human mind and behavior, so it can help you find a solution ⓐ your problem.

How do I become less nervous?

It was five minutes before Jisu's big presentation in front of the whole class. Feeling nervous, Jisu was carefully studying her notes in her chair. Then, her teacher came over and told her ⓑ stand tall like Wonder Woman. After standing tall for a few minutes, Jisu did not feel nervous anymore. ⓒ , she was confident that she would make a great presentation.

21 위 글의 빈칸 ⓐ와 ⓑ에 공통으로 들어갈 알맞은 전치사를 고르시오.

① to   ② on   ③ for

④ in   ⑤ at

22 위 글의 빈칸 ⓒ에 알맞은 것을 고르시오.

① For example   ② However

③ In addition   ④ In fact

⑤ Thus

[23~25] 다음 글을 읽고 물음에 답하시오.

Who can help me feel better?

When he graduates from high school next year, Taeho wants to become a professional farmer. However, he has never told anyone about it. He is worried that his parents or his friends will not understand. ⓐWanting to clear his mind, Taeho decided to take a day trip on a train by himself. On the train, he told a complete stranger sitting beside him about his problem. He had no idea why he did it. However, he felt much better when he got off the train. Strangely enough, we often tell strangers about our problems just like Taeho. That is because we do not have to worry about being judged or seeing them again. If you have a problem that you cannot share with your family or friends, try talking to a stranger. You will feel much better.

23 위 글의 주제로 알맞은 것을 고르시오.

① how to meet a complete stranger
② how to feel better when we have a problem
③ how to clear our mind
④ why Taeho wants to be a professional farmer
⑤ why we tell a teacher about our problem

24 밑줄 친 ⓐ를 부사절로 알맞게 고친 것을 고르시오.

① As he wants to clear his mind
② Because he wanted to clear his mind
③ Though he wanted to clear his mind
④ If he wanted to clear his mind
⑤ After he wanted to clear his mind

25 According to the passage, which is NOT true?

① Taeho wants to become a professional farmer after graduation from high school.
② Taeho has never told anyone about becoming a professional farmer.
③ When we have a problem that we cannot share with our family or friends, we will feel much better by trying talking to a stranger.
④ Taeho took a day trip on a train by himself as he wanted to clear his mind.
⑤ Taeho knew why he told a complete stranger about his problem.

[26~29] 다음 글을 읽고 물음에 답하시오.

How do I turn a rival into a friend?

Benjamin Franklin once had a political rival who did not like him at all. (①) Franklin wanted to become friends with him, so he came up with a plan. (②) His rival had a rare book. (③) When Franklin returned the book, he thanked him deeply. (④) Since that day, his rival became not only a political supporter but also a good friend. (⑤) Franklin famously said, "Enemies who do you one favor will want to do more." If you want to turn a rival into a friend, don't do your rival a favor. ____ⓐ____, ask your rival to do you a favor.

26 위 글의 빈칸 ⓐ에 들어갈 말로 알맞은 것을 고르시오.

① However   ② For instance
③ Nonetheless   ④ In fact
⑤ Instead

27 위 글의 흐름으로 보아, 주어진 문장이 들어가기에 가장 적절한 곳은?

> Franklin asked his rival to lend him the book for a few days.

①   ②   ③   ④   ⑤

28 위 글에 나타난 Franklin에 대한 설명으로 가장 적절한 것을 고르시오.

① wicked   ② honest   ③ wise
④ timid   ⑤ evil

29 What did Franklin's political rival do for Franklin? Answer in English with 7 words.

➡ _____

출제율 90%

01 다음 영영풀이가 가리키는 것을 고르시오.

> someone who hates you and wants to harm you

① stranger   ② supporter
③ psychologist   ④ rival
⑤ enemy

출제율 95%

02 다음 우리말을 주어진 단어를 이용하여 영작하시오.

(1) 네 자신에게 너무 많은 부담을 주지 마라. (pressure, too, on)

➡ _____

(2) 두 발을 벌리고 서라. (with, feet)

➡ _____

(3) 내가 식당에 전화해서 예약할게요. (make, restaurant)

➡ _____

[03~05] 다음 대화를 읽고 물음에 답하시오.

Minsu: Shall we have seafood spaghetti for dinner?

Emma: Sure. I'll stop by the store on the way home.

Minsu: You don't have to do that. We already have what we need.

Emma: Oh, I see. Then, I'll be back home by 6 to help you cook.

출제율 90%

03 What is Minsu going to cook for dinner?

➡ _____

출제율 95%

04 Why doesn't Emma have to stop by the store?

➡ _____

출제율 90%

05 By when will Emma be back home to help Minsu?

➡ _____

출제율 95%

06 다음 대화가 자연스럽게 이어지도록 순서대로 배열하시오.

(A) He was probably bored. Why don't you play with him more often?

(B) O.K., I will. I hope he will stop chewing my shoes.

(C) What happened to your shoes? Aren't they new?

(D) Yes, but my dog chewed them. He does it all the time. I'm worried about him.

➡ _____

[07~08] 다음 대화를 읽고 물음에 답하시오.

Jack: Mom, what time are we going to Grandma's place tomorrow morning?

Mom: About 8 a.m. I'm going to bake cookies for her before we go.

Jack: Then, should I get up early to help you?

Mom: (A)그럴 필요 없단다. (have) Your dad will help me.

Jack: O.K, then. Good night, Mom!

출제율 90%

07 위 대화의 밑줄 친 (A)의 우리말을 주어진 단어를 사용하여 영작하시오. (4 words)

➡ _____

08 위 대화의 내용과 일치하지 <u>않는</u> 것은?

① Jack is supposed to visit his grandma with her mother.

② Jack is going to his grandma's place about 8 a.m. tomorrow morning.

③ Jack doesn't need to help his mom tomorrow morning.

④ Jack's mom is planning to bake cookies for Jack's grandma at night.

⑤ Jack's father is going to help Jack's mom to bake cookies.

[09~10] 다음 대화를 읽고 물음에 답하시오.

Yuri: Hi, Jaden. Sports Day is next Friday. I can't wait!

Jaden: Really? I'm actually worried about it.

Yuri: Why? Aren't you good at sports?

Jaden: (A) Yes, I am, but I'm worried about the 800-meter relay.

Yuri: What do you mean?

Jaden: (B) I'm the last runner. What if our team loses because of me?

Yuri: (C) I think you're putting too much pressure on yourself.

Jaden: (D) Really? Don't you think I should practice every day?

Yuri: (E) It's just a school race. It's not about winning or losing.

Jaden: I guess you're right, Yuri. I'm lucky to have a friend like you.

09 위 대화의 (A)~(E) 중 주어진 문장이 들어가기에 적절한 곳은?

> No, you don't have to do that.

① (A) ② (B) ③ (C) ④ (D) ⑤ (E)

10 위 대화의 내용과 일치하지 <u>않는</u> 것은?

① 운동회가 다음 주 금요일이다.

② Jaden은 운동을 잘하지만 800미터 릴레이가 걱정된다.

③ Jaden은 자신 때문에 팀이 질까봐 걱정한다.

④ 유리는 Jaden이 스스로에게 너무 많은 압박을 주고 있는 것 같다고 생각한다.

⑤ 유리는 이기거나 지는 것이 중요한 경기는 아니지만, Jaden이 매일 연습해야 한다고 생각한다.

11 다음 대화의 내용과 일치하지 <u>않는</u> 것은?

B: You look a bit nervous.

G: I'm worried about my swimming competition this Saturday.

B: Don't worry. You're such a good swimmer. Just relax and enjoy yourself!

G: Thanks. I feel much better now.

① 소녀는 긴장한 것 같아 보인다.

② 소녀는 다음 주 토요일에 있는 수영대회를 걱정하고 있다.

③ 소녀는 수영을 아주 잘한다.

④ 소년은 소녀에게 긴장을 풀고 즐기라고 하였다.

⑤ 소녀는 소년의 격려 덕분에 기분이 훨씬 괜찮아졌다.

12 다음 중 어법상 올바른 문장을 <u>모두</u> 고르면?

① Opened the drawer, he took out a letter.

② There being no bus service, we had to walk all the way home.

③ Worked hard to finish the project in time, Chris was taken to hospital.

④ Knowing not what to do, she asked him for help.

⑤ Director Bong winning the great awards, the fans in Korea felt proud of his films.

[13~14] 다음 중 빈칸에 들어갈 수 <u>없는</u> 말을 고르시오.

출제율 100%

13

The princess Elsa in the castle was not only _____ but also generous.

① beautiful ② friendly ③ lovely
④ truly ⑤ wise

출제율 95%

14

My grandmother not only wrote a lot about her memories on her family and friends but also _____.

① wished that I would lead a happy life
② was sure that her children would be happy
③ was satisfied with a quiet life
④ proud of her family members
⑤ wanted to be remembered by us

출제율 95%

15 다음 각 문장의 부사절을 알맞은 분사구문으로 전환하시오.

(1) When we use green energy vehicles, we can reduce a good amount of CO_2 in the air.

➡ _____, we can reduce a good amount of CO_2 in the air.

(2) Because Anne didn't come back, her husband waited for three hours.

➡ _____, her husband waited for three hours.

(3) As Shane had not been invited to the final match, he stayed at home all day long.

➡ _____, Shane stayed at home all day long.

출제율 95%

16 다음 중 우리말과 그 영작이 바르게 짝지어지지 <u>않은</u> 것은?

① Ben은 영어뿐만 아니라 중국어도 말할 수 있다.
→ Ben can speak not only English but also Chinese.

② 그 배우는 드라마뿐만 아니라 영화도 찍고 있다.
→ The actor is filming not only a drama but also a movie.

③ 아이들뿐만 아니라 그들의 엄마도 펭수를 좋아한다.
→ Not only the kids but also their mom like Pengsu.

④ BTS는 한국에서뿐만 아니라 일본에서도 콘서트를 열 것이다.
→ BTS will hold a concert not only in Korea but also in Japan.

⑤ 불고기는 맛있을 뿐만 아니라 영양가도 있다.
→ Bulgogi is not only delicious but also nutritious.

[17~18] 다음 글을 읽고 물음에 답하시오.

How confident do you feel about yourself? (A)Wanting to find the answer to this question, we created a test about confidence. Thirty students took the test. The average score was nine. Eighteen students scored above the average score. Thus, ____ⓐ____ percent of the students felt quite confident about themselves.

출제율 90%

17 위 글의 빈칸 ⓐ에 들어갈 알맞은 말을 영어로 쓰시오.

➡ _____

18 위 글의 밑줄 친 (A)를 부사절로 고쳐 쓰시오.

➡ _____

_____

[19~20] 다음 글을 읽고 물음에 답하시오.

Do you think you have a ⓐ problem? (A)아마 많은 다른 사람들이 여러분과 똑같은 고민을 가지고 있을 것이다. Psychology is the study of the human mind and behavior, so it can help you find a solution to your problem.

19 주어진 영영풀이에 해당하는 단어를 빈칸 ⓐ에 써 넣으시오.

being the only one of its kind

➡ _____

20 위 글의 밑줄 친 (A)의 우리말에 맞게 chances를 이용하여 10 단어로 영작하시오.

➡ _____

_____

[21~23] 다음 글을 읽고 물음에 답하시오.

How do I become less nervous?

It was five minutes before Jisu's big presentation in front of the whole class. (①) Feeling nervous, Jisu was carefully studying her notes in her chair. (②) Then, her teacher came over and told her to stand tall like Wonder Woman. (③) In fact, she was confident that she would make a great presentation. (④) According to Amy Cuddy, a famous psychologist, we can become more confident just by standing tall for two minutes before stressful events. (⑤) Our bodies change our minds, and our minds can change our behavior. Do you want to feel confident? Stand with your feet apart, and place your hands on your hips. ⓐYou will not only feel sure about yourself but also look confident to other people.

21 위 글의 흐름으로 보아, 주어진 문장이 들어가기에 가장 적절한 곳은?

After standing tall for a few minutes, Jisu did not feel nervous anymore.

① ② ③ ④ ⑤

22 What did Jisu's teacher advise Jisu to do?

➡ _____

_____

23 위 글의 밑줄 친 ⓐ와 그 뜻이 다른 것을 고르시오.

① You will not only feel sure about yourself but look confident to other people.
② You will not simply feel sure about yourself but look confident to other people.
③ You will not just feel sure about yourself but also look confident to other people.
④ You will not merely feel sure about yourself but also look confident to other people.
⑤ You will not feel sure about yourself but look confident to other people.

[01~03] 다음 대화를 읽고 물음에 답하시오.

> Yuri: Hi, Jaden. Sports Day is next Friday. I can't wait!
>
> Jaden: Really? I'm actually worried about it.
>
> Yuri: Why? Aren't you good at sports?
>
> Jaden: Yes, I am, but I'm worried about the 800-meter relay.
>
> Yuri: What do you mean?
>
> Jaden: I'm the last runner. What if our team loses because of me?
>
> Yuri: I think you're putting too much pressure on yourself.
>
> Jaden: Really? Don't you think I should practice every day?
>
> Yuri: No, you don't have to do that. It's just a school race. It's not about winning or losing.
>
> Jaden: I guess you're right, Yuri. I'm lucky to have a friend like you.

01 What is Yuri looking forward to?

➡ _____

02 As the last runner of the 800-meter relay, what is Jaden worried about?

➡ _____
_____

03 Why does Yuri think Jaden doesn't have to practice every day?

➡ _____
_____

04 다음 우리말에 맞도록 괄호 안에 주어진 어휘를 알맞게 배열하시오.

(1) Bob과 Tom이 길을 걷고 있었을 때, 그들은 Julie가 노래 부르는 것을 봤다. (down, street, walking, the)

➡ _____, Bob and Tom saw Julie singing.

(2) 비록 Jane은 아버지의 뜻을 알지 못했지만, 그가 말한 대로 하기로 결심했다. (what, not, meant, knowing, her father)

➡ _____,
Jane decided to do as he told.

(3) 그 비행기에 남은 좌석이 있다면, 나는 오늘 저녁에 LA로 갈 것이다. (seats, there, the plane, left, any, on, being)

➡ _____,
I will go to L.A. this evening.

(4) 마음을 정리하고 싶었기 때문에, Karen은 회사를 그만두겠다고 사장에게 말했다. (clear, wanting, mind, to, her)

➡ _____, Karen told the boss that she'd quit the company.

05 다음 그림을 보고, 내용에 맞게 〈보기〉에서 알맞은 단어를 각각 선택하여, 어법에 맞게 대화의 빈칸에 채워 넣으시오.

┌─ 보기 ┐
- not / but / both / only / either / neither / also / nor / and
- 반드시 한 번씩만 사용할 것.
- 빈칸의 위치에 따라 대·소문자 구분할 것.

Jina: You know when Mom's birthday is?

Jihun: Sure. It's in November, isn't it?

Jina: Yeah, on which day?

Jihun: It probably falls on before or after the cookie stick *Pepero* day. So, it's _____ 10th, or 12th?

Jina: _____ 10th _____ 12th is right. It's 18th, just a week after *Pepero* day. _____ _____ Dad _____ _____ you don't care about Mom.

Jihun: Sorry for that. Instead, what should _____ Dad _____ I do?

[06~08] 다음 글을 읽고 물음에 답하시오.

The hardest time in my life

The hardest time in my life was when my grandmother passed away five years ago. When I was younger, she took care of me most of the time. ⓐNot having her around, I felt sad and lonely. One day, I found my grandmother's diary. ⓑShe not only wrote a lot about her memories but also wished that I would lead a happy life. From this experience, I have learned that I should try to be happy just as she wished.

06 위 글의 밑줄 친 ⓐ를 부사절로 고쳐 쓰시오.

➡ _____

07 위 글의 밑줄 친 ⓑ를 not only로 시작하여 바꿔 쓰시오.

➡ _____

08 위 글의 필자가 할머니의 일기장을 통해 얻은 교훈을 우리말에 쓰시오.

➡ _____
_____

[09~11] 다음 대화를 읽고 물음에 답하시오.

A: Who ate the cookies?

B: (*Touching his* __ⓐ__) I don't know. Maybe the dog ate them.

A: I can tell that you're (A)[lying / laying] because you're touching your __ⓐ__.

C: This is an example of the Pinocchio Effect. People experience the Pinocchio Effect when they tell a lie. (B)[Not only they / Not only do they] feel (C)[even if / as if] their nose is getting hotter, but also the temperature around their eyes (D)[raises / rises].

09 위 글의 빈칸 ⓐ에 공통으로 들어갈 알맞은 말을 쓰시오.

➡ _____

10 Why do people touch their nose when they tell a lie? Fill in the blanks (A) and (B) with suitable words.

Because they feel as if not only their nose is (A)_____ _____, but also the temperature around their eyes (B)_____.

11 위 글의 괄호 (A)~(D)에서 문맥상 알맞은 낱말을 골라 쓰시오.

➡ (A) _____ (B) _____
(C) _____ (D) _____

01 다음 대화를 읽고 대화의 내용과 일치하도록 빈칸을 완성하시오.

> Jack: Mom, what time are we going to Grandma's place tomorrow morning?
>
> Mom: About 8 a.m. I'm going to bake cookies for her before we go.
>
> Jack: Then, should I get up early to help you?
>
> Mom: You don't have to. Your dad will help me.
>
> Jack: O.K, then. Good night, Mom!

> I'm looking forward to visiting (A)_____ tomorrow. We're going to leave about 8 a.m tomorrow. My mom is planning to (B)_____ for my grandma. (C)_____ is going to help her early in the morning. I can't wait to see my grandma!

02 다음 내용을 바탕으로 다른 사람에게 공감과 조언을 하는 편지의 빈칸을 알맞게 채우시오.

Situation	Feelings
• have just moved to a new school	• lonely
• have nobody to talk to	• feel like crying
• ask one of my classmates to show me her notes	• showed me her notes, started to talk about herself
• Asking for help	• help you make new friends

> To someone who (A)_____,
> I understand how (B)_____ you might be feeling now. I had to go to a new school like you because my whole family moved to Gunsan, a small city in Korea. (C)_____, I felt like crying on the first day at my new school. However, a small thing made the situation better. I asked one of my classmates to show me her notes. Then, she not only (D)_____. That was how she became my new friend. Asking for help sometimes (E)_____. I wish you all the best.

단원별 모의고사

01 다음 우리말에 맞게 빈칸을 완성하시오. (철자가 주어진 것은 그 철자로 시작할 것.)

(1) 그녀는 판매를 올리기 위한 새로운 아이디어를 떠올렸다.

➡ She _____ _____ _____ a new idea for increasing sales.

(2) 그는 저녁을 먹으러 우리집에 들렀다.

➡ He c_____ _____ to my house for dinner.

(3) 내가 돌아왔을 때, 이미 모두가 가버렸다.

➡ When I _____ _____, everybody was already gone.

02 다음 문장의 빈칸에 들어갈 말을 〈보기〉에서 골라 쓰시오.

┌─ 보기 ─────────────────────┐
competition / text message / prepare / mind / anxious / unique
└────────────────────────────┘

(1) He sent a _____ to his dad.

(2) You don't have to be _____ about the exam.

(3) Everyone's fingerprint is _____.

(4) While I cook the pasta, would you _____ the sauce?

(5) I went for a walk to clear my _____.

(6) I'm worried about my swimming _____.

03 우리말과 일치하도록 주어진 단어를 배열하여 영작하시오.

(1) 당신은 정치적인 사안에 관심이 있나요?

(the / in / you / are / issue / interested / political)

➡ _____

_____

(2) 당신은 매일 연설 준비를 할 필요가 없어요.

(every day / prepare / you / your / don't / to / speech / have)

➡ _____

_____

(3) 나는 우리의 발표가 전혀 걱정되지 않아.

(worried / about / at / our / all / I'm / presentation / not)

➡ _____

_____

04 다음 짝지어진 대화가 어색한 것은?

① A: What don't I have to do on Stress-Free Day?

B: You don't have to clean the classroom.

② A: I'm worried about my grade on the science test.

B: You don't have to be good at every subject.

③ A: I'm concerned about my weight. I think I'm too fat.

B: You don't need to worry about your weight. You look great.

④ A: I'm afraid that I'll make a mistake on my math test.

B: You don't have to worry too much.

⑤ A: I'm worried about my family. We don't talk to each other much these days.

B: You look a bit nervous. You don't need to talk to each other.

[05~06] 다음 대화를 읽고 물음에 답하시오.

> B: You look a bit nervous.
> G: Well, I'm worried about my presentation in history class.
> B: Don't worry. You've prepared a lot. You'll do a great job.
> G: Thanks. I feel much better now.

05 What is the girl concerned about?

➡ _____

_____

06 Why does the boy think the girl will do a great job?

➡ _____

_____

07 다음 대화를 읽고 대답할 수 <u>없는</u> 것은?

> Jack: Mom, what time are we going to Grandma's place tomorrow morning?
> Mom: About 8 a.m. I'm going to bake cookies for her before we go.
> Jack: Then, should I get up early to help you?
> Mom: You don't have to. Your dad will help me.
> Jack: O.K, then. Good night, Mom!

① What is Jack going to do with his mom?
② What is Jack's mom going to do for his grandma?
③ Who will help Jack's mom in the morning?
④ When are Jack and his mom going to his grandma's place tomorrow?
⑤ What time is Jack's mom going to get up to bake cookies?

[08~09] 다음 대화를 읽고 물음에 답하시오.

> Emily: Shall we try that new Mexican restaurant tomorrow?
> Tom: Why not? I'll call the restaurant to _____(A)_____ for us.
> Emily: You don't have to call them. You can do it online.
> Tom: Oh, I see. How convenient!

08 위 대화의 빈칸 (A)에 '예약하다'를 3 단어로 쓰시오.

➡ _____

09 위 대화의 내용과 일치하지 <u>않는</u> 것은?

① Emily는 Tom에게 내일 새로 생긴 멕시코 레스토랑에 가자고 제안한다.
② Tom은 멕시코 레스토랑에 가는 것이 별로 마음에 들지 않는다.
③ Tom은 레스토랑에 전화로 예약할 필요가 없다.
④ 레스토랑 예약은 온라인으로 할 수 있다.
⑤ Tom은 온라인 예약이 편리하다고 생각한다.

10 다음 대화가 자연스럽게 이어지도록 순서대로 배열하시오.

> (A) Thanks. I feel much better now.
> (B) You look a bit nervous.
> (C) I'm worried about my swimming competition this Saturday.
> (D) Don't worry. You're such a good swimmer. Just relax and enjoy yourself!

➡ _____

11 다음 대화의 (A)~(C)에 들어갈 말이 바르게 짝지어진 것은?

> Jane: What happened to your shoes? Aren't they new?
>
> Brian: Yes, but my dog chewed them. He does it all the time. I'm (A)[worrying / worried] about him.
>
> Jane: He was probably (B)[boring / bored]. Why don't you play with him more often?
>
> Brian: O.K., I will. I hope he will stop (C) [to chew / chewing] my shoes.

	(A)	(B)	(C)
①	worrying	boring	to chew
②	worrying	bored	chewing
③	worried	bored	to chew
④	worried	bored	chewing
⑤	worried	boring	to chew

12 다음 대화와 일치하도록 빈칸을 완성하시오.

> B: You look a bit nervous.
>
> G: I'm worried about my swimming competition this Saturday.
>
> B: Don't worry. You're such a good swimmer. Just relax and enjoy yourself!
>
> G: Thanks. I feel much better now.

> The girl looked (A)_____.
> She was so worried because of (B)_____. It'll be held on (C)_____. The boy already knew she is a good swimmer, so he encouraged her, by saying (D)"_____". Thanks to the boy, the girl felt relieved.

[13~14] 다음 주어진 우리말을 영작한 것으로 옳은 것은?

13
> 지수는 자신에 대한 확신을 느꼈을 뿐만 아니라, 타인들에게도 자신감에 차 보였다.

① Jisu felt not only sure about herself but looked also confident to other people.

② Not only Jisu felt sure about herself but also other people looked confident.

③ Jisu not only felt sure about herself but looked confident to other people.

④ Not only did feel Jisu sure about herself but she also looked confident to other people.

⑤ Jisu not only felt sure about herself but also looked confidently to other people.

14
> Franklin은 기타를 연주할 수 있을 뿐만 아니라, 피아노 조율도 할 수 있다.

① Franklin can play not only the guitar, but also tune the piano.

② Franklin not only can play the guitar, but also can he tune the piano.

③ Not only can Franklin play the guitar, does he also tune the piano.

④ Not only can Franklin play the guitar, but he can tune the piano.

⑤ Not Franklin only can play the guitar, but can he also tune the piano.

15 다음 각 문장의 밑줄 친 분사구문을 부사절로 바꿀 때 어법상 <u>어색한</u> 것은?

① <u>Visiting Vladivostok</u>, she could learn the Russian dance.

→ When she visited Vladivostok,

② <u>Seen from the high sky,</u> the city seems to be made of the lego bricks.

→ If it is seen from the high sky,

③ <u>There being nothing to eat,</u> the mice moved to another city.

→ Since there was nothing to eat,

④ <u>It being cold but fine,</u> we went on a picnic.

→ Though it was cold but fine,

⑤ <u>Completing the final review,</u> Roberto went out for a walk with his pets.

→ After he completed the final review,

16 다음 그림을 보고, 주어진 단어들을 알맞게 배열하여 빈칸을 채우시오.

(Sam, Minju, are, joining, and, in, both, interested, a club)

➡ _____

_____ and doing volunteer work.

17 다음 각 문장의 밑줄 친 부사절을 분사구문으로 바꾼 것 중 옳은 것은?

① <u>While Babe was watching TV,</u> his pet puppies fell asleep.

→ Watching TV,

② <u>Because she went to bed earlier last night,</u> Reon woke up at dawn.

→ She going to bed earlier last night,

③ <u>If you cut the wrong wire,</u> the box will explode.

→ Cutting the wrong wire,

④ <u>If it is fine tomorrow,</u> we will go fishing in the sea.

→ Being fine tomorrow,

⑤ <u>When it is seen from a spaceship,</u> the Earth is blue.

→ Seen from a spaceship,

[18~19] 다음 중에서 <u>틀린</u> 문장을 찾아 기호를 쓰고, 바르게 고쳐 문장을 다시 쓰시오.

18 ① Finding the smartphone she had lost, Emilia cried out with joy.

② Someone having touched the tires of her car, Clara didn't use it that morning.

③ Seeing its master, the dog wagged its tail.

④ Julie having seen him before, she decided to make friends with Charles.

⑤ Speaking in front of many people for a long time, the director felt quite tired.

➡ _____

_____

19 ① Do both Michael and his employees know how the company survived?

② Can either you or your partner explain to me what's happening in this building?

③ Not only you but also they warned us of the danger of the viruses.

④ Not only can he fly the drones, but he also makes some drones himself.

⑤ Neither the president nor his secretaries wants to know the basic causes of the problem.

➡ _____

_____

[20~22] 다음 글을 읽고 물음에 답하시오.

①The hardest time in my life was my first grade in middle school. When my family moved to Gunsan, I had to go to a new school. ②Had no friends at school, I felt sad and lonely. One day, I asked one of my ③classmate to show me her notes. She not only helped me but also ④became a good friend. From this experience, I have learned that ____ⓐ____ is a good way ⑤to make friends.

20 위 글의 밑줄 친 ①~⑤에서 어법상 어색한 것을 두 개 골라 바르게 고치고 그 이유를 밝히시오.

➡ _____

이유: _____

_____

21 위 글의 빈칸 ⓐ에 알맞은 것을 고르시오.

① asking for help
② keeping silent
③ inquiring questions
④ moving to a new school
⑤ showing notes

22 According to the passage, which is NOT true?

① The writer had to go to a new school when her family moved to Gunsan.
② The writer's hardest time in her life was her first grade in middle school.
③ The writer had some friends at the new school.
④ One of the writer's classmates not only helped her but also became a good friend.
⑤ The writer learned a good way to make friends.

[23~25] 다음 글을 읽고 물음에 답하시오.

_____ⓐ_____

①When he graduates from high school next year, Taeho wants to become a professional farmer. ②Having no friends, he has never told anyone about it. ③He is worried that his parents or his friends will not understand. ④Wanting to clear his mind, Taeho decided to take a day trip on a train by himself. ⑤On the train, he told a complete stranger sitting beside him about his problem. He had no idea why he did it. However, he felt much better when he got off the train. Strangely enough, we often tell strangers about our problems just like Taeho. That is because we do not have to worry about being judged or seeing them again. If you have a problem that you cannot share with your family or friends, try talking to a stranger. You will feel much better.

23 위 글의 빈칸 ⓐ에 알맞은 것을 고르시오.

① How do I become less nervous?
② Who can help me feel better?
③ Why has Taeho never told anyone about his problem?
④ How do I turn a rival into a friend?
⑤ How does psychology answer our questions?

24 Why did Taeho take a day trip on a train by himself?

➡ _____

_____

25 위 글의 ①~⑤ 중에서 흐름상 어색한 것을 고르시오.

①   ②   ③   ④   ⑤

MEMO

Lesson 6

Find Your Passion

🎙 의사소통 기능

- 불만족 표현하기
  I'm not satisfied with this T-shirt.

- 다짐 말하기
  I promise I won't be late again.

🎙 언어 형식

- 관계부사
  He wanted to create a place **where** people
  could try his innovative food.

- 접속부사 however, thus
  Some dishes were even decorated with flowers.
  Customers, **however**, were unhappy.
  He wanted to cook much more quickly and easily.
  Thus, he invented new machines for his kitchen.

Words & Expressions

Key Words

- **actor** [ǽktər] 몡 배우
- **appreciate** [əprí:ʃièit] 동 진가를 알아보다, 고마워하다
- **arts high school** 예술 고등학교
- **blueberry** [blú:bèri] 몡 블루베리
- **check** [tʃek] 몡 계산서
- **complain** [kəmpléin] 동 불평하다
- **completely** [kəmplí:tli] 부 완전하게
- **creative** [kriéitiv] 혭 창의적인, 창조적인
- **crush** [krʌʃ] 동 으깨다
- **customer** [kʌ́stəmər] 몡 고객, 소비자
- **decide** [disáid] 동 결정하다
- **decorate** [dékərèit] 동 장식하다, 꾸미다
- **device** [diváis] 몡 도구
- **dish** [diʃ] 몡 음식, 요리
- **draw** [drɔː] 동 그리다
- **fantastic** [fæntǽstik] 혭 환상적인
- **few** [fju:] 혭 소수의, 거의 없는
- **finish** [fíniʃ] 동 끝마치다
- **fix** [fiks] 동 수리하다
- **form** [fɔːrm] 몡 서류
- **fresh** [freʃ] 혭 신선한
- **gladly** [glǽdli] 부 기꺼이
- **grand** [grænd] 혭 웅장한, 위대한
- **happen** [hǽpən] 동 일어나다
- **honestly** [ánistli] 부 솔직하게, 솔직히

- **inconvenience** [ìnkənví:njəns] 몡 불편, 애로
- **innovative** [ínəvèitiv] 혭 획기적인
- **inventor** [invéntər] 몡 발명가
- **ma'am** [mæm] 몡 (여성을 정중히 부르는 말) 부인
- **meal** [mi:l] 몡 식사
- **passion** [pǽʃən] 몡 열정, 흥미
- **pay** [pei] 동 지불하다, 지급하다
- **promise** [prάmis] 동 약속하다, 다짐하다
- **provide** [prəváid] 동 제공하다
- **pursue** [pərsú:] 동 추구하다, 추진하다
- **rare** [rɛər] 혭 덜 익은, 살짝 익힌
- **real** [rí:əl] 혭 사실적인
- **reason** [rí:zn] 몡 이유
- **role** [roul] 몡 역할, 배역
- **satisfied** [sǽtisfàid] 혭 만족한
- **sell** [sel] 동 팔다
- **slice** [slais] 몡 한 조각, 일부
- **successful** [səksésfəl] 혭 성공적인
- **supper** [sʌ́pər] 몡 만찬, 저녁 식사
- **surely** [ʃúərli] 부 확실히, 분명히
- **tank** [tæŋk] 몡 (물·기름 등의) 탱크
- **throughout** [θru:áut] 전 ~ 동안 내내
- **unfortunately** [ənfɔ́:rtʃənətli] 부 불행하게도
- **uniquely** [ju:ní:kli] 부 독특하게
- **yet** [jet] 부 아직

Key Expressions

- **as a result** 결과적으로
- **be interested in** ~에 관심이 있다
- **be used to** ~에 익숙하다
- **do one's best** 최선을 다하다
- **feel like -ing** ~할 마음이 나다
- **fill out** 작성하다
- **have a bite of** 한 입 베어 물다
- **have a look at** ~을 살펴보다
- **not anymore** 더 이상 아니다
- **now that** ~이기 때문에, ~이므로

- **of all time** 역대, 지금껏
- **put ... in charge of ~** ~에게 …의 책임을 맡기다
- **put up** 내붙이다, 게시하다
- **scare away** 겁주어 쫓아내다
- **take charge of** ~의 책임을 지다, ~을 떠맡다
- **take a class** 수업을 듣다
- **take on** ~을 떠맡다
- **That's the reason why ~.** 그것이 ~하는 이유이다.
- **turn off** ~을 끄다

Word Power

※ 서로 비슷한 뜻을 가진 어휘

- □ **check** 계산서 – **bill** 계산서
- □ **complain** 불평하다 – **criticize** 비난하다
- □ **completely** 완전히 – **thoroughly** 철저하게
- □ **creative** 창의적인 – **original** 독창적인
- □ **decide** 결정하다 – **determine** 결정하다
- □ **fix** 수리하다 – **repair** 수리하다

- □ **happen** 일어나다 – **occur** 일어나다
- □ **provide** 제공하다 – **supply** 제공하다
- □ **pursue** 추구하다 – **seek** 찾다, 추구하다
- □ **reason** 이유 – **cause** 원인
- □ **supper** 저녁 식사 – **dinner** 저녁 식사
- □ **surely** 확실히 – **certainly** 확실하게

※ 서로 반대되는 뜻을 가진 어휘

- □ **completely** 완전하게 ↔ **incompletely** 불완전하게
- □ **fantastic** 환상적인 ↔ **realistic** 현실적인, 현실성 있는
- □ **convenience** 편리함 ↔ **inconvenience** 불편

- □ **rare** 덜 익은 ↔ **well-done** 잘 익은
- □ **satisfied** 만족한 ↔ **dissatisfied** 불만족한
- □ **sell** 팔다 ↔ **purchase** 구입하다

※ 동사 – 명사

- □ **appreciate** 진가를 알아보다 – **appreciation** 진가의 인정
- □ **complain** 불평하다 – **complaint** 불평
- □ **decide** 결정하다 – **decision** 결정
- □ **decorate** 장식하다 – **decoration** 장식

- □ **innovate** 혁신하다 – **innovation** 혁신
- □ **pay** 지불하다 – **payment** 지불
- □ **provide** 제공하다 – **provision** 공급
- □ **pursue** 추구하다 – **pursuit** 추구

※ 접두사 un-

- □ **clear** 명백한 – **unclear** 불확실한
- □ **creative** 창의적인 – **uncreative** 창의적이지 않은
- □ **easy** 쉬운 – **uneasy** 불편한
- □ **fortunate** 행운의 – **unfortunate** 불행한
- □ **happy** 행복한 – **unhappy** 불행한

- □ **natural** 자연스러운 – **unnatural** 자연스럽지 않은
- □ **real** 사실적인 – **unreal** 사실적이지 않은
- □ **successful** 성공적인 – **unsuccessful** 성공적이지 않은
- □ **usual** 흔한 – **unusual** 흔치 않은

English Dictionary

- □ **appreciate** 진가를 알아보다
  → to like something because one recognizes its good qualities
  어떤 것의 좋은 점을 인정하여 그것을 좋아하다

- □ **complain** 불평하다
  → to say that you are annoyed, not satisfied, or unhappy about something or someone
  어떤 것이나 누군가에 대해 짜증나거나 불만족스럽거나 불쾌하다고 말하다

- □ **crush** 으깨다
  → to press something so hard that it breaks or is damaged
  어떤 것을 세게 눌러서 깨지거나 손상되게 하다

- □ **customer** 고객, 소비자
  → someone who buys goods or services from a shop, company, etc.
  상점, 회사 등으로부터 상품이나 서비스를 구입하는 사람

- □ **decorate** 장식하다, 꾸미다
  → to make something look more nice by putting something pretty on it
  어떤 예쁜 것을 올려놓아 어떤 것을 더 좋아 보이게 만들다

- □ **fix** 수리하다
  → to repair something that is broken or not working properly
  망가지거나 제대로 작동하지 않는 것을 수리하다

- □ **form** 서류
  → an official document with spaces where you write information
  당신이 정보를 적을 여백을 가진 공식적인 문서

- □ **pursue** 추구하다, 추진하다
  → to make efforts to achieve a particular aim or result, often over a long period of time
  종종 오랜 시간에 걸쳐, 어떤 특정 목표나 결과를 달성하기 위해 노력하다

- □ **rare** 덜 익은, 살짝 익힌
  → cooked a short time; still red inside
  잠깐 요리된; 속이 아직 붉은

01 다음 짝지어진 단어의 관계가 같도록 빈칸에 알맞은 말은?

> check – bill : determine – _____

① complain　② cause　③ crush
④ device　⑤ decide

02 주어진 영어 설명에 맞게 문장의 빈칸에 알맞은 말을 쓰시오.

> It is unnecessary to _____ the argument any further.

> <영어 설명> to make efforts to achieve a particular aim or result, often over a long period of time

➡ _____

03 다음 주어진 단어를 사용하여 자연스러운 문장을 만들 수 없는 것은?

> provide slice promise fix

① I'll see what I can do but I can't _____ anything.
② They're sending an engineer to _____ the phone.
③ I usually have a _____ of bread every morning.
④ Photographs of actors _____ the walls of the restaurant.
⑤ Teachers _____ a model for children to imitate.

04 다음 빈칸에 들어갈 알맞은 말을 고르시오.

> Find your _____ and follow your dreams.

① passion　② device
③ convenience　④ expression
⑤ contact

05 밑줄 친 부분의 의미로 알맞지 <u>않은</u> 것은?

① They managed to <u>scare</u> the bears <u>away</u>. (겁주어 쫓아내다)
② Could you <u>fill out</u> these forms? (작성하다)
③ I <u>was</u> not <u>used</u> to carrying a tray with one hand. (~에 사용되었다)
④ I don't feel ready to <u>take on</u> new responsibilities. (떠맡다)
⑤ To <u>take the class</u>, you have to be able to use a computer. (수업을 듣다)

06 다음 빈칸에 공통으로 들어갈 말로 알맞은 것을 고르시오.

> • You will take charge _____ the company.
> • To my thinking, he's one of the greatest comedians _____ all time.

① in　② of　③ with
④ at　⑤ for

01 다음 영영풀이에 알맞은 어휘를 〈보기〉에서 찾아 쓰시오.

> ┌─ 보기 ─┐
> form   complain
> customer   appreciate

(1) to say that you are annoyed, not satisfied, or unhappy about something or someone

➡ _____

(2) someone who buys goods or services from a shop, company, etc.

➡ _____

(3) to like something because one recognizes its good qualities

➡ _____

(4) an official document with spaces where you write information

➡ _____

02 다음 짝지어진 두 단어의 관계가 같도록 빈칸에 알맞은 말을 쓰시오.

(1) decide : decision = complain : _____

(2) completely : incompletely
= natural : _____

03 다음 우리말에 맞도록 빈칸에 알맞은 말을 쓰시오.

(1) 그것은 획기적인 디자인 덕분에 곧 인기 있게 되었다.

➡ It soon became popular thanks to its _____ design.

(2) 나는 내 방을 꽃으로 장식하고 싶어.

➡ I want to _____ my room with flowers.

(3) 그는 그의 어린 딸에게 안전장치를 만들어 주었다.

➡ He made a safety _____ for his baby daughter.

(4) 그녀는 이 영화에서 주인공을 연기한다.

➡ She plays the main _____ in this movie.

04 우리말에 맞게 한 단어를 추가하여 주어진 어구를 알맞게 배열하시오.

(1) 나는 패션에 대한 열정을 갖고 있다.
(a, I, fashion, have, for)

➡ _____

(2) 그 새 식당은 밝고 다채로운 간판을 세웠다.
(the new restaurant, sign, and, bright, up, a, colorful)

➡ _____
_____

(3) 양해해 주셔서 감사드리며 불편을 끼쳐드린 점 사과드립니다.
(we, you, your, understanding, and, inconvenience, thank, apologize, any, for)

➡ _____
_____

(4) 이제 겨울이니까, 나는 주말마다 스키 타러 갈 거야.
(I'm, weekend, winter, it's, now, go, going, skiing, every, to)

➡ _____
_____

Conversation

① 불만족 표현하기

> **I'm not satisfied with this T-shirt.** 나는 이 티셔츠가 마음에 들지 않아.

- 'I'm not satisfied with A.'는 '나는 A가 마음에 들지 않는다.'는 의미로 불만족을 나타내는 표현으로, 'I'm not happy with ~.'라고 표현하기도 한다. 불만족을 나타낼 때는 'not satisfied with ~', 'not happy with ~', 'not pleased with ~'와 함께 'unhappy with ~', 'dissatisfied with ~'를 사용하여 'I'm unhappy with ~', 'I'm dissatisfied with ~' 또는 'I don't like ~'라고 할 수도 있다.

- 불만족에 대하여 물을 때는 'Are you dissatisfied with ~?' 또는 'Are you unhappy with ~?(~이 마음에 안 드니?)' 등과 같은 표현을 사용한다.

- 고민이나 불만족의 원인을 물어볼 때는 'Is something worrying you?(무슨 걱정거리가 있나요?)' 또는 'Is there something bothering you?(뭔가 걸리는 일이 있나요?)', 'Is there anything wrong?(뭐 잘못된 일 있니?)', 'What happened?(무슨 일 있니?)'와 같은 표현을 사용하고, 무슨 문제가 있는지 물어볼 때는 'Is something wrong?(뭐가 잘못되었니?)' 또는 'What's wrong (with you)?(뭐가 잘못됐나요?)', 'Why are you disappointed?(왜 실망스러운가요?)'와 같은 표현을 쓸 수도 있다.

불만족 표현하기

- I'm not satisfied with ~. 나는 ~가 만족스럽지 않아.
- I don't like ~. 나는 ~가 안 좋아.
- I'm not happy with ~. 나는 ~가 마음에 들지 않아.
- I'm unhappy with ~. 나는 ~가 마음에 들지 않아.
- I'm dissatisfied with ~. 나는 ~가 불만스러워요.

핵심 Check

1. 다음 밑줄 친 (A)의 우리말과 일치하도록 주어진 표현을 이용하여 영어로 쓰시오.

   M: Hello, ma'am. How can I help you?

   W: I bought this phone only a week ago, but it sometimes turns off by itself.

   M: Oh, I see. May I have a look at it? (Pause) We're sorry for the inconvenience. It'll take a few hours to fix it.

   W: (A)그 휴대전화가 만족스럽지 않아요. (the phone, satisfied) I'd like a new one.

   M: Of course. I just need to fill out this form.

   ➡ _____

❷ 다짐 말하기

I promise I won't be late again. 다시는 늦지 않겠다고 약속할게요.

- 'I promise to ~.'는 '~하겠다고 약속합니다.'의 뜻으로 확실하게 하겠다는 다짐을 나타내는 말이다. promise를 쓸 때는 to부정사나 'that 주어+동사'의 형태가 따라온다. 상대방에게 확실하게 '~하겠다.'는 의미로 확실성을 나타내는 'make sure(확실하게 하다)'를 사용하여 'I will make sure that 주어+동사 ~'라고 할 수도 있다.

- 다짐이나 확실한 일을 나타내는 표현에는 sure(확실한), certain(확신하는), positive(긍정적인) 등을 사용하여 'I'm sure (that) ~.'이라고 하거나 'I'm certain (that) ~.' 또는 'I'm positive about ~.(나는 ~에 대해 확신한다.)'라고 할 수 있고, '맹세하다'라는 의미의 'swear'를 사용하여 'I swear I will ~.'이라는 표현을 사용할 수 있다.

- '확실하다'라는 의미로 'I'm 100 percent sure.(나는 100% 장담해.)' 또는 'It is obvious/clear that ~.(~가 분명하다.)'를 쓰기도 한다. 'bet'은 '내기를 걸다, 틀림없다'의 뜻으로 'I bet that ~.'이라고 하면 '틀림없이 ~이다.'라는 뜻이 된다. 앞으로 할 일이나 일어날 일에 대하여 상대방에게 확신을 주거나, 원하는 것이나 좋은 일이 일어날 것이 확실함을 나타낼 때는 'I have no doubt that ~.(~할 거라고 믿는다., ~을 믿어 의심치 않는다., ~할 거라고 확신한다.)'이라는 표현을 사용한다.

다짐 말하기

- I promise to ~. 나는 ~하겠다고 약속해.
- I promise you that I'll ~. 나는 ~하겠다고 약속드릴게요.
- She will make sure that ~. 그녀는 반드시 ~하도록 할 거다.
- He swears he will ~. 그는 ~하겠다고 약속한다.
- I'm sure that ~. 나는 반드시 ~할 것이다.
- I'm certain that ~. 나는 확실히 ~할 것이다.

핵심 Check

2. 다음 대화의 밑줄 친 (A)의 우리말에 해당하는 적절한 표현을 쓰시오.

B: Mom, I want to take cooking classes.

W: What? I thought you were interested in sports.

B: I was but not anymore. I want to become a chef.

W: Are you sure? Cooking is hard work.

M: Don't worry. (A)최선을 다하겠다고 약속할게요. (do, promise)

W: O.K., then.

➡ _____

Listen & Speak 1 A-1

B: Wow! Did you draw this?

G: I did. Do you like it?

B: Yes, the bread and the milk ❶look so real. ❷I feel like having a bite of the bread.

G: Thanks, but ❸I'm not satisfied with it. It's not ❹unique.

B: I don't think ❺so. I think it's a fantastic drawing.

B: 우와! 이거 네가 그린 거야?
G: 내가 그렸어. 마음에 들어?
B: 응, 빵이랑 우유가 정말 진짜 같아. 빵을 한 입 먹고 싶어지는데.
G: 고마워. 하지만 이건 만족스럽진 않아. 독창적이지 않아.
B: 난 그렇게 생각 안 해. 정말 멋진 그림인 것 같아.

❶ look+형용사: ~하게 보이다
❷ feel like ~ing: ~하고 싶다
❸ 'be not satisfied with'는 불만족을 표현하는 말이다.
❹ unique: 독창적인
❺ so는 'It's not unique.'를 대신하고 있다.

Check(√) True or False

(1) The girl is satisfied with what she drew. T ☐ F ☐

(2) The boy thinks the bread and the milk look so real. T ☐ F ☐

Listen & Speak 1 A-2

M: Hello, ma'am. How can I help you?

W: I bought this phone only a week ago, but it sometimes turns off ❶ by itself.

M: Oh, I see. May I ❷have a look at it? (*Pause*) We're sorry for the ❸ inconvenience. ❹It'll take a few hours to fix it.

W: ❺I'm not satisfied with the phone. I'd like a new ❻one.

M: Of course. I just need to ❼fill out this form.

M: 안녕하세요, 고객님. 무엇을 도와드릴까요?
W: 이 휴대전화를 겨우 일주일 전에 샀는데, 가끔 저절로 꺼져요.
M: 오, 그렇군요. 제가 좀 봐도 될까요? 불편을 드려 죄송합니다. 고치는 데 몇 시간 정도 걸릴 거예요.
W: 이 휴대전화가 만족스럽지 않아요. 새것을 원해요.
M: 물론이죠. 이 서류만 작성하면 됩니다.

❶ by itself: 스스로, 저절로 = naturally, automatically(자동으로)
❷ have a look at: ~을 한 번 보다, it은 this phone을 가리킨다.
❸ inconvenience: 불편
❹ take: (시간이) 걸리다, fix: 고치다, 수리하다
❺ 'be not satisfied with'는 불만족을 표현하는 말이다.
❻ one은 phone을 대신해서 쓰인 부정대명사이다.
❼ fill out a form: 서식을 작성하다

Check(√) True or False

(3) The woman bought the phone a few weeks ago. T ☐ F ☐

(4) The man needs to fill out a form. T ☐ F ☐

Listen & Speak 2 A-1

G: Wow, I like this blueberry jam. Where did you buy it?

B: I made it ❶myself.

G: Really? ❷This is better than any other jam I've ever had. You should sell it.

B: Do you think people would want to buy this?

G: Of course. ❸I promise I'll be your first customer.

❶ 강조 용법으로 쓰인 재귀대명사이다.

❷ '비교급+than any other+단수 명사'로 최상급의 의미이다. jam 뒤에는 관계대명사 that이 생략되어 있는 형태로 관계사절이 선행사인 jam을 수식하고 있다.

❸ 다짐을 말할 때 쓰는 표현이다. promise 뒤에는 구체적인 내용을 명사절로 써서 나타내며, "I promise to be your first customer."로 바꿔 쓸 수 있다.

Listen & Speak 2 A-2

B: Mom, I want to go to an arts high school. I want to become an actor.

W: What? I thought you were interested in science.

B: I was but ❶not anymore. I want to become a movie star.

W: Are you sure you want to be an actor?

B: Yes, I'll learn ❷how to act. ❸I promise I'll do my best.

❶ 'not anymore'는 'I'm not interested in science anymore.'에서 중복되는 것을 생략하고 쓴 표현이다.

❷ 'how to act'는 '의문사+to부정사'로 learn의 목적어 역할을 하고 있다.

❸ 다짐을 말할 때 쓰는 표현으로 'I promise to do my best.'로 바꿔 쓸 수 있다.

Communicate A

Man: Are you enjoying your meal?

Woman: Well, the bread was good, and the salad was fresh.

Man: How about your steak?

Woman: Honestly, ❶I'm not satisfied with the steak. It's too ❷rare for me.

Man: I'm sorry. Would you like me to bring you another one?

Woman: ❸That's O.K. I need to be going. Let me just have the check, please.

Man: I'm really sorry. You won't have to pay for the steak.

Woman: O.K. Thanks.

Man: ❹I promise we'll provide you with a better experience next time you visit.

❶ 'be not satisfied with'는 불만족을 표현하는 말이다.

❷ rare: 설익은, 덜 익은

❸ That은 다른 것으로 가져다 주겠다는 앞 문장의 내용을 받고 있다.

❹ 다짐을 말할 때 쓰는 표현이다.

Progress Check 1

M: Hello, ma'am. How can I help you?

W: I got this hat as a gift yesterday, ❶but I'm not satisfied with the color.

M: Oh, I see. We have this hat in different colors.

W: Do you have ❷one in blue?

M: Yes, we ❸do. I'll get ❷one for you.

W: Thanks.

❶ 'be not satisfied with'는 불만족을 표현하는 말이다.

❷ one은 hat을 대신해서 쓰인 부정대명사이다.

❸ do는 'have the hat in blue'를 대신하는 대동사이다.

Progress Check 2

B: Mom, I want to ❶take cooking classes.

W: What? I thought you were interested in sports.

B: I was but ❷not anymore. I want to become a chef.

W: Are you sure? Cooking is hard work.

B: Don't worry. ❸I promise I'll do my best.

W: O.K., ❹then.

❶ take classes: 수업을 듣다

❷ 'not anymore'는 'I'm not interested in sports anymore.'에서 중복되는 것을 생략하고 쓴 표현이다.

❸ 다짐을 말할 때 쓰는 표현으로 'I promise to do my best.'로 바꿔 쓸 수 있다.

❹ then은 'If you promise you'll do your best'를 대신한다고 볼 수 있다.

Progress Check 3

G: Dad, I want to watch a movie on TV now.

M: ❶Have you finished your homework?

G: No, but ❷I promise I'll finish it after I watch TV.

❶ 현재완료의 완료 용법이다.

❷ 다짐을 말할 때 쓰는 표현으로 'I promise to finish it after I watch TV.'로 바꿔 쓸 수 있다.

● 다음 우리말과 일치하도록 빈칸에 알맞은 말을 쓰시오.

Listen & Speak 1 A-1

B: Wow! Did you draw this?

G: I _____ . Do you like _____ ?

B: Yes, the bread and the milk _____ _____ _____ . I _____
_____ _____ _____ _____ _____ the bread.

G: Thanks, but _____ _____ _____ _____ it. It's not _____ .

B: I don't think _____ . I think it's a _____ _____ .

Listen & Speak 1 A-2

M: Hello, ma'am. _____ _____ I _____ you?

W: I bought this phone _____ _____ _____ _____ , but it
_____ _____ _____ _____ _____ _____ .

M: Oh, I see. May I _____ _____ _____ _____ it? (*Pause*)
We're sorry for the _____ . It'll _____ a _____ _____
_____ fix it.

W: _____ _____ _____ _____ the phone. I'd like a new
_____ .

M: Of course. I just need to _____ _____ this _____ .

Listen & Speak 2 A-1

G: Wow, I like this blueberry jam. Where did you buy it?

B: I made it _____ .

G: Really? This is _____ _____ _____ _____ _____ I've
ever had. You should sell _____ .

B: Do you think people _____ want to buy this?

G: Of course. _____ _____ _____ _____ your first customer.

Listen & Speak 2 A-2

B: Mom, I want to go to an arts high school. I want to become an actor.

W: What? I thought you _____ _____ _____ science.

B: I was but _____ _____ . I _____ _____ become a movie
star.

W: _____ you _____ you want to be an actor?

B: Yes, I'll learn _____ _____ _____ . _____ _____ _____
_____ my best.

B: 우와! 이거 네가 그린 거야?

G: 내가 그렸어. 마음에 들어?

B: 응, 빵이랑 우유가 정말 진짜 같아. 빵
을 한 입 먹고 싶어지는데.

G: 고마워, 하지만 이건 만족스럽진 않
아. 독창적이지 않아.

B: 난 그렇게 생각 안 해. 정말 멋진 그림
인 것 같아.

M: 안녕하세요, 고객님. 무엇을 도와드릴
까요?

W: 이 휴대전화를 겨우 일주일 전에 샀
는데, 가끔 저절로 꺼져요.

M: 오, 그렇군요. 제가 좀 봐도 될까요?
불편을 드려 죄송합니다. 고치는 데
몇 시간 정도 걸릴 거예요.

W: 그 휴대전화가 만족스럽지 않아요.
새것을 원해요.

M: 물론이죠. 이 서류만 작성하면 됩니다.

G: 우와, 이 블루베리 잼 마음에 든다. 어
디서 샀어?

B: 직접 만든 거야.

G: 정말? 내가 지금껏 먹어본 잼 중에
제일 좋아. 팔아도 되겠어.

B: 사람들이 이걸 사길 원할 거라고 생각
해?

G: 물론이지. 내가 너의 첫 손님이 되겠
다고 약속할게.

B: 엄마, 저 예술 고등학교에 가고 싶어
요. 배우가 되고 싶어요.

W: 뭐라고? 네가 과학에 관심이 있다고
생각했는데.

B: 그랬었는데 더는 아니에요. 저는 영화
배우가 되고 싶어요.

W: 배우가 되고 싶은 게 확실하니?

B: 네, 연기하는 방법을 배울 거예요. 최
선을 다하겠다고 약속할게요.

Communicate A

Man: Are you enjoying _____ _____?

Woman: Well, the bread was _____, and the salad was _____.

Man: How _____ your steak?

Woman: Honestly, _____ _____ _____ _____ the steak. It's too _____ for me.

Man: I'm sorry. Would you like me _____ _____ you _____ _____?

Woman: That's O.K. I need to _____ _____. Let me just _____ the _____, please.

Man: I'm really sorry. You _____ _____ _____ pay for the steak.

Woman: O.K. Thanks.

Man: _____ _____ _____ _____ you _____ a better experience next time you visit.

Progress Check 1

M: Hello, ma'am. _____ _____ _____ help you?

W: I _____ this hat _____ a gift yesterday, but _____ _____ _____ _____ the color.

M: Oh, I see. We have this hat _____ different colors.

W: Do you have _____ _____ _____?

M: Yes, we _____. I'll _____ _____ for you.

W: Thanks.

Progress Check 2

B: Mom, I want to _____ cooking _____.

W: What? I thought you were _____ _____ sports.

B: I was but _____ _____. I want to become a chef.

W: Are you sure? Cooking is hard work.

B: Don't _____. _____ _____ _____ _____ my best.

W: O.K., _____.

Progress Check 3

G: Dad, I want to watch a movie _____ TV now.

M: _____ you _____ your homework?

G: No, but _____ _____ _____ _____ _____ it after I watch TV.

01 다음 빈칸 (A)에 알맞은 문장을 고르시오.

> B: Wow! Did you draw this?
> G: I did. Do you like it?
> B: Yes, the bread and the milk look so real. I feel like having a bite of the bread.
> G: Thanks, but _____(A)_____. It's not unique.
> B: I don't think so. I think it's a fantastic drawing.

① I'm pleased with it
② I'm not satisfied with it
③ I think I can make it more real
④ I think it's rather natural
⑤ I think it looks like real bread and milk

02 밑줄 친 우리말을 주어진 어구를 이용해 영작하시오.

> G: Wow, I like this blueberry jam. Where did you buy it?
> B: I made it myself.
> G: Really? This is better than any other jam I've ever had. You should sell it.
> B: Do you think people would want to buy this?
> G: Of course. 내가 너의 첫 손님이 되겠다고 약속할게. (promise, be first customer, 7 단어)

➡ _____

03 다음 대화가 자연스럽게 연결되도록 (A)~(D)를 적절하게 배열하시오.

> M: Hello, ma'am. How can I help you?
> (A) I'm not satisfied with the phone. I'd like a new one.
> (B) Oh, I see. May I have a look at it? (*Pause*) We're sorry for the inconvenience. It'll take a few hours to fix it.
> (C) I bought this phone only a week ago, but it sometimes turns off by itself.
> (D) Of course. I just need to fill out this form.

➡ _____

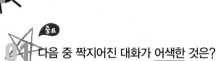

01 다음 중 짝지어진 대화가 <u>어색한</u> 것은?

① A: Wow! Did you draw this?

B: Yes, I did. Do you like it?

② A: I'm not satisfied with the phone. I'd like a new one.

B: Of course. I just need to fill out this form.

③ A: Are you sure you want to be an actor?

B: Yes, I'll learn how to act. I promise I'll do my best.

④ A: I was but not anymore. I want to become a chef.

B: I thought you were interested in sports.

⑤ A: Are you enjoying your meal?

B: Well, the bread was good, and the salad was fresh.

[02~05] 다음 대화를 읽고 물음에 답하시오.

M: Hello, ma'am. How can I help you?

W: I got this hat as a gift yesterday, but I'm not satisfied with _____(A)_____.

M: Oh, I see. We have this hat in different colors.

W: (a)파란 것도 있나요? (one, have, in)

M: _____(B)_____ I'll get one for you.

W: Thanks.

02 빈칸 (A)에 알맞은 말을 고르시오.

① the color   ② the shape

③ its convenience   ④ its size

⑤ its price

03 위 대화의 빈칸 (B)에 들어갈 말로 알맞은 말을 we를 포함한 3 단어로 쓰시오.

➡ _____

04 밑줄 친 (a)의 우리말에 맞게 괄호 안에 주어진 어휘를 이용하여 영작하시오.

➡ _____

05 위 대화의 내용과 일치하는 것은?

① The man is a customer.

② The woman bought a hat yesterday.

③ The woman is satisfied with the gift.

④ The woman has a blue hat.

⑤ The man will get a hat for the woman.

[06~07] 다음 대화를 읽고 물음에 답하시오.

B: Mom, I want to go to an arts high school. I want to become an actor.

W: What? I thought you were interested in science.

B: I was but (a)더는 아니에요. I want to become a movie star.

W: Are you sure you want to be an actor?

B: Yes, I'll learn how to act. _____(A)_____

06 위 대화의 빈칸 (A)에 들어갈 말로 알맞은 것은?

① Do you want me to do my best?

② I don't want to try my best.

③ Let me wish good luck.

④ I hope I'll do my best.

⑤ I promise I'll do my best.

07 밑줄 친 (a)의 우리말에 맞게 두 단어로 영작하시오.

➡ _____

08 주어진 글 사이에 대화가 자연스럽게 연결되도록 (A)~(D)를 적절하게 배열하시오.

> M: Hello, ma'am. How can I help you?

> (A) Do you have one in blue?
> (B) Oh, I see. We have this hat in different colors.
> (C) I got this hat as a gift yesterday, but I'm not satisfied with the color.
> (D) Yes, we do. I'll get one for you.

> W: Thanks.

➡ _____

[09~12] 다음 대화를 읽고 물음에 답하시오.

> Man: Are you enjoying your meal?
> Woman: Well, the bread was good, and the salad was fresh.
> Man: How about your steak?
> Woman: Honestly, _____(A)_____. It's too rare for me.
> Man: I'm sorry. Would you like me to bring you another __(B)__?
> Woman: That's O.K. I need to be going. Let me just have the check, please.
> Man: I'm really sorry. You won't have to pay for the steak.
> Woman: O.K. Thanks.
> Man: I promise we'll provide you with a better experience (a)다음에 방문하실 때는.

09 위 대화의 빈칸 (A)에 알맞은 말은?

① I enjoyed a lot
② I think this restaurant is very good
③ I think the service is not so good
④ I'm not satisfied with the steak
⑤ it's very good and delicious

10 위 대화의 빈칸 (B)에 알맞은 말을 부정대명사를 이용하여 쓰시오.

➡ _____

11 위 대화를 읽고 대답할 수 없는 것은?

① What does the woman think about the salad?
② Does the man always serve the steak rare?
③ Did the woman enjoy the steak?
④ Will the woman pay for the steak?
⑤ Will the man serve the woman better next time she visits?

12 위 대화의 밑줄 친 (a)의 우리말을 'time'을 이용하여 영작하시오.

➡ _____

13 다음 대화의 밑줄 친 부분의 의도로 알맞은 것은?

> G: Dad, I want to watch a movie on TV now.
> M: Have you finished your homework?
> G: No, but I promise I'll finish it after I watch TV.

① 불만족 표현하기
② 희망 표현하기
③ 설명하기
④ 경험 말하기
⑤ 다짐 말하기

[01~03] 다음 대화를 읽고 물음에 답하시오.

Man: Are you enjoying your meal?

Woman: Well, the bread was good, and the salad was fresh.

(A) That's O.K. I need to be going. Let me just have the check, please.

(B) Honestly, I'm not satisfied with the steak. It's too rare for me.

(C) I'm sorry. Would you like me to bring you another one?

(D) How about your steak?

Man: I'm really sorry. (a)스테이크 값은 지불하지 않으셔도 됩니다. (won't, the steak)

Woman: O.K. Thanks.

Man: I promise we'll provide you with a better experience next time you visit.

01 위 대화의 (A)~(D)를 알맞은 순서로 배열하시오.

➡ _____

02 괄호 안에 주어진 어휘를 이용하여 밑줄 친 우리말 (a)에 맞게 8 단어로 쓰시오.

➡ _____

03 Why isn't the woman satisfied with the steak? Use the word 'because'.

➡ _____
_____
_____

[04~05] 다음 대화를 읽고 물음에 답하시오.

M: Hello, ma'am. How can I help you?

W: I bought this phone only a week ago, but it sometimes turns off (a)저절로.

M: Oh, I see. May I have a look at it? (Pause) We're sorry for the inconvenience. It'll take a few hours to fix it.

W: _____ (A) _____ I'd like a new one.

M: Of course. I just need to fill out this form.

04 위 대화의 빈칸 (A)에 '전화기가 만족스럽지 않음'을 표현하는 말을 6 단어로 쓰시오.

➡ _____

05 밑줄 친 (a)의 우리말을 2 단어로 쓰시오.

➡ _____

06 다음 대화에서 어법상 어색한 것을 찾아 바르게 고치시오. (2개)

B: Wow! Did you draw this?

G: I was. Do you like it?

B: Yes, the bread and the milk look so real. I feel like to have a bite of the bread.

G: Thanks, but I'm not satisfied with it. It's not unique.

B: I don't think so. I think it's a fantastic drawing.

(1) _____ ➡ _____

(2) _____ ➡ _____

Grammar

① 관계부사

> * He wanted to create a place **where** people could try his innovative food.
>   그는 사람들이 그의 획기적인 음식을 먹어볼 수 있는 장소를 만들기를 원했다.
>
> * That's the reason **why** he hasn't finished the painting yet.
>   그것이 그가 아직 그림을 끝내지 못한 이유이다.

■ 관계부사는 접속사와 부사의 역할을 동시에 하는 것으로 선행사를 수식한다.

* I remember **the day**. We first met **on the day**.
  = I remember the day **when** we first met. 나는 우리가 처음 만난 날을 기억한다.
* That is **the building**. My uncle works **in the building**.
  = That is the building **where** my uncle works. 저기가 나의 삼촌이 일하는 건물이다.

■ 선행사가 장소, 시간, 이유, 방법 등의 명사일 때 전치사와 관계대명사로 표현 가능하며, 생략 등 각각의 용례도 조금씩 다르다.

(1) 장소(where): This is **the house**. Da Vinci lived **in the house**.
  → This is the house **which[that]** da Vinci lived **in**.
  → This is the house **in which** da Vinci lived. (in that (×))
  → This is the house **where** da Vinci lived. 이곳이 다빈치가 살았던 집이다.

(2) 시간(when): This is **the day**. Da Vinci was born **on the day**.
  → This is the day **which[that]** da Vinci was born **on**.
  → This is the day **on which** da Vinci was born. (on that (×))
  → This is the day **when** da Vinci was born. 이 날이 다빈치가 태어난 날이다.

(3) 이유(why): This is **the reason**. Da Vinci is a genius **for the reason**.
  → This is the reason **which[that]** da Vinci is a genius **for**.
  → This is the reason **for which** da Vinci is a genius. (for that (×))
  → This is the reason **why** da Vinci is a genius. 이것이 다빈치가 천재인 이유이다.
  → This is **why** da Vinci is a genius. (the reason 또는 why 둘 중의 하나 생략 가능)

(4) 방법(how): This is **the way**. Da Vinci escaped **in the way**.
  → This is the way **which[that]** da Vinci escaped **in**.
  → This is the way **in which** da Vinci escaped. (in that (×))
  → This is **the way how** da Vinci escaped.(×) (the way와 how를 같이 쓸 수 없다.
  → This is **the way** da Vinci escaped. 이것이 다빈치가 탈출한 방법이다.
  → This is **how** da Vinci escaped. (the way 또는 how 둘 중의 하나만 써야 한다.)

핵심 Check

1. 괄호 안에서 알맞은 말을 고르시오.

   (1) Sumi doesn't tell me the reason (why / which) she cried yesterday.

   (2) This is the year (how / when) the teacher decided to start a business.

2 접속부사

> • Some dishes were even decorated with flowers. Customers, **however**, were unhappy. 몇몇 음식들은 심지어 꽃으로 장식되었다. 하지만, 손님들은 불만족스러워했다.
>
> • He wanted to cook much more quickly and easily. **Thus**, he invented new machines for his kitchen. 그는 훨씬 더 빠르고 더 쉽게 요리하고 싶어 했다. 따라서 그는 그의 부엌을 위해 새로운 기계들을 발명하였다.

■ 접속부사는 앞에 제시된 문장의 내용을 부가적으로 연결하는 역할을 하며, 앞 문장과 대조되는 상황일 때는 'however'(그러나)와 같은 역접을, 자연스러운 인과 관계일 때는 'thus'(그러므로)와 같은 순접을 쓴다. 또한, 접속부사는 접속사가 아니라 부사이므로 문장들을 직접 연결할 수는 없다. 문장의 접속사 역할을 하는 세미콜론 뒤 또는 문장 맨 앞이나 뒤에서 쉼표와 함께 쓰이며, 문장 중간에 올 때는 앞뒤에 쉼표가 오게 된다.

• David is active, **however**, his son is quiet and shy. David은 활동적이지만, 그의 아들은 조용하고 부끄럼을 탄다.

• The road was blocked. **Thus**, we had to go back. 길이 막혀서, 우리는 되돌아가야 했다.

■ 같은 의미의 문장을 접속사, 접속부사 등으로 표현할 수 있다.

• **Because** it rained yesterday, the ground is wet. 어제 비가 와서, 땅이 젖었다.

= **Because of** the rain yesterday, the ground is wet. 어제 비 때문에, 땅이 젖었다.

= It rained yesterday. **Thus**, the ground is wet. 어제 비가 왔다. 그래서 땅이 젖었다.

• **Though** he was small, he jumped the hurdle. 비록 그는 작았지만, 장애물을 뛰어넘었다.

= He was small. **However**, he jumped the hurdle. 그는 작았다. 하지만 그는 장애물을 뛰어넘었다.

■ 그 밖의 다양한 접속부사나 연결어들의 종류와 의미

(1) 역접: 대조, 양보 (however, still, on the contrary, nevertheless 등)

(2) 인과, 결과 (thus, therefore, so, hence, consequently, as a result)

(3) 예시 (for example, for instance)

(4) 부가, 추가 (in addition, furthermore, moreover 등)

(5) 유사 (likewise, similarly, in the same way 등)

• She didn't like to eat it. **Nevertheless**, she did it.
그녀는 그것을 먹고 싶지 않았다. 그럼에도 불구하고 결국은 그것을 먹었다.

• **For example**, a virus that causes severe symptoms may be less likely to be transmitted.
예를 들어, 심각한 증상을 초래하는 바이러스는 전염이 덜 될지도 모른다.

핵심 Check

2. 다음 빈칸에 however 또는 thus를 사용하여 두 문장을 연결하시오.

(1) Mary wants to buy a new pen. _____, she doesn't have enough money.

(2) The soldiers threatened the citizens. _____, the public was very upset.

01 다음 빈칸에 들어갈 말로 알맞은 것은?

> The concert was cancelled due to the virus. _____, the singer and her fans were very disappointed.

① However　　　② For example　　　③ Thus
④ Similarly　　　⑤ Instead

02 다음 두 문장을 한 문장으로 연결할 때, 각각의 빈칸에 들어갈 알맞은 말을 써 넣으시오.

(1) Tom bought the house. A famous musician lived in the house.
　➡ Tom bought the house _____ _____ a famous musician lived.
　➡ Tom bought the house _____ a famous musician lived.
(2) I want to know the reason. Mina was angry for the reason.
　➡ I want to know the reason _____ _____ Mina was angry.
　➡ I want to know the reason _____ Mina was angry.

03 다음 밑줄 친 부분 중 어법상 옳지 <u>않은</u> 것을 고르시오.

① That is the restaurant <u>where</u> I found my credit card.
② Venice is the city <u>where</u> Marco Polo was born in.
③ I'm interested in the house <u>where</u> the singer lived.
④ They don't know the reason <u>why</u> their mother left them.
⑤ Eric developed the way in <u>which</u> he could make much money.

04 다음 빈칸에 however 또는 thus 중 알맞은 단어를 써 넣으시오.

(1) Megan wanted to buy me coffee. _____, I don't like caffeine.
(2) It is proved that sleep helps with your memory. _____, it is important to get enough sleep to get good grades.
(3) Fred has been sick since last night. He looks more lively than anybody else, _____.
(4) Sharon is a small and weak child. _____, she has the courage enough to fight against injustice.
(5) The film is based on real events. _____, it gives the audience a more realistic feeling.

01 다음 중 어법상 어색한 것은?

① Do you remember the day when we first met?
② This is the library where you can enjoy reading 3D books.
③ Sujin will show Peter the way how she could solve the problem.
④ This is the kindergarten where my mom is working.
⑤ Judy is wondering about the reason why her brother is so happy.

[02~03] 다음 중 밑줄 친 부분이 문맥상 어색한 것을 고르시오.

02 ① Clara bought her son a bag that he wanted. However, he didn't seem to be happy with it.
② Ben learned about the importance of the environment. Thus, he decided to save electricity every day.
③ Watson was very hungry; however, he handed out his food to the poor.
④ William has lived next to the park for 3 years. Thus, he has never been there.
⑤ I have never been to Japan. I know and speak Japanese very well, however.

03 ① Jane can speak Chinese. In addition, she can speak German.
② The movie was very disappointing. Therefore, the actors' performances were excellent.
③ Monkeys do not plan for the future. On the other hand, we human beings live by planning.
④ Anna often feels tired. So, she's going to take vitamins.
⑤ Liz has been learning to swim for 5 years. Nevertheless, she is really bad at swimming.

[04~05] 다음 우리말을 어법상 알맞게 영작한 것을 고르시오.

04

| 그 회의가 끝나게 될 시간을 아십니까? |

① Do you know when will the meeting be over?
② When do you know the time the meeting will be over?
③ Do you know the time at when the meeting will be over?
④ Do you know the time which the meeting will be over?
⑤ Do you know the time when the meeting will be over?

05

| 이것이 내가 성공한 이유이다. |

① This is why I succeeded.
② This is the reason which I succeeded.
③ This is the reason why I succeeded for.
④ This is which I succeeded for.
⑤ This is the reason on which I succeeded.

서답형

06 다음 〈보기〉에 주어진 단어들을 한 번씩만 사용해서 글의 흐름에 알맞게 빈칸을 채워 넣으시오.

┌─── 보기 ───

Therefore, For example, However,
Moreover, Similarly

└─────────

① Shakespeare invented many words in his works. _____, he took the noun 'elbow' and turned it into the verb.

(2) It was very cold. _____, the wind blew hard.

(3) A son is likely to follow his father. _____, a daughter tends to go after her mother.

(4) Lily has a passive personality. _____, she actively works and raises her voice for the poor.

(5) The world economy became even worse than before. _____, lots of people lost their jobs.

[07~08] 다음 중 글의 흐름상 However 또는 Thus가 바르게 쓰인 문장은?

07 ① Judy lost David's phone number. However, she couldn't contact him.

② All the passengers saw the accident. Thus, most of them could stay calm.

③ My boyfriend prepared our dinner. However, my family were happy about it.

④ The sea was stormy. Thus, they set sail.

⑤ The teacher explained the solution of the question. However, Lisa felt that the answer was wrong.

08 ① Both of us watched the movie. Thus, we couldn't understand the story of it.

② The doctor explained that Sarah would be fine. However, I felt relieved.

③ Jerome studied hard not to lose the opportunity. Thus, he finally got the job.

④ Robert fixed the car himself. However, he knew of the car better than anyone.

⑤ Ann asked him a math problem. Thus, he couldn't solve the hard problem.

[09~10] 다음 중 어법상 옳지 않은 문장은?

09 ① She told me the reason for which her son became a world famous pianist.

② She told me the reason why her son became a world famous pianist.

③ She told me the reason which her son became a world famous pianist for.

④ She told me why her son became a world famous pianist.

⑤ She told me the reason in which her son became a world famous pianist.

10 ① Michael showed me the way which he escaped from the prison in.

② Michael showed me the way he escaped from the prison.

③ Michael showed me the way in how he escaped from the prison.

④ Michael showed me how he escaped from the prison.

⑤ Michael showed me the way in which he escaped from the prison.

[11~12] 다음 두 문장을 한 문장으로 표현할 때, 빈칸에 들어갈 알맞은 말을 쓰시오.

서답형

11

• Jason often goes to the local market.
• He can find fresh vegetables there.

➡ Jason often goes to the local market _____ he can find fresh vegetables.

서답형

12

• Now is the time.
• The babies go to sleep at the time.

➡ Now is the time _____ the babies go to sleep.

[13~14] 우리말과 일치하도록 괄호 안에 주어진 어구들을 바르게 배열하시오.

서답형

13

나의 어머니는 2차 세계대전이 발생했던 해에 태어나셨다.
→ My (World War Ⅱ, the year, broke, born, was, when, out, in, mother).

➡ My _____
_____ .

서답형

14

많은 사람들이 지하철이 30분이나 도착하지 않은 이유를 알고 싶어 한다.
Many people want to know (has, for, the subway, why, 30 minutes, arrived, not).

➡ Many people want to know _____
_____ .

15 다음 〈보기〉의 문장과 가장 가까운 뜻을 가진 문장을 고르시오.

┤ 보기 ├

Dahyun had five pieces of pizza and two burgers. She was still hungry, however.

① Since Dahyun had five pieces of pizza and two burgers, she was still hungry.
② As Dahyun had five pieces of pizza and two burgers, she was still hungry.
③ Though Dahyun had five pieces of pizza and two burgers, she was still hungry.
④ Unless Dahyun had five pieces of pizza and two burgers, she was still hungry.
⑤ Once Dahyun had five pieces of pizza and two burgers, she was still hungry.

서답형

16 다음 그림을 보고 자연스러운 문장이 되도록 괄호 안에 주어진 어구를 바르게 배열하여 빈칸을 완성하시오.

(1)

➡ Seokbong _____
_____ , looking at his poor handwriting. (his mother, couldn't understand, them, about, the way, straight, cut)

(2)

➡ My friends were surprised _____
_____ . (rich, how, hear, be, I, could, to)

01 다음 괄호 안에서 어법상 알맞은 것을 고르시오.

> Da Vinci believed that people would soon appreciate his creative cooking. (However / Thus), that never happened.

중요

02 다음 우리말과 일치하도록 괄호 안에 주어진 단어들을 바르게 배열하여 문장을 완성하되, 빈칸에 해당하는 Thus와 However 중에서 문맥상 알맞은 접속부사를 선택하여 문두에 쓰시오.

(1) 다빈치는 몇몇 음식들을 심지어 꽃으로 장식했다. _____, 손님들은 고기 요리에 익숙했기 때문에 불만족스러워했다. (unhappy, customers, because, used, were, were, to, they)
➡ Da Vinci even decorated some foods with flowers. _____

_____ meat dishes.

(2) 그는 훨씬 더 빠르고 더 쉽게 요리하고 싶어 했다. _____, 그는 그의 부엌을 위해 새로운 기계들을 발명했다. (new machines, kitchen, he, for, his, invented)
➡ He wanted to cook much more quickly and easily. _____

_____.

(3) 당신의 몸이 당신의 마음을 바꿀 수 있다. _____, 당신의 마음도 당신의 행동을 바꿀 수 있다. (can, as, your mind, your behavior, change, well)
➡ Your body can change your mind.

_____

_____.

(4) Mina는 마음을 정리하고 싶었다. _____, 그녀는 혼자 하루 여행을 떠나기로 결심했다. (by herself, to take, she, a day trip, decided)
➡ Mina wanted to clear her mind.

_____.

03 다음 (A)와 (B) 두 문장을 한 문장으로 연결할 때, 주어진 〈조건〉에 맞게 영작하시오.

> ┤ 조건 ├
> 1. (A)의 위에서부터 순서대로 영작할 것.
> 2. (A)가 앞에 오는 문장일 것.
> 3. 가급적 '선행사+관계부사'로 영작할 것.
> 4. 관계부사는 생략하지 말 것. (that은 사용할 수 없음.)

(A)	(B)
They found a special cave.	She could be world famous in the way.
The singer told me the way.	I can see the life coming back in the season.
My favorite season is spring.	The Korean national football team beat Brazil at the stadium.
Please tell your mom the reason.	My first daughter was born on the day.
That is the soccer stadium.	You hid the letter from Grace for the reason.
I remember the day.	Their ancestors spent the winter in the cave.

(1) _____

_____

(2) _____

(3) _____

_____

(4) _____

_____

(5) _____

_____

(6) _____

04 다음은 어느 백화점 내부의 모습이다. 그림을 참고하여, 관계부사와 각각의 번호에 주어진 표현들을 모두 사용하여 문장을 완성하시오.

(1) restaurant, she, make a hamburger
➡ A receipt was handed over to a man at _____.

(2) charity box, a girl, put some money
➡ There was _____
_____.

(3) the cafe, we, talk over tea and coffee
➡ This was _____
_____.

(4) laptop, she, write a marketing report
➡ Brenda brought _____
_____.

05 다음 글의 빈칸 (A)~(D)에 들어갈 알맞은 접속부사를 However 또는 Thus만을 사용하여 써 넣으시오.

Da Vinci believed that people would soon appreciate his creative cooking. (A)_____, that never happened. He created machines that could crush vegetables and pull spaghetti. Surely, they were all very innovative. (B)_____, most of them were too big or too difficult to use. Da Vinci never became a successful cook. (C)_____, he showed great interest in cooking throughout his life. Now you know all about his secret passion for cooking. (D)_____, you will never look at *The Last Supper* the same way.

06 다음 밑줄 친 ①~⑥에서 어색한 곳을 모두 찾아 고치시오. (단, 본문에 있는 단어만을 사용하여 수정할 것)

When he graduates from high school next year, Taeho wants to become a professional farmer. ①However, he has never told anyone about it. He is worried that his parents or his friends will not understand. ②As he wanted to clear his mind, Taeho decided to take a day trip on a train by himself. On the train, he told a complete stranger sitting beside him about his problem. He didn't know the reason ③why he did it. ④Thus, he felt much better when he got off the train. Strangely enough, we often tell strangers about our problems just like Taeho. That is ⑤because we do not have to worry about being judged or seeing them again. ⑥However, if you have a problem that you cannot share with your family or friends, try talking to a stranger. You will feel much better.

➡ _____

07 다음 그림을 보고 괄호 안의 단어를 배열하여 빈칸을 알맞게 채우시오.

(in, with, she, the pool, when, played, the summer vacation)

➡ Minju could never forget _____
_____ her cousins.

Da Vinci the Cook

Leonardo da Vinci is known as one of the greatest painters of all time. He was also a great inventor, scientist, and musician. Very few people, however, know that da Vinci was also a creative cook.

In 1473, twenty-year-old da Vinci worked as a cook at a restaurant in Florence, Italy. When he took charge of the kitchen, da Vinci changed the menu completely. He made simple but artistic dishes like fish with a few carrot slices. Some dishes were even decorated with flowers. Customers, however, were unhappy because they were used to dishes with big servings of meat. As a result, da Vinci lost his job.

A few years later, da Vinci opened a restaurant with his friend Sandro Botticelli. He wanted to create a place where people could try his innovative food. They put up a beautifully painted sign and made a uniquely written menu. Da Vinci believed that people would soon appreciate his creative cooking. Unfortunately, that never happened.

---

of all time 역대, 지금껏

few 소수의, 거의 없는

creative 창의적인, 창조적인

take charge of ~의 책임을 지다, ~을 떠맡다

dish 음식, 요리

slice 한 조각, 일부

decorate 장식하다, 꾸미다

customer 손님, 고객

be used to ~에 익숙하다

innovative 획기적인

put up 내붙이다, 게시하다

uniquely 독특하게

appreciate 진가를 알아보다, 고마워하다

unfortunately 불행하게도

 확인문제

● 다음 문장이 본문의 내용과 일치하면 T, 일치하지 않으면 F를 쓰시오.

1 Leonardo da Vinci is known as one of the greatest painters of all time. ☐

2 Customers liked da Vinci's dishes decorated with flowers. ☐

3 Leonardo da Vinci once ran a restaurant with his friend. ☐

4 People appreciated da Vinci's creative cooking. ☐

In the early 1480s, da Vinci began to work for Ludovico Sforza in Milan. He was given many different roles, such as a musician, a painter, and an engineer. He was also put in charge of the kitchen. He was happy to be given another chance to pursue his passion for cooking. Da Vinci did not stop at cooking creative dishes. He wanted to cook much more quickly and easily. Thus, he invented new machines for his kitchen. He created machines that could crush vegetables and pull spaghetti. He even made a device that could scare frogs away from the water tank. Surely, they were all very innovative, but most of them were too big or too difficult to use.

In 1495, Sforza asked da Vinci to make a grand painting, which was based on the last supper of Jesus, on the wall of a church in Milan. Da Vinci gladly took on the project because he had always been interested in food. He spent a lot of time cooking all kinds of food to decide what to put on the table in his picture. "Da Vinci has wasted his time in the kitchen for over a year. That's the reason why he hasn't finished the painting yet," complained the people from the church to Sforza.

Although da Vinci never became a successful cook, he showed great interest in cooking throughout his life. He was not only a great painter but also a creative cook. Now that you know all about his secret passion for cooking, you will never look at *The Last Supper* the same way.

put … in charge of …에게 ~의 책임을 맡기다

pursue 추구하다, 추진하다

passion 열정, 흥미

tank (물·기름 등의) 탱크

surely 확실히, 분명히

grand 웅장한, 위대한

supper 만찬, 저녁 식사

take on 떠맡다

reason 이유

complain 불평하다

throughout ~ 동안 내내

now that ~이기 때문에, ~이므로

 **확인문제**

● 다음 문장이 본문의 내용과 일치하면 T, 일치하지 않으면 F를 쓰시오.

1 Da Vinci was happy to be given another chance to pursue his passion for cooking. ☐

2 Da Vinci stopped at cooking creative dishes. ☐

3 Da Vinci never became a successful cook. ☐

4 Da Vinci was not a great painter but a creative cook. ☐

● 우리말을 참고하여 빈칸에 알맞은 말을 쓰시오.

1 Da Vinci _____ _____

2 Leonardo da Vinci _____ _____ _____ one of the greatest _____ _____ _____ _____ .

3 He was _____ a great inventor, scientist, and musician.

4 Very _____ people, _____ , know that da Vinci was also a _____ cook.

5 In 1473, _____ da Vinci worked _____ a cook at a restaurant in Florence, Italy.

6 When he _____ _____ _____ the kitchen, da Vinci changed the menu _____ .

7 He made simple _____ artistic dishes _____ fish with _____ _____ carrot slices.

8 Some dishes _____ _____ _____ _____ flowers.

9 Customers, _____ , were unhappy because they _____ _____ _____ dishes with big _____ of meat.

10 _____ _____ _____ , da Vinci lost his job.

11 _____ _____ years later, da Vinci opened a restaurant with his friend Sandro Botticelli.

12 He wanted to create a place _____ people could try his _____ food.

13 They put up a _____ _____ sign and made a _____ _____ menu.

14 Da Vinci believed that people _____ soon _____ his _____ cooking.

15 Unfortunately, that never _____ .

1 요리사 다빈치

2 레오나르도 다빈치는 역대 가장 위대한 화가들 중의 한 명으로 알려져 있다.

3 그는 또한 위대한 발명가, 과학자, 그리고 음악가였다.

4 하지만, 극히 소수의 사람들만이 또한 그가 창의적인 요리사였다는 것을 안다.

5 1473년, 스무 살의 레오나르도 다빈치는 이탈리아 플로렌스에 있는 음식점에서 요리사로 일했다.

6 그가 부엌을 책임지게 되었을 때, 다빈치는 메뉴를 완전히 바꿔 버렸다.

7 그는 약간의 당근 조각을 곁들인 생선과 같이 간단하지만 예술적인 음식을 만들었다.

8 몇몇 음식들은 심지어 꽃으로 장식되었다.

9 하지만, 손님들은 많은 양의 고기 요리에 익숙했었기 때문에 불만족스러워했다.

10 그 결과, 다빈치는 그의 직업을 잃었다.

11 몇 년 후, 다빈치는 그의 친구인 산드로 보티첼리와 함께 음식점을 열었다.

12 그는 사람들이 그의 획기적인 음식을 먹어 볼 수 있는 장소로 만들기를 원했다.

13 그들은 아름답게 그려진 간판을 내걸었고 독특하게 써진 메뉴를 만들었다.

14 다빈치는 사람들이 곧 그의 창의적인 요리의 진가를 알아볼 것이라고 믿었다.

15 불행히도, 그런 일은 결코 일어나지 않았다.

16 In the early 1480s, da Vinci began _____ _____ for Ludovico Sforza in Milan.

17 He _____ _____ many different roles, _____ _____ a musician, a painter, and an engineer.

18 He _____ also _____ _____ _____ _____ _____ the kitchen.

19 He was happy _____ _____ _____ _____ chance _____ _____ his passion for cooking.

20 Da Vinci did not _____ _____ cooking creative dishes.

21 He wanted to cook _____ _____ quickly and easily.

22 _____, he invented new machines for his kitchen.

23 He created machines _____ could crush vegetables and pull spaghetti.

24 He even made a device _____ could _____ frogs _____ the water tank.

25 Surely, they were all very innovative, but most of them _____ _____ big or _____ difficult _____ use.

26 In 1495, Sforza asked da Vinci _____ _____ a grand painting, _____ _____ _____ _____ the last supper of Jesus, on the wall of a church in Milan.

27 Da Vinci gladly _____ _____ the project because he _____ always _____ interested in food.

28 He spent _____ _____ _____ time _____ all kinds of food to decide _____ _____ _____ on the table in his picture.

29 "Da Vinci has wasted his time in the kitchen _____ _____ a year. That's the reason _____ he hasn't finished the painting yet," complained the people from the church _____ Sforza.

30 _____ da Vinci never became a successful cook, he showed great interest in cooking _____ his life.

31 He was _____ _____ a great painter _____ _____ a creative cook.

32 _____ _____ you know all about his secret passion for cooking, you will never look at *The Last Supper* _____ _____ _____ .

16 1480년대 초반에, 다빈치는 밀라노에서 루도비코 스포르차를 위해 일하기 시작했다.

17 그는 음악가, 화가, 그리고 공학자와 같은 많은 역할들을 부여받았다.

18 그는 또한 주방을 책임지게 되었다.

19 그는 요리를 향한 그의 열정을 추구할 또 다른 기회를 얻게 되어 행복했다.

20 다빈치는 창의적인 요리를 만드는 것에 멈추지 않았다.

21 그는 훨씬 더 빠르고 쉽게 요리하고 싶어했다.

22 따라서, 그는 그의 주방에서 사용할 새로운 기계들을 발명하였다.

23 그는 채소를 으깨고 스파게티를 뽑는 기계들을 만들었다.

24 그는 심지어 개구리를 겁주어 물탱크에서 쫓아낼 수 있는 기구도 만들었다.

25 확실히 그것들은 모두 매우 획기적이었지만, 그것들 중 대부분은 사용하기에 너무 크거나 너무 어려웠다.

26 1495년, 스포르차는 다빈치에게 웅장한 그림을 밀라노에 있는 교회의 벽에 그려 달라고 부탁했는데, 그것은 예수의 최후의 만찬을 바탕으로 한 것이었다.

27 다빈치는 기꺼이 그 작업을 맡았는데, 그가 항상 음식에 흥미를 가졌기 때문이었다.

28 그는 그림 속 식탁 위에 어떤 음식을 올릴지 결정하기 위해 모든 종류의 음식을 요리하느라 많은 시간을 썼다.

29 "다빈치는 1년 넘게 부엌에서 시간을 낭비해 오고 있습니다. 그것이 그가 아직도 그림을 끝내지 못한 이유입니다."라고 교회 사람들이 스포르차에게 불평을 했다.

30 다빈치는 결코 성공적인 요리사는 되지 못했지만 그는 그의 생애 내내 요리에 대한 큰 흥미를 보여 주었다.

31 그는 훌륭한 화가일 뿐만 아니라 창의적인 요리사였다.

32 이제 여러분은 요리에 대한 그의 비밀스런 열정을 모두 알게 되었기 때문에 〈최후의 만찬〉을 절대 같은 식으로는 보지 않을 것이다.

● 우리말을 참고하여 본문을 영작하시오.

1 요리사 다빈치

➡ _____

2 레오나르도 다빈치는 역대 가장 위대한 화가들 중의 한 명으로 알려져 있다.

➡ _____

3 그는 또한 위대한 발명가, 과학자, 그리고 음악가였다.

➡ _____

4 하지만, 극히 소수의 사람들만이 또한 그가 창의적인 요리사였다는 것을 안다.

➡ _____

5 1473년, 스무 살의 레오나르도 다빈치는 이탈리아 플로렌스에 있는 음식점에서 요리사로 일했다.

➡ _____

6 그가 부엌을 책임지게 되었을 때, 다빈치는 메뉴를 완전히 바꿔 버렸다.

➡ _____

7 그는 약간의 당근 조각을 곁들인 생선과 같이 간단하지만 예술적인 음식을 만들었다.

➡ _____

8 몇몇 음식들은 심지어 꽃으로 장식되었다.

➡ _____

9 하지만, 손님들은 많은 양의 고기 요리에 익숙했었기 때문에 불만족스러워했다.

➡ _____

10 그 결과, 다빈치는 그의 직업을 잃었다.

➡ _____

11 몇 년 후, 다빈치는 그의 친구인 산드로 보티첼리와 함께 음식점을 열었다.

➡ _____

12 그는 사람들이 그의 획기적인 음식을 먹어 볼 수 있는 장소로 만들기를 원했다.

➡ _____

13 그들은 아름답게 그려진 간판을 내걸었고 독특하게 써진 메뉴를 만들었다.

➡ _____

14 다빈치는 사람들이 곧 그의 창의적인 요리의 진가를 알아볼 것이라고 믿었다.

➡ _____

15 불행히도, 그런 일은 결코 일어나지 않았다.

➡ _____

16 1480년대 초반에, 다빈치는 밀라노에서 루도비코 스포르차를 위해 일하기 시작했다.

➡ _____

17 그는 음악가, 화가, 그리고 공학자와 같은 많은 역할들을 부여받았다.

➡ _____

18 그는 또한 주방을 책임지게 되었다.

➡ _____

19 그는 요리를 향한 그의 열정을 추구할 또 다른 기회를 얻게 되어 행복했다.

➡ _____

20 다빈치는 창의적인 요리를 만드는 것에 멈추지 않았다.

➡ _____

21 그는 훨씬 더 빠르고 쉽게 요리하고 싶어했다.

➡ _____

22 따라서, 그는 그의 주방에서 사용할 새로운 기계들을 발명하였다.

➡ _____

23 그는 채소를 으깨고 스파게티를 뽑는 기계들을 만들었다.

➡ _____

24 그는 심지어 개구리를 겁주어 물탱크에서 쫓아낼 수 있는 기구도 만들었다.

➡ _____

25 확실히 그것들은 모두 매우 획기적이었지만, 그것들 중 대부분은 사용하기에 너무 크거나 너무 어려웠다.

➡ _____

26 1495년, 스포르차는 다빈치에게 웅장한 그림을 밀라노에 있는 교회의 벽에 그려 달라고 부탁했는데, 그것은 예수의 최후의 만찬을 바탕으로 한 것이었다.

➡ _____

_____

27 다빈치는 기꺼이 그 작업을 맡았는데, 그가 항상 음식에 흥미를 가졌기 때문이었다.

➡ _____

28 그는 그림 속 식탁 위에 어떤 음식을 올릴지 결정하기 위해 모든 종류의 음식을 요리하느라 많은 시간을 썼다.

➡ _____

29 "다빈치는 1년 넘게 부엌에서 시간을 낭비해 오고 있습니다. 그것이 그가 아직도 그림을 끝내지 못한 이유입니다."라고 교회 사람들이 스포르차에게 불평을 했다.

➡ _____

_____

30 다빈치는 결코 성공적인 요리사는 되지 못했지만 그는 그의 생애 내내 요리에 대한 큰 흥미를 보여 주었다.

➡ _____

_____

31 그는 훌륭한 화가일 뿐만 아니라 창의적인 요리사였다.

➡ _____

32 이제 여러분은 요리에 대한 그의 비밀스런 열정을 모두 알게 되었기 때문에 〈최후의 만찬〉을 절대 같은 식으로는 보지 않을 것이다.

➡ _____

_____

[01~03] 다음 글을 읽고 물음에 답하시오.

Leonardo da Vinci is known as one of the greatest painters of all time. He was also a great inventor, scientist, and musician. Very few people, however, know that da Vinci was also _____(A)_____.

In 1473, twenty-year-old da Vinci worked as a cook at a restaurant in Florence, Italy. When he took charge of the kitchen, da Vinci changed the menu completely. He made simple but artistic dishes like fish with a few carrot slices. Some dishes were even decorated with flowers. Customers, however, were unhappy because they were used to dishes with big servings of meat. As a result, da Vinci lost his job.

A few years later, da Vinci opened a restaurant with his friend Sandro Botticelli. He wanted to create a place where people could try his innovative food. They put up a beautifully painted sign and made a uniquely written menu. Da Vinci believed that people would soon _____(B)_____ his creative cooking. Unfortunately, that never happened.

01 위 글의 빈칸 (A)에 들어갈 알맞은 말을 고르시오.

① a good barista
② a creative cook
③ a great psychologist
④ an innovative physician
⑤ a natural philosopher

서답형

02 주어진 영영풀이를 참고하여 빈칸 (B)에 들어갈 단어를 철자 a로 시작하여 쓰시오.

> to like something because you recognize its good qualities

➡ _____

중요

03 According to the passage, which is NOT true?

① Da Vinci is known as one of the greatest painters.
② Da Vinci was also a great inventor and musician.
③ Da Vinci made simple but artistic dishes like fish with a few carrot slices.
④ Da Vinci lost his job because customers liked dishes decorated with flowers.
⑤ Da Vinci opened a restaurant with Sandro Botticelli.

[04~06] 다음 글을 읽고 물음에 답하시오.

In the early 1480s, da Vinci began to work for Ludovico Sforza in Milan. He was given many different roles, such as a musician, a painter, and an engineer. He was also put in charge of the kitchen. He was happy to be given another chance to pursue his passion ____ⓐ____ cooking. Da Vinci did not stop at cooking creative dishes. He wanted to cook much more quickly and easily. ____ⓑ____, he invented new machines for his kitchen. He created machines that could crush vegetables and pull spaghetti. He even made a device that could scare frogs away ____ⓒ____ the water tank. Surely, they were all very innovative, but most of them were too big or too difficult ____ⓓ____.

04 위 글의 빈칸 ⓐ와 ⓒ에 들어갈 전치사가 바르게 짝지어진 것은?

① on – for   ② on – to
③ for – from   ④ for – for
⑤ in – from

서답형

05 위 글의 빈칸 ⓑ에 들어갈 알맞은 말을 고르시오.

① Thus ② As a result
③ Surely ④ However
⑤ Unfortunately

서답형

06 위 글의 빈칸 ⓓ에 use를 알맞은 형태로 쓰시오.

➡ ____________________

[07~09] 다음 글을 읽고 물음에 답하시오.

In 1495, Sforza asked da Vinci to make a ①grand painting, which was based on the last supper of Jesus, on the wall of a church in Milan.

(A) "Da Vinci has ②wasted his time in the kitchen for over a year. That's the reason why he hasn't finished the painting yet," ③commended the people from the church to Sforza.

(B) He spent a lot of time cooking all kinds of food to decide what to put on the table in his picture.

(C) Da Vinci ④gladly took on the project because he had always been interested in food.

Although da Vinci never became a ⑤successful cook, he showed great interest in cooking throughout his life. He was not only a great painter but also a creative cook. ___ⓐ___ you know all about his secret passion for cooking, you will never look at *The Last Supper* the same way.

07 위 글의 (A)~(C)의 순서로 가장 적절한 것은?

① (A)-(C)-(B) ② (B)-(A)-(C)
③ (B)-(C)-(A) ④ (C)-(A)-(B)
⑤ (C)-(B)-(A)

08 위 글의 빈칸 ⓐ에 'As' 대신 쓸 수 있는 말을 두 단어로 쓰시오.

➡ ____________________

중요

09 위 글의 밑줄 친 ①~⑤에서 문맥상 어색한 것을 고르시오.

① ② ③ ④ ⑤

[10~12] 다음 글을 읽고 물음에 답하시오.

Leonardo da Vinci is known as one of the greatest (A)[painter / painters] of all time. He was also a great inventor, scientist, and musician. Very few people, however, know that da Vinci was also a creative cook.

In 1473, twenty-year-old da Vinci worked as a cook at a restaurant in Florence, Italy. When he took charge of the kitchen, da Vinci changed the menu completely. He made simple but artistic dishes like fish with (B)[a few / a little] carrot slices. Some dishes were even decorated with flowers. Customers, however, were unhappy because they were used to dishes with big servings of meat. As a result, da Vinci (C)[got / lost] his job.

A few years later, da Vinci opened a restaurant with his friend Sandro Botticelli. He wanted to create a place where people could try his innovative food. They put up a beautifully painted ⓐsign and made a uniquely written menu. Da Vinci believed that people would soon appreciate his creative cooking. Unfortunately, that never happened.

10 위 글의 괄호 (A)~(C)에서 문맥이나 어법상 알맞은 낱말을 골라 쓰시오.

➡ (A) ________ (B) ________ (C) ________

중요

11 Which question CANNOT be answered after reading the passage?

① Do many people know that da Vinci was a creative cook?

② What was da Vinci's job in 1473?

③ What did da Vinci do when he took charge of the kitchen?

④ How long did da Vinci work as a cook?

⑤ Why did da Vinci lose his job?

12 위 글의 밑줄 친 ⓐsign과 같은 의미로 쓰인 것을 고르시오.

① Headaches may be a sign of stress.

② Many building signs are written in English.

③ He gave a thumbs-up sign.

④ He signed to me to enter the garden.

⑤ There is no sign of habitation.

[13~15] 다음 글을 읽고 물음에 답하시오.

In the early 1480s, da Vinci began to work for Ludovico Sforza in Milan. He was given many different roles, such as a musician, a painter, and an engineer. He was also put in charge of the kitchen. He was happy to be given another chance to pursue his passion for cooking. ⓐDa Vinci did not stop at cooking creative dishes. ⓑHe wanted to cook much more quickly and easily.(only, also) Thus, he invented new machines for his kitchen. He created machines that could crush vegetables and pull spaghetti. He even made a device ⓒ개구리를 겁주어 물탱크 에서 쫓아낼 수 있는.(frogs, that, away, could, the water tank, scare, from) Surely, they were all very ___(A)___, but most of them were too big or too difficult to use.

13 위 글의 빈칸 (A)에 들어갈 말로 적절한 것은?

① common   ② routine   ③ plain

④ traditional   ⑤ innovative

서답형

14 위 글의 밑줄 친 문장 ⓐ와 ⓑ를 괄호 안에 주어진 어휘를 이용하여 한 문장으로 쓰시오.

➡ _____

_____

15 위 글의 밑줄 친 ⓒ의 우리말에 맞게 괄호 안에 주어진 어휘 를 배열하시오.

➡ _____

[16~19] 다음 글을 읽고 물음에 답하시오.

In 1495, Sforza asked da Vinci to make a grand painting, which was based on the last supper of Jesus, on the wall of a church in Milan. Da Vinci gladly took on the project because he had always been interested in food. ⓐ그는 그림 속 식탁 위에 어떤 음식을 올릴 지 결정하기 위해 모든 종류의 음식을 요리하느라 많은 시간을 썼다. "Da Vinci has ___(A)___ his time in the kitchen for over a year. That's the reason why he hasn't finished the painting yet," complained the people from the church to Sforza.

___(B)___ da Vinci never became a successful cook, he showed great interest in cooking throughout his life. He was not only a great painter but also a creative cook. Now that you know all about his secret passion for cooking, you will never look at *The Last Supper* the same way.

16 위 글의 빈칸 (A)에 들어갈 말로 알맞은 것은?

① saved   ② wasted   ③ kept
④ prevented   ⑤ recovered

17 빈칸 (B)에 들어갈 알맞은 말을 고르시오.

① When   ② Since   ③ If
④ Although   ⑤ Unless

서답형

18 위 글의 밑줄 친 ⓐ의 우리말에 맞게 주어진 어휘를 배열하시오.

> he, all kinds, on the table, what, time, spent, in his picture, a lot of, cooking, food, decide, put, of, to, to

➡ _____
_____

19 Which question CANNOT be answered after reading the passage?

① What did da Vinci ask Sforza to do to make a grand painting?
② What was the grand painting based on?
③ Why did da Vinci gladly take on the project?
④ Why did da Vinci spend a lot of time cooking all kinds of food?
⑤ Why will we never look at *The Last Supper* the same way?

[20~22] 다음 글을 읽고 물음에 답하시오.

In the early 1480s, da Vinci began to work for Ludovico Sforza in Milan. He was given many different roles, such as a musician, a painter, and an engineer.

(A) Surely, they were all very innovative, but most of them were too big or too difficult to use.

(B) He was also put in charge of the kitchen. He was happy to be given another chance to ___ⓐ___ his passion for cooking. Da Vinci did not stop at cooking creative dishes. He wanted to cook much more quickly and easily.

(C) Thus, he invented new machines for his kitchen. He created machines that could crush vegetables and pull spaghetti. He even made a device that could scare frogs away from the water tank.

서답형

20 주어진 영영풀이에 해당하는 말을 빈칸 ⓐ에 철자 p로 시작하여 쓰시오.

> to make efforts to achieve a particular aim or result, often over a long period of time

➡ _____

21 위 글의 (A)~(C)의 순서로 가장 적절한 것은?

① (A)-(C)-(B)   ② (B)-(A)-(C)
③ (B)-(C)-(A)   ④ (C)-(A)-(B)
⑤ (C)-(B)-(A)

22 위 글에서 다빈치가 루도비코 스포르차를 위해 한 일에 해당하지 <u>않는</u> 것을 고르시오.

① 과학자   ② 주방장   ③ 화가
④ 기술자   ⑤ 음악가

[01~03] 다음 글을 읽고 물음에 답하시오.

Leonardo da Vinci is known as one of the greatest painters of all time. He was also a great inventor, scientist, and musician. Very few people, however, know that da Vinci was also a creative cook.

In 1473, twenty-year-old da Vinci worked as a cook at a restaurant in Florence, Italy. When he took charge of the kitchen, da Vinci changed the menu completely. He made simple but artistic dishes like fish with a few carrot slices. Some dishes were even decorated with flowers. Customers, however, were unhappy because they were used to dishes with big servings of meat. As a result, da Vinci lost his job.

A few years later, da Vinci opened a restaurant with his friend Sandro Botticelli. ⓐ그는 사람들이 그의 획기적인 음식을 먹어 볼 수 있는 장소로 만들기를 원했다. They put up a beautifully painted sign and made a uniquely written menu. Da Vinci believed that people would soon appreciate his creative cooking. Unfortunately, ⓑthat never happened.

01 Why did da Vinci lose his job? Answer in English using the words, 'It's because, creative and satisfied.'

➡ _____

_____

02 밑줄 친 ⓐ의 우리말에 맞게 'a place, try, innovative'를 이용하여 13 단어로 영작하시오.

➡ _____

_____

03 위 글의 밑줄 친 ⓑthat이 가리키는 것을 본문에서 찾아 쓰시오.

➡ _____

[04~06] 다음 글을 읽고 물음에 답하시오.

In the early 1480s, da Vinci began to work for Ludovico Sforza in Milan. He was given many different roles, such as a musician, a painter, and an engineer. He was also put in charge of the kitchen. ⓐHe was happy to be given the other chance to pursue his passion for cooking. Da Vinci did not stop at cooking creative dishes. He wanted to cook much more quickly and easily. Thus, he invented new machines for his kitchen. He created machines that could crush vegetables and pull spaghetti. He even made a device that could scare frogs away from the water tank. Surely, ⓑthey were all very innovative, but most of them were too big or too difficult to use.

04 What did da Vinci do to cook much more quickly and easily?

➡ _____

05 밑줄 친 ⓐ에서 어색한 것을 찾아 바르게 고치시오.

_____ ➡ _____

06 위 글의 밑줄 친 ⓑthey가 가리키는 것을 본문에서 찾아 쓰시오.

➡ _____

[07~09] 다음 글을 읽고 물음에 답하시오.

In 1495, Sforza asked da Vinci to make a grand painting, ⓐwhich was based on the last supper of Jesus, on the wall of a church in Milan. Da Vinci gladly took on the project because he had always been interested in food. He spent a lot of time cooking all kinds of food to decide what to put on the table in his picture. "Da Vinci has wasted his time in the kitchen for over a year. That's the reason why he hasn't finished the painting yet," complained the people from the church to Sforza.

Although da Vinci never became a successful cook, he showed great interest in cooking throughout his life. ⓑHe was not only a great painter but also a creative cook. Now that you know all about his secret passion for cooking, you will never look at *The Last Supper* the same way.

07 위 글의 밑줄 친 ⓐ를 접속사를 사용하여 바꿔 쓰시오.

➡ _____

08 위 글의 밑줄 친 ⓑ를 'as well as'를 이용하여 바꿔 쓰시오.

➡ _____

09 Why did da Vinci spend a lot of time cooking all kinds of food? Fill in the blank with suitable words.

➡ It was to _____

_____ .

[10~12] 다음 글을 읽고 물음에 답하시오.

In 1473, twenty-year-old da Vinci worked as a cook at a restaurant in Florence, Italy. When he took charge of the kitchen, da Vinci changed the menu (A)[complete / completely]. He made simple but artistic dishes like fish with a few carrot slices. Some dishes were even decorated with flowers. Customers, ⓐ , were (B)[happy / unhappy] because they were used to dishes with big servings of meat. As a result, da Vinci lost his job.

A few years later, da Vinci opened a restaurant with his friend Sandro Botticelli. He wanted to create a place where people could try his innovative food. ⓑThey put up a beautifully painted sign and made a uniquely written menu. Da Vinci believed that people would soon (C)[appreciate / depreciate] his creative cooking. Unfortunately, that never happened.

10 위 글의 빈칸 ⓐ에 알맞은 말을 쓰시오.

➡ _____

11 위 글의 괄호 (A)~(C)에서 문맥이나 어법상 알맞은 낱말을 고르시오.

➡ (A) _____ (B) _____ (C) _____

12 위 글의 밑줄 친 ⓑThey가 가리키는 것을 본문에서 찾아 쓰시오.

➡ _____

Write

My name is Kim Jieun. I am an artist who uses technology. There was a
주격 관계대명사   선행사(시간)
special moment when I decided what I wanted to be. Back in 2030, I made
         관계부사   관계대명사
a small statue using technology. It was a great chance to learn about using
          분사구문   형용사적 용법   전치사+동명사
technology for arts. Thus, I decided to go to a technical high school. After I

graduated from high school, I entered Korea Art College and learned more
자동사+전치사   타동사(전치사 불필요)
about arts and technology. This year, I held my first exhibition. I am very

satisfied with my life.
감정을 나타내는 과거분사

구문해설 • **statue**: 동상 • **hold**: 개최하다 • **exhibition**: 전시회 • **satisfied with**: ～에 만족하는

내 이름은 김지은이다. 나는 기술을 사용하는 예술가다. 내가 예술가가 되기로 결심했을 때 특별한 순간이 있었다. 2030년에, 나는 기술을 사용해 작은 동상을 만들었다. 그것은 예술을 위한 기술을 배우는 데에 아주 좋은 기회였다. 따라서, 나는 기술 고등학교에 진학하기로 결심했다. 고등학교를 졸업한 뒤, 나는 한국 예술 대학에 입학해서 예술과 기술에 대해 더 배웠다. 올해, 나는 내 첫 전시회를 열었다. 나는 내 인생에 매우 만족한다.

Link

Some people think creativity is the most important thing to consider when
                                   최상급   형용사적 용법
they choose their career. They like to come up with new ideas and design new
                            명사적 용법(like의 목적어)   to come과 병렬 관계
things. Thus, they want to work at a place where they can use their creativity.
     결과를 이끄는 접속부사   관계부사(= in which)

구문해설 • **creativity**: 창의력 • **come up with**: ～을 생각해 내다

어떤 사람들은 직업을 선택할 때 고려해야 할 가장 중요한 것은 창의력이라고 생각한다. 그들은 새로운 아이디어를 떠올리고 새로운 것들을 구상하기를 좋아한다. 따라서, 그들은 그들의 창의력을 발휘할 수 있는 곳에서 일하기를 원한다.

Watch and Think Share

Winston Churchill is known for being the Prime Minister of the United
                  ～로 알려지다
Kingdom during World War II. Very few people, however, know that he
during: 특정 기간 (for 다음에는 보통 숫자로 나타내는 기간이 나옴)   역접의 접속부사
was also a historian, a painter, and a writer. He even won the Nobel Prize in
                                              심지어
Literature in 1953.

구문해설 • **Prime Minister**: 수상 • **historian**: 사학자 • **the Nobel Prize in Literature**: 노벨 문학상

Winston Churchill은 제2차 세계대전 중 영국의 수상이었던 것으로 알려져 있다. 하지만, 극소수의 사람들은 그가 또한 사학자이며, 화가이자, 작가임을 알고 있다. 심지어 그는 1953년에 노벨 문학상을 수상하기도 했다.

영역별 핵심문제

01 〈보기〉의 밑줄 친 어휘와 같은 의미로 쓰인 것을 고르시오.

┌─ 보기 ┐
Let me have the check, please.
└──────┘

① Can I have the check, please?
② They carried out security checks at the airport.
③ Would you please check if I filled out this card right?
④ I need to cash this check.
⑤ Cars are checked as they come off the production line.

02 다음 대화의 빈칸에 〈영영풀이〉에 해당하는 어휘를 쓰시오.

A: What are you going to do tomorrow?
B: I'm going to _____ the Christmas tree.

<영영 풀이> to make something look more attractive by putting something pretty on it

➡ _____

03 괄호 안에 주어진 어휘를 이용하여 빈칸에 알맞게 쓰시오.

• It is _____ for a large asteroid to come so close to Earth. (usual)
• _____, I won't be able to attend the meeting. (fortunate)

*asteroid: 소행성

04 다음 영영풀이에 해당하는 단어를 주어진 철자로 시작하여 빈칸에 쓰고, 알맞은 것을 골라 문장을 완성하시오.

• r_____: why someone decides to do something, or the cause or explanation for something that happens
• r_____: cooked a short time; still red inside

(1) Do you have a _____ for being so late?
(2) My father likes _____ meat that is still a little pink inside.

05 다음 짝지어진 단어의 관계가 같도록 빈칸에 알맞은 말을 쓰시오. (철자 p로 시작할 것)

rare : well-done = sell : _____

06 다음 문장의 빈칸에 공통으로 들어갈 알맞은 말을 쓰시오.

• They _____ him in charge of the park.
• He _____ up a sign saying, "No pets."
• Fire engines arrived to _____ out a fire.
• I have a sweater you can _____ on.

07 다음 중 짝지어진 대화가 <u>어색한</u> 것은?

① A: I'm not satisfied with this bag.
B: Why not?
A: I don't like the color.

② A: These plants are dying.
B: I'm sorry. I promise I'll water them more often.

③ A: I want to become a movie star.
B: I promise I'll do my best.

④ A: Have you finished your homework?
B: No, but I promise I'll finish it after I watch TV.

⑤ A: Do you have this in a smaller size?
B: No, I'm sorry, but the smaller ones are all sold out. I promise I'll have one for you by next week.

[08~10] 다음 대화를 읽고 물음에 답하시오.

G: Wow, I like this blueberry jam. Where did you buy it?
(A) Do you think people would want to buy this?
(B) Really? This is better than any other jam I've ever had. You should sell it.
(C) I made it myself.
(D) Of course. _____ (a)

08 위 대화의 빈칸 (a)에 첫 손님이 되겠다는 다짐을 말하는 표현을 7 단어로 쓰시오.

➡ _____

09 주어진 글 다음의 대화가 자연스럽게 연결되도록 (A)~(D)를 순서대로 가장 적절하게 배열한 것은?

① (B) – (A) – (C) – (D)
② (B) – (C) – (A) – (D)
③ (C) – (B) – (A) – (D)
④ (C) – (B) – (D) – (A)
⑤ (C) – (D) – (B) – (A)

10 위 대화의 내용과 일치하지 <u>않는</u> 것은?

① 소녀는 블루베리 잼이 마음에 든다.
② 블루베리 잼은 사 온 것이다.
③ 블루베리 잼은 소녀가 먹어본 잼 중에 제일 좋았다.
④ 소녀는 사람들이 블루베리 잼을 사기를 원할 거라고 생각한다.
⑤ 소녀는 첫 손님이 되겠다고 약속한다.

11 다음 주어진 문장을 둘로 나눌 때, 원래 문장과 의미가 가장 가까운 것은?

> Although Tracy lived alone in that big apartment, she rarely felt lonely.
> → Tracy lived alone in that big apartment. _____, _____.

① Fortunately, she felt lonely.
② Consequently, she rarely felt lonely.
③ Instead, she felt lonely.
④ Nevertheless, she rarely felt lonely.
⑤ Therefore, she rarely felt lonely.

[12~13] 다음 중 어법상 어색한 문장을 고르시오.

12 ① This is the hotel where the singer stayed last week.

② This is the hotel that the singer stayed in last week.

③ This is the hotel which the singer stayed last week.

④ This is the hotel in which the singer stayed last week.

⑤ This is the hotel which the singer stayed in last week.

13 ① Would you tell us the reason why Sandra hasn't come yet?

② The house where the photographer lived had a beautiful studio.

③ Timothy can't forget the day when Anne left Paris for New York.

④ An auditorium is a large space or building in which is used for events such as meetings or concerts.

⑤ Now is the time when they should start to produce the cure for the disease.

14 다음 괄호 안에서 어법상 알맞은 것을 고르시오.

(1) Da Vinci did not feel well. (However / Thus), he still kept painting.

(2) Dr. Kim required that everyone present at the lecture wear a mask. (However / Thus), most of them didn't take it seriously.

(3) Everything she said turned out to be untrue. (However / Thus), many people were disappointed with her.

(4) My grandmother has rarely brushed her teeth after meals. (However / Thus), despite her age of 90, she has healthy teeth.

(5) James was in deep sleep after working all night. (However / Thus), he didn't answer the phone.

(6) Da Vinci had always been interested in food. (However / Thus), when he was asked to make a painting of the last supper of Jesus, he gladly took on the project.

15 다음 그림을 보고 괄호 안의 단어를 배열하여 빈칸을 알맞게 채우시오.

(1)

➡ People were not interested in _____ _____. (da Vinci, his, cooking, made, creative, how)

(2)

➡ At school, I like lunchtime best _____

_____.

(have, with, can, when, a, my friends, meal, I, delicious)

[16~17] 다음 밑줄 친 부분 중 어법상 어색한 것을 고르시오.

16 ① Let her know <u>how</u> the machines work in such a hot and humid environment.

② That evening was the moment <u>when</u> I fell in love with the princess.

③ I will show you the way <u>how</u> the magician escaped from the steel box.

④ Tom can't forget the day <u>when</u> he first ate cold bean soup noodles.

⑤ Does Sarah know the reason <u>why</u> her husband came here?

17 ① Venice is the city <u>where</u> Marco used to live in.

② That is the square <u>where</u> I picked up her credit cards.

③ This is the building <u>in which</u> my parents met for the first time.

④ I remember the shop <u>which</u> I bought some souvenirs at.

⑤ The town <u>where</u> she's going to move is not far from here.

18 다음 밑줄 친 부분의 쓰임이 〈보기〉와 같은 것은?

Friday is the day <u>when</u> my daughter goes to the pool to learn swimming.

① Mina was taking a shower <u>when</u> someone visited her.

② I wonder <u>when</u> you will leave here for Africa to volunteer.

③ No one knows <u>when</u> the virus disease could be treated properly.

④ I like the Christmas season <u>when</u> I can meet all my family.

⑤ <u>When</u> does she think she can call me?

19 다음 접속부사가 쓰인 두 문장을 한 문장으로 적절하게 바꾼 것을 고르시오.

His explanation was unclear. Thus, I didn't understand it.

① Although his explanation was unclear, I didn't understand it.

② Whereas his explanation was unclear, I didn't understand it.

③ As soon as his explanation was unclear, I didn't understand it.

④ Since his explanation was unclear, I didn't understand it.

⑤ Unless his explanation was unclear, I didn't understand it.

Reading

[20~22] 다음 글을 읽고 물음에 답하시오.

Leonardo da Vinci is known as one of the greatest painters of all time. He was also a great inventor, scientist, and musician. Very ⓐ_____ people, however, know that da Vinci was also a creative cook.

In 1473, twenty-year-old da Vinci worked as a cook at a restaurant in Florence, Italy. When he took charge of the kitchen, da Vinci changed the menu completely. (①) He made simple but artistic dishes like fish with a few carrot slices. (②) Some dishes were even decorated with flowers. (③) As a result, da Vinci lost his job.

A few years later, da Vinci opened a restaurant with his friend Sandro Botticelli. (④) He wanted to create a place where people could try his innovative food. (⑤) They put up a beautifully painted sign and made a uniquely written menu. Da Vinci believed that people would soon appreciate his creative cooking. Unfortunately, that never happened.

20 위 글의 빈칸 ⓐ에 들어갈 알맞은 말을 고르시오.

① many   ② few   ③ a few
④ little   ⑤ a little

21 위 글의 흐름으로 보아, 주어진 문장이 들어가기에 가장 적절한 곳은?

> Customers, however, were unhappy because they were used to dishes with big servings of meat.

①   ②   ③   ④   ⑤

22 What did da Vinci do when he took charge of the kitchen?

➡ _____

[23~25] 다음 글을 읽고 물음에 답하시오.

In the early 1480s, da Vinci began to work for Ludovico Sforza in Milan. He was given many different roles, ___ⓐ___ a musician, a painter, and an engineer. He was also put in charge of the kitchen. He was happy to be given another chance to pursue his passion for cooking. Da Vinci did not stop at cooking creative dishes. He wanted to cook much more quickly and easily. Thus, he invented new machines for his kitchen. He created machines ___ⓑ___ could crush vegetables and pull spaghetti. He even made a device ___ⓑ___ could scare frogs away from the water tank. Surely, they were all very innovative, but ⓒ그것들 중 대부분은 사용하기에 너무 크거나 너무 어려웠다.

23 위 글의 빈칸 ⓐ에 들어갈 말로 like 대신 쓸 수 있는 말을 쓰시오. (two words)

➡ _____

24 위 글의 빈칸 ⓑ에 공통으로 들어갈 알맞은 말을 쓰시오.

➡ _____

25 위 글의 밑줄 친 ⓒ의 우리말에 맞게 주어진 어휘를 이용하여 11 단어로 영작하시오.

> them, too, most, difficult, use, or

➡ _____

[26~28] 다음 글을 읽고 물음에 답하시오.

In 1495, Sforza asked da Vinci to make a grand painting, which was based on the last supper of Jesus, on the wall of a church in Milan. (①) He spent a lot of time cooking all kinds of food to decide what to put on the table in his picture. (②) "Da Vinci has wasted his time in the kitchen for over a year. That's the reason ____ⓐ____ he hasn't finished the painting yet," complained the people from the church to Sforza.

(③) Although da Vinci never became a successful cook, he showed great interest in cooking throughout his life. (④) He was not only a great painter but also a creative cook. Now that you know all about his secret passion for cooking, you will never look at *The Last Supper* the same way. (⑤)

26 위 글의 빈칸 ⓐ에 들어갈 말로 알맞은 것을 고르시오.

① when ② where ③ how
④ why ⑤ what

27 위 글의 흐름으로 보아, 주어진 문장이 들어가기에 가장 적절한 곳은?

Da Vinci gladly took on the project because he had always been interested in food.

①   ②   ③   ④   ⑤

28 What was the grand painting based on? Answer in English with 9 words.

➡ _____

[29~30] 다음 글을 읽고 물음에 답하시오.

Some people think creativity is the most important thing ⓐto consider when they choose their career. They like to come up with new ideas and design new things. Thus, they want to work at a place ⓑ그들의 창의력을 발휘할 수 있는 곳에서(use, creativity).

29 위 글의 밑줄 친 ⓐ와 문법적 쓰임이 같은 것을 고르시오.

① I need some time to consider.
② They sat down to consider the problem.
③ It is important to consider the cost of repairs.
④ I decided to consider the money he borrowed lost.
⑤ Everyone in the office is meeting to consider forming a union.

30 위 글의 밑줄 친 ⓑ의 우리말에 맞게 주어진 어휘를 이용하여 6 단어로 영작하시오.

➡ _____

출제율 90%

01 다음 중 짝지어진 단어의 관계가 나머지와 다른 것은?

① inconvenience – convenience
② sell – purchase
③ check – bill
④ satisfied – dissatisfied
⑤ creative – uncreative

출제율 100%

02 다음 밑줄 친 부분의 의미로 알맞지 않은 것은?

① We would appreciate you letting us know of any problems. (고마워하다)
② I really don't feel like working anymore. (~할 마음이 나다)
③ It's not a quiet island anymore. (더 이상 ~ 아니다)
④ Don't you want to have a bite of this burger? (~을 한 입 베어 물다)
⑤ Now that I finally know I'll take care of you. (이제)

출제율 95%

03 다음 빈칸에 공통으로 들어갈 알맞은 말을 쓰시오.

• I was put in _____ of the office.
• He took _____ of the farm after his father's death.

출제율 95%

04 다음 주어진 우리말에 맞게 빈칸을 채우시오. (철자가 주어진 경우 주어진 철자로 시작할 것)

(1) 그는 역대 최고의 선수라고 불려요.
➡ He is called the greatest player _____ _____ t_____.

(2) Frank는 거리에서 사람들이 자기를 알아보는 것에 익숙해 있다.
➡ Frank is u_____ _____ being recognized in the street.

(3) 코알라는 호주 고유의 동물이다.
➡ The koala is u_____ to Australia.

[05~07] 다음 대화를 읽고 물음에 답하시오.

B: Wow! Did you draw this?
G: I ⓐdid. Do you like it?
B: Yes, the bread and the milk look so ⓑreally. (A)빵을 한 입 먹고 싶어지는데.
G: Thanks, but I'm not satisfied ⓒwith it. It's not ⓓunique.
B: I don't think ⓔso. I think it's a fantastic drawing.

출제율 90%

05 위 대화의 밑줄 친 ⓐ~ⓔ 중 어법상 어색한 것을 고르시오.

① ⓐ ② ⓑ ③ ⓒ ④ ⓓ ⑤ ⓔ

06 위 대화를 읽고 대답할 수 <u>없는</u> 질문을 고르시오.

① Who drew the drawing?

② Does the girl like the drawing?

③ Does the boy think the bread and the milk look so real?

④ Does the boy think the drawing is fantastic?

⑤ What is unique in the drawing?

07 위 대화의 밑줄 친 (A)의 우리말에 맞게 영작하시오. (9 단어)

➡ _____

[08~10] 다음 대화를 읽고 물음에 답하시오.

Man: Are you enjoying your meal?

Woman: Well, the bread was good, and the salad was fresh.

Man: How about your steak?

Woman: Honestly, _____(A)_____. It's too rare for me.

Man: I'm sorry. Would you like me to bring you another one?

Woman: That's O.K. I need to be going. Let me just have the check, please.

Man: I'm really sorry. You won't have to pay for the steak.

Woman: O.K. Thanks.

Man: I promise we'll provide you with a better experience next time you visit.

08 위 대화의 빈칸 (A)에 들어갈 말로 어울리지 <u>않는</u> 것을 고르시오.

① I'm not pitiful with the steak

② I'm not satisfied with the steak

③ I'm dissatisfied with the steak

④ I'm not happy with the steak

⑤ I don't like the steak

09 What does the woman ask the man to do?

➡ _____

10 위 대화의 내용과 일치하지 <u>않는</u> 것은?

① 여자는 빵에는 만족했고, 샐러드에는 실망했다.

② 여자는 스테이크에 만족하지 않았다.

③ 남자는 다른 스테이크로 가져다 주겠다고 제안한다.

④ 여자는 스테이크 값을 지불하지 않아도 된다.

⑤ 남자는 다음 방문 때는 더 좋은 경험을 드리겠다고 약속한다.

11 다음 빈칸에 접속부사 however 또는 thus 중에서 알맞은 것을 선택하여 써 넣으시오.

(1) Leonardo da Vinci is known as one of the greatest painters and also a great inventor, scientist, and musician. Very few people, _____, know that da Vinci was a creative cook.

(2) Customers who saw da Vinci's creative food were unhappy because they were used to dishes with big servings of meat. _____, da Vinci lost his job.

(3) Da Vinci wanted to make creative food much more quickly and easily. _____, he invented new machines that could crush vegetables and pull spaghetti.

(4) Da Vinci never became a successful cook when he lived. _____, he showed great interest in cooking throughout his life.

(5) I have learned all about the secret passion for cooking of da Vinci. _____, I think I will never look at *The Last Supper* the same way as before.

출제율 95%

12 다음 글의 빈칸 ①~⑤에 들어갈 단어가 <u>잘못된</u> 것은?

> In 1495, Sforza asked da Vinci to make a grand painting, ①_____ was based on the last supper of Jesus, on the wall of a church in Milan. Da Vinci gladly took on the project ②_____ he had always been interested in food. He spent a lot of time cooking all kinds of food to decide ③_____ to put on the table in his picture. "Da Vinci has wasted his time in the kitchen for over a year. That's the ④_____ why he hasn't finished the painting ⑤_____," complained the people from the church to Sforza.

① which ② because ③ that
④ reason ⑤ yet

출제율 95%

13 다음 그림을 보고 괄호 안의 단어를 배열하여 빈칸을 알맞게 채우시오.

> People complained that da Vinci wasted too much time on food and that was
> _____.
>
> (the painting, why, finished, he, earlier, the reason, hadn't)

출제율 100%

14 다음 두 문장을 가능하다면 선행사와 관계부사를 모두 써서 한 문장으로 쓰시오. (단, 관계부사는 반드시 사용해야 함)

(1) • Jamaica is the country.
   • International reggae festivals take place every summer in Jamaica.
   ➡ _____
   _____

(2) • Show your brother the way.
   • You solved the puzzle in such a short time in that way.
   ➡ _____
   _____

(3) • Everyone but me knows the day.
   • I will be transferred to Jeju island on the day.
   ➡ _____
   _____

(4) • Katherine won't tell her teacher the reason.
   • She ran out of the classroom for that reason.
   ➡ _____
   _____

15 다음 그림을 보고 괄호 안의 단어를 배열하여 빈칸을 알맞게 채우시오. 출제율 90%

(pizza, people, line up, to eat, have to, all night, where)

➡ That is the famous restaurant _____

_____ .

16 위 글의 빈칸 (A)에 주어진 두 문장을 한 문장으로 바꾸어 쓰시오. 출제율 95%

• He wanted to create a place.
• People could try his innovative food at the place.

➡ _____

_____

[16~18] 다음 글을 읽고 물음에 답하시오.

Leonardo da Vinci is known as one of the greatest painters of all time. He was also a great inventor, scientist, and musician. Very few people, however, know that da Vinci was also a creative cook.

In 1473, twenty-year-old da Vinci worked as a cook at a restaurant in Florence, Italy. When he took charge of the kitchen, da Vinci changed the menu completely. He made simple but artistic dishes like fish with a few carrot slices. Some dishes were even decorated with flowers. Customers, however, were unhappy because they were ⓐused to dishes with big servings of meat. As a result, da Vinci lost his job.

A few years later, da Vinci opened a restaurant with his friend Sandro Botticelli. _____(A)_____ . They put up a beautifully painted sign and made a uniquely written menu. Da Vinci believed that people would soon appreciate his creative cooking. Unfortunately, that never happened.

17 위 글의 밑줄 친 ⓐ와 바꿔 쓸 수 있는 것을 고르시오. 출제율 95%

① utilized ② accustomed
③ served ④ applied
⑤ spent

18 위 글의 제목으로 알맞은 것을 고르시오. 출제율 100%

① Why Is da Vinci Famous?
② How to Become a Cook
③ What to do as a Cook
④ Jack of All Trades: Leonardo da Vinci
⑤ Unachieved Dream of da Vinci

[19~22] 다음 글을 읽고 물음에 답하시오.

In the early 1480s, da Vinci began to work for Ludovico Sforza in Milan. He was given many different roles, such as a musician, a painter, and an engineer. He was also put in charge of the kitchen. He was happy to be given another chance to pursue his passion for cooking. Da Vinci did not stop __ⓐ__ cooking creative dishes. He wanted to cook much more quickly and easily. Thus, he invented new machines for his kitchen. He created machines that could crush vegetables and pull spaghetti. He even made a device that could scare frogs away from the water tank. Surely, they were all very innovative, but (A)most of them were too big or too difficult to use.

출제율 90%

19 위 글의 빈칸 ⓐ에 알맞은 말을 쓰시오.

➡ _____

출제율 100%

20 Which question can be answered after reading the passage?

① Who was Ludovico Sforza in Milan?

② What did da Vinci ask Ludovico Sforza to work for?

③ Why did da Vinci want to cook more differently?

④ Why did da Vinci invent new machines for his kitchen?

⑤ How could the device scare frogs away from the water tank?

출제율 95%

21 다음 문장에서 위 글의 내용과 <u>다른</u> 부분을 찾아서 고치시오.

Da Vinci was happy to have another chance to pursue his passion for painting.

_____ ➡ _____

출제율 90%

22 밑줄 친 (A)를 that을 이용하여 바꿔 쓰시오.

➡ _____

_____

단원별 예상문제 **159**

[01~03] 다음 대화를 읽고 물음에 답하시오.

> M: Hello, ma'am. How can I help you?
> W: I bought this phone only a week ago, but it sometimes _____ (A) _____.
> M: Oh, I see. May I have a look at it? (Pause) We're sorry for the _____ (B) _____. It'll take a few hours to fix it.
> W: (C)I don't like the phone. I'd like a new one.
> M: Of course. I just need to fill out this form.

01 다음 customer service report를 참고하여 빈칸 (A)를 알맞게 채우시오.

CUSTOMER SERVICE REPORT	
(1) Product	☐ TV ✓ Phone ☐ Refrigerator
(2) Problem	☐ It doesn't turn on. ✓ It turns off by itself.
(3) Service needed	☐ Fix broken parts. ✓ Provide a new one.

➡ _____

02 다음 영영풀이에 해당하는 말을 빈칸 (B)에 쓰시오.

> problems caused by something which annoy or affect you

➡ _____

03 위 대화의 밑줄 친 (C)와 같은 뜻의 말을 'satisfied'를 이용하여 쓰시오.

➡ _____

04 다음 주어진 문장의 밑줄 친 부분을 다시 쓰고자 한다. 빈칸에 알맞은 관계부사를 써 넣으시오.

(1) The exhausted employee needs a place to rest <u>in which</u> she can refresh her mind.
   ➡ The exhausted employee needs a place to rest _____ she can refresh her mind.

(2) Lunar New Year's Day is the day <u>on which</u> people gather and eat together.
   ➡ Lunar New Year's Day is the day _____ people gather and eat together.

(3) The police are trying to find out <u>the way in which</u> he escaped from the heavily guarded prison.
   ➡ The police are trying to find out _____ he escaped from the heavily guarded prison.

(4) No one knew the reason <u>for which</u> Brian cried while performing on his concert stage.
   ➡ No one knew the reason _____ Brian cried while performing on his concert stage.

(5) His funeral will be held next Friday <u>on which</u> all of his children will gather together.
   ➡ His funeral will be held next Friday _____ all of his children will gather together.

05 다음 〈보기〉에 주어진 단어들을 한 번씩만 사용해서 글의 흐름에 알맞게 빈칸을 채우시오.

> ┤ 보기 ├
> Thus, However, For example, In addition, In other words

(1) Da Vinci constantly made unique and creative dishes. _____, he was an experimental cook.

(2) Da Vinci wanted to be a successful cook. _____, people did not think of him as a cook.

(3) Da Vinci designed a device to crush vegetables. _____, he invented a machine to pull pasta out.

(4) Da Vinci was interested in cooking. _____, he thought long about what food to put on "*the Last Supper*" table.

(5) Da Vinci is known for his talents in various areas. _____, he is a painter, architect, mathematician and musician.

[06~08] 다음 글을 읽고 물음에 답하시오.

Leonardo da Vinci is known as one of the greatest painters of all time. He was also a great inventor, scientist, and musician. Very few people, however, know that da Vinci was also a creative cook.

ⓐIn 1473, twenty-years-old da Vinci worked as a cook at a restaurant in Florence, Italy. When he took charge of the kitchen, da Vinci changed the menu completely. He made simple but artistic dishes like fish with a few carrot slices. Some dishes were even decorated with flowers. Customers, however, were unhappy because they were used to dishes with big servings of meat.   (A) , da Vinci lost his job.

A few years later, da Vinci opened a restaurant with his friend Sandro Botticelli. He wanted to create a place where people could try his innovative food. They put up a beautifully painted sign and made a uniquely written menu. Da Vinci believed that people would soon appreciate his creative cooking. Unfortunately, that never happened.

06 위 글의 빈칸 (A)에 들어갈 알맞은 말을 3 단어의 영어로 쓰시오.

➡ _____

07 위 글의 밑줄 친 ⓐ에서 어법상 어색한 것을 찾아 바르게 고치시오.

_____ ➡ _____

08 Why did da Vinci lose his job?

➡ _____

01 다음 그림을 보고 〈보기〉의 표현을 이용하여 다음 대화의 빈칸에 알맞은 말을 쓰시오.

┌─ 보기 ─────────────────────┐
  (1) drawing / color
  (2) steak / rare
└────────────────────────┘

A: I'm not satisfied with this _____.
B: Why not?
A: _____.

02 다음 그림을 보고 〈보기〉의 단어들을 활용하여, 자유롭게 관계부사가 들어간 문장을 2개 만드시오. (단, 꼭 써야 할 단어는 포함해야 한다.)

(1)   (2)   (3)

┌─ 보기 ─────────────────────┐
  선행사: the place, the day, how / 꼭 써야 할 단어: eat(또는 not eat), the apple
└────────────────────────┘

(1) _____
(2) _____
(3) _____

03 다음 내용을 바탕으로 20년 뒤 자신의 꿈이 이루어졌다고 가정하고 쓴 자서전의 빈칸을 채우시오.

┌──┐
  2030 made a small statue using technology, 2031 entered Korea Technical High School,
 2034 entered Korea Art College, 2040 held my first exhibition, an artist who uses technology
└──┘

My name is Kim Jieun. I am (A)_____ who uses technology. There was a special moment when I decided what I wanted to be. Back in 2030, I made a small statue (B)_____. It was a great chance to learn about (B)_____ for arts. Thus, I decided to go to a (C)_____ high school. After I graduated from high school, I entered Korea Art College and learned more about arts and technology. This year, I held (D)_____. I am very satisfied with my life.

단원별 모의고사

01 다음 짝지어진 단어의 관계가 같도록 빈칸에 알맞은 말을 쓰시오. (철자 p로 시작하여 쓸 것.)

> surely – certainly : supply – _____

02 주어진 영어 설명에 맞게 문장의 빈칸에 알맞은 말을 쓰시오.

> The car was completely _____ed under the truck.

> <영어설명> to press something so hard that it breaks or is damaged

➡ _____

03 다음 빈칸에 알맞은 말로 짝지어진 것을 고르시오.

> • We _____ our happiness for the rest of our lives.
> • I've never heard him _____ about anything.

① determine – provide
② decorate – appreciate
③ decorate – complain
④ pursue – complain
⑤ pursue – provide

04 다음 문장에 공통으로 들어갈 말은?

> • She was put in charge _____ the matter.
> • He is the greatest speaker _____ all time.

① by   ② with   ③ from
④ to   ⑤ of

05 우리말에 맞게 빈칸에 알맞은 말을 철자 t로 시작하여 쓰시오.

> 그 박물관은 연중 내내 매일 문을 연다.
> ➡ The museum is open daily _____ the year.

➡ _____

06 다음 영영풀이를 참고하여 빈칸에 알맞은 말을 쓰시오.

> to repair something that is broken or not working properly

> Can you organize someone to come over and _____ it?

➡ _____

[07~09] 다음 대화를 읽고 물음에 답하시오.

> B: Mom, I want to go to an arts high school. I want to become an actor.
> W: What? I thought you were interested in science.
> B: I was but not anymore. I want to become a movie star.
> W: Are you sure you want to be an actor?
> B: Yes, ⓐI'll learn how to act. ⓑI promise I'll do my best.

07 위 대화의 밑줄 친 ⓐ를 'should'를 이용하여 바꿔 쓰시오.

➡ _____

08 위 대화의 밑줄 친 ⓑ를 'sure'를 이용하여 바꿔 쓰시오.

➡ _____

09 Why does the boy want to go to an arts high school? Answer with the words "It's because."

➡ _____

[10~12] 다음 대화를 읽고 물음에 답하시오.

M: Hello, ma'am. How can I help you?
W: I bought this phone only a week ago, but it sometimes turns off by itself. (①)
M: Oh, I see. (②) (*Pause*) We're sorry for the inconvenience. It'll take a few hours to fix it.
W: I'm not satisfied with the phone. (③) I'd like a new one. (④)
M: Of course. I just need to fill out this form. (⑤)

10 위 대화의 (①)~(⑤) 중에서 주어진 문장이 들어가기에 가장 적절한 곳은?

| May I have a look at it? |

①   ②   ③   ④   ⑤

11 What is the problem of the phone the woman bought?

➡ _____

12 If the woman had her phone repaired, how long would it take to repair it?

➡ _____

[13~14] 다음 주어진 두 개의 문장을 같은 내용의 하나의 문장으로 바르게 옮긴 것은?

13
| Sam didn't have breakfast. However, he didn't feel hungry. |

① If he had breakfast, Sam wouldn't feel hungry.
② Since he didn't have breakfast, Sam felt hungry.
③ Though he didn't have breakfast, Sam didn't feel hungry.
④ As he didn't have breakfast, Sam didn't feel hungry.
⑤ Before he didn't have breakfast, Sam didn't feel hungry.

14
| The students had close contact with a patient in the PC cafe. Thus, they were infected with the virus. |

① Although the students had close contact with a patient in the PC cafe, they were infected with the virus.
② Since the students didn't have close contact with a patient in the PC cafe, they were infected with the virus.
③ As the students had close contact with a patient in the PC cafe, they were not infected with the virus.
④ Because the students had close contact with a patient in the PC cafe, they were infected with the virus.
⑤ Whereas the students had close contact with a patient in the PC cafe, they were infected with the virus.

15 다음 각 문장의 밑줄 친 '전치사+관계대명사'를 관계부사로 바꿀 때 어법상 어색한 것은?

① Paris is the city in which many artists come to live.
　→ Paris is the city where many artists come to live.

② Donald will never forget the moment at which he saw the killer.
　→ Donald will never forget the moment when he saw the killer.

③ She will tell you the reason for which you failed the test.
　→ She will tell you the reason why you failed the test.

④ That's the way in which Paul persuaded the customer companies.
　→ That's the way how Paul persuaded the customer companies.

⑤ This is the restaurant in which we had Bulgogi last month.
　→ This is the restaurant where we had Bulgogi last month.

16 다음 각 문장의 밑줄 친 관계부사를 관계대명사를 이용해서 전환한 문장으로 옳지 않은 것은?

① Hongkong is the city where Henry was born.
　→ Hongkong is the city which Henry was born in.

② Do you know the reason why Jerome didn't come?
　→ Do you know the reason for which Jerome didn't come?

③ Teach me how the machine works.
　→ Teach me the way in which the machine works.

④ The accident happened on the day when the president came back.
　→ The accident happened on the day which the president came back in.

⑤ All of us saw the building where your mother works.
　→ All of us saw the building which your mother works in.

17 다음 각 그림을 보고, 주어진 어구를 알맞게 배열하되, 반드시 However나 Thus 중 하나로 시작하는 문장을 만드시오.

(1)

➡ The hedgehog just wanted to get along with the dog. ＿＿＿＿＿＿＿
＿＿＿＿＿＿＿＿＿. (painful, so, that, the dog, it, ran away, was)

(2)

➡ Today is the day when Sumi's parents are on duty for lunch. ＿＿＿＿＿＿＿
＿＿＿＿＿＿＿＿＿＿＿＿.
(side dishes, Sumi, a lot of, asked for)

[18~19] 다음 글을 읽고 물음에 답하시오.

Leonardo da Vinci is known as one of the greatest painters of all time. He was also a great inventor, scientist, and musician. Very few people, however, know that da Vinci was also a creative cook.

In 1473, twenty-year-old da Vinci worked as a cook at a restaurant in Florence, Italy. When he took charge of the kitchen, da Vinci changed the menu completely. He made simple but artistic dishes like fish with a few carrot slices. Some dishes were even decorated with flowers. Customers, however, were unhappy because they were used to dishes with big servings of meat. As a result, da Vinci lost his job.

18 위 글에 언급된 다빈치의 직업이 <u>아닌</u> 것은?

① 화가　　　② 발명가　　　③ 조각가
④ 음악가　　⑤ 요리사

19 When he took charge of the kitchen, what did da Vinci do with his dishes? Answer with 6 words.

➡ _____

[20~22] 다음 글을 읽고 물음에 답하시오.

My name is Kim Jieun. I am an artist who uses technology. There was a special moment ___ⓐ___ I decided what I wanted to be. (①) Back in 2030, I made a small statue using technology. (②) It was a great chance to learn about using technology for arts. (③) After I graduated from high school, I entered Korea Art College and learned more about arts and technology. (④) This year, I held my first exhibition. (⑤) I am very satisfied with my life.

20 위 글의 빈칸 ⓐ에 알맞은 것을 고르시오.

① what　　② why　　③ how
④ where　　⑤ when

21 위 글의 흐름으로 보아, 주어진 문장이 들어가기에 가장 적절한 곳은?

> Thus, I decided to go to a technical high school.

①　　　②　　　③　　　④　　　⑤

22 According to the passage, which is NOT true?

① Jieun is an artist who uses technology.
② Jieun's special moment was in 2030.
③ Jieun had a great chance to learn about using technology for arts.
④ Jieun decided to leave Korea Art College.
⑤ Jieun is very satisfied with her life.

INSIGHT
on the textbook

교과서 파헤치기

※ 다음 영어를 우리말로 쓰시오.

01	greenhouse		22	breathe
02	harvest		23	destroy
03	ad(= advertisement)		24	waterfall
04	exhibition		25	trail
05	underwater		26	intangible
06	marine		27	jellyfish
07	nationwide		28	press
08	overseas		29	underground
09	promote		30	suitable
10	bridge		31	audience
11	community		32	overwork
12	moved		33	path
13	heritage		34	realize
14	environment		35	wish for
15	seafood		36	happen to
16	several		37	walk along
17	breadwinner		38	a couple of
18	female		39	get into
19	volcanic		40	be suitable for
20	worldwide		41	give a talk
21	complete		42	a little bit
			43	be good for

※ 다음 우리말을 영어로 쓰시오.

01 폭포

02 광고

03 경로, 길

04 과로하다

05 교량, 다리

06 좁은 길

07 지하의

08 세계적으로

09 화산의, 화산 작용에 의한

10 온실

11 파괴하다

12 전시회, 박람회

13 홍보하다, 촉진하다

14 완성[완료]하다

15 몇몇의

16 생계를 책임지는 사람, 가장

17 적합한, 적절한

18 여성의

19 누르다; 언론, 기자

20 지역 공동체

21 무형의, 만질 수 없는

22 수중의, 물속에서

23 해파리

24 해양의, 바다의

25 수확하다

26 청중

27 유산

28 호흡하다

29 전국적인

30 해외의

31 깨닫다, 인식하다

32 단단히. 꽉

33 (북 등을 치는) 소리, (심장의) 고동

34 풍년

35 휴가가다

36 ~에 들어가다

37 우연히 ~하다

38 ~을 따라 걷다

39 ~에 유익하다

40 계속해서 ~하다

41 힘을 북돋아 주다, 격려하다

42 거들어 주다, 돕다

43 발표하다

※ 다음 영영풀이에 알맞은 단어를 <보기>에서 골라 쓴 후, 우리말 뜻을 쓰시오.

1   _____ : to gather a crop: _____

2   _____ : under the surface of the ground: _____

3   _____ : to finish making or doing something: _____

4   _____ : one of a series of regular movements or hitting actions: _____

5   _____ : a place where a stream or river falls from a high place: _____

6   _____ : right or appropriate for a particular purpose or occasion: _____

7   _____ : to take air into your lungs and send it out again: _____

8   _____ : the people who live in the same area, town, etc.: _____

9   _____ : the traditional beliefs, values, customs of a family, country, or society:

    _____

10 _____ : having value but not existing physically: _____

11 _____ : to or in a foreign country that is across the sea: _____

12 _____ : fish and shellfish that live in the ocean and are used for food: _____

13 _____ : to damage something so badly that it no longer exists, works, etc.: _____

14 _____ : a picture, set of words, or a short film, intended to persuade people to

    buy: _____

15 _____ : a structure built over something such as a river so that people or vehicles

    can get across: _____

16 _____ : the member of a family who earns the money to support the others:

    _____

보기			
destroy	breadwinner	community	suitable
intangible	overseas	harvest	seafood
bridge	complete	waterfall	ad
heritage	breathe	beat	underground

※ 다음 우리말과 일치하도록 빈칸에 알맞은 말을 쓰시오.

해석

Listen & Speak 1 A-1

G: Wow, _____ _____ the _____ in this _____. I wonder _____ _____ _____ _____ _____ _____.

B: That's Gwangandaegyo in Busan.

G: _____ _____ you _____ that?

B: I _____ _____ _____ my family _____ _____.

G: 와, 이 광고에 나오는 다리 좀 봐. 어디에서 찍은 사진인지 궁금하네.
B: 부산의 광안대교야.
G: 그걸 어떻게 아니?
B: 작년 여름에 우리 가족들과 그곳에 갔었거든.

Listen & Speak 1 A-2

B: _____ _____ there. _____ _____ _____ _____ there are so many people _____ _____ _____.

G: They're _____ _____ _____ _____ the new bakery there.

B: Why? Is it _____?

G: Yes. It was _____ a TV program.

B: Really? We _____ _____ their bread _____.

G: Sure.

B: 저기 좀 봐. 왜 저렇게 많은 사람들이 줄을 서서 기다리고 있는지 궁금하네.
G: 새로 생긴 제과점에 들어가려고 기다리고 있는 거야.
B: 왜? 유명한 곳이야?
G: 맞아. TV 프로그램에 나왔어.
B: 정말? 그럼 우리 저곳의 빵을 먹어 봐야겠다.
G: 그래.

Listen & Speak 2 A-1

W: Excuse me, _____ _____ _____ _____ an audio guide.

M: _____ you _____.

W: Could you _____ _____ _____ _____ _____ _____ _____?

M: Sure. _____ this button, and it'll tell you _____ _____ _____.

W: 실례합니다, 음성 가이드를 대여하고 싶은데요.
M: 여기 있습니다.
W: 어떻게 사용하는지 설명해 주실 수 있나요?
M: 물론이죠. 이 버튼을 누르면, 무엇을 해야 할지 말해 줄 겁니다.

Listen & Speak 2 A-2

B: _____ you _____ _____ this summer?

G: I'm _____ _____ Jejudo to _____ the Jeju Olle Trail.

B: The Jeju Olle Trail? _____ _____ _____ _____ _____ _____ _____ _____?

G: It's a _____ _____ _____ _____ Jejudo.

B: Oh, I see. I hope you _____ _____ _____!

B: 이번 여름에 어디 갈 거야?
G: 제주 올레길을 따라 걸으러 제주도에 갈 거야.
B: 제주 올레길? 그게 무엇인지 설명해 줄래?
G: 제주도 둘레에 있는 긴 하이킹 코스야.
B: 오, 그렇구나. 즐거운 여행이 되길 바랄게!

Communication A

Jaden: Do you hear that? _____ _____ _____ that music is _____
_____.

Yuri: I think it's coming from _____ _____. Do you want to go
and _____ _____ _____?

Jaden: Yes, I love that _____ _____. Is it _____ Korean music?

Yuri: Yes, it's _____ nongak. It's _____ _____ _____ _____
band music.

Jaden: Nongak? _____ _____ _____ _____ _____ _____ _____
more about it?

Yuri: It's _____ used to _____ _____ farmers and _____
_____ a _____ _____.

Jaden: I see. Look! Some people _____ _____ _____ the _____.

Yuri: Yes, that's a big _____ _____ nongak. Dancing together
_____ the music.

Jaden: _____ _____ them.

Yuri: Sure. _____ _____?

Jaden: 저거 들리니? 저 음악이 어디
서 오는 것인지 궁금하네.
유리: 저기서 나오는 것 같은데. 가서 확
인해 볼래?
Jaden: 그래, 저 강한 비트가 마음에
들어. 그게 한국의 전통 음악이
니?
유리: 맞아, 농악이라고 해. 공동체 악단
음악의 한 종류야.
Jaden: 농악? 그것에 대해 좀 더 설명
해 줄래?
유리: 그건 전통적으로 농부들의 힘을
북돋아 주고 풍년을 기원하기 위
해 사용되었어.
Jaden: 그렇구나. 봐! 몇몇 사람들이
리듬에 맞춰 춤추고 있어.
유리: 그래, 그게 농악의 큰 부분이야.
함께 춤추는 것이 음악을 완성하
지.
Jaden: 저들과 함께 하자.
유리: 물론이야. 왜 안 되겠어?

Progree Check 1

W: Look over there. _____ _____ _____ _____
_____ _____ _____ on the road.

M: _____ _____ people are _____ _____ _____ this
weekend.

W: Really? Then, _____ _____ _____ go somewhere, _____?

M: O.K.

W: 저기 좀 봐요. 도로에 왜 저렇게 차
가 많은지 궁금하네요.
M: 많은 사람들이 이번 주말에 휴가를
가거든요.
W: 정말로요? 그럼, 우리도 어디 가는
게 어떤가요?
M: 좋아요.

Progree Check 2

B: _____ me, I'd like to use a _____ _____.

W: O.K. You can use this machine.

B: Could you explain _____ _____ _____ _____ _____ _____?

W: Sure. _____ the button for _____ _____, and then _____
the start button.

B: Thank you.

B: 실례합니다, 복사기를 좀 쓰고 싶은
데요.
W: 알겠어요. 이 기계를 써도 돼요.
B: 어떻게 양면 복사를 하는지 설명해
주실 수 있나요?
W: 물론이죠. 양면 복사 버튼을 누르고,
시작 버튼을 누르세요.
B: 감사합니다.

※ 다음 우리말에 맞도록 대화를 영어로 쓰시오.

Listen & Speak 1 A-1

G: _____

B: _____

G: _____

B: _____

해석

G: 와, 이 광고에 나오는 다리 좀 봐. 어디에서 찍은 사진인지 궁금하네.
B: 부산의 광안대교야.
G: 그걸 어떻게 아니?
B: 작년 여름에 우리 가족들과 그곳에 갔었거든.

Listen & Speak 1 A-2

B: _____

G: _____

B: _____

G: _____

B: _____

G: _____

B: 저기 좀 봐. 왜 저렇게 많은 사람들이 줄을 서서 기다리고 있는지 궁금하네.
G: 새로 생긴 제과점에 들어가려고 기다리고 있는 거야.
B: 왜? 유명한 곳이야?
G: 맞아. TV 프로그램에 나왔어.
B: 정말? 그럼 우리 저곳의 빵을 먹어 봐야겠다.
G: 그래.

Listen & Speak 2 A-1

W: _____

M: _____

W: _____

M: _____

W: 실례합니다, 음성 가이드를 대여하고 싶은데요.
M: 여기 있습니다.
W: 어떻게 사용하는지 설명해 주실 수 있나요?
M: 물론이죠. 이 버튼을 누르면, 무엇을 해야 할지 말해 줄 겁니다.

Listen & Speak 2 A-2

B: _____

G: _____

B: _____

G: _____

B: _____

B: 이번 여름에 어디 갈 거야?
G: 제주 올레길을 따라 걸으러 제주도에 갈 거야.
B: 제주 올레길? 그게 무엇인지 설명해 줄래?
G: 제주도 둘레에 있는 긴 하이킹 코스야.
B: 오, 그렇구나. 즐거운 여행이 되길 바랄게!

Communication A

Jaden: _____

Yuri: _____

Jaden: _____

Yuri: _____

Jaden: _____

Yuri: _____

Jaden: _____

Yuri: _____

Jaden: _____

Yuri: _____

Jaden: 저거 들리니? 저 음악이 어디서 오는 것인지 궁금하네.

유리: 저기서 나오는 것 같은데. 가서 확인해 볼래?

Jaden: 그래, 저 강한 비트가 마음에 들어. 그게 한국의 전통 음악이니?

유리: 맞아, 농악이라고 해. 공동체 악단 음악의 한 종류야.

Jaden: 농악? 그것에 대해 좀 더 설명해 줄래?

유리: 그건 전통적으로 농부들의 힘을 북돋아 주고 풍년을 기원하기 위해 사용되었어.

Jaden: 그렇구나. 봐! 몇몇 사람들이 리듬에 맞춰 춤추고 있어.

유리: 그래, 그게 농악의 큰 부분이야. 함께 춤추는 것이 음악을 완성하지.

Jaden: 저들과 함께 하자.

유리: 물론이야. 왜 안 되겠어?

Progree Check 1

W: _____

M: _____

W: _____

M: _____

W: 저기 좀 봐요. 도로에 왜 저렇게 차가 많은지 궁금하네요.

M: 많은 사람들이 이번 주말에 휴가를 가거든요.

W: 정말로요? 그럼, 우리도 어디 가는 게 어떤가요?

M: 좋아요.

Progree Check 2

B: _____

W: _____

B: _____

W: _____

B: _____

B: 실례합니다, 복사기를 좀 쓰고 싶은데요.

W: 알겠어요. 이 기계를 써도 돼요.

B: 어떻게 양면 복사를 하는지 설명해 주실 수 있나요?

W: 물론이죠. 양면 복사 버튼을 누르고, 시작 버튼을 누르세요.

B: 감사합니다.

※ 다음 우리말과 일치하도록 빈칸에 알맞은 것을 골라 쓰시오.

1 _____, _____ _____ of Korea
A. Divers   B. Female   C. Haenyeo

2 For the past _____ years, the _____ photographer Zin Kim has _____ the culture of Jeju haenyeo _____.
A. promoted   B. several   C. worldwide   D. underwater

3 Haenyeo are Korean _____ divers who _____ seafood _____ any _____ devices.
A. without   B. female   C. breathing   D. harvest

4 Their culture _____ UNESCO's _____ Cultural _____ in 2016.
A. Heritage   B. Intangible   C. made   D. list

5 At her studio _____ week, Zin Kim was _____ about her _____ of _____ pictures of haenyeo.
A. interviewed   B. taking   C. last   D. experience

6 Q. How did you _____ photos of haenyeo?
A. interested   B. in   C. become   D. taking

7 _____ _____, I _____ _____ take pictures of a haenyeo.
A. happened   B. day   C. to   D. one

8 I _____ _____ _____ _____ that she was enjoying her job.
A. to   B. was   C. find   D. surprised

9 _____ then, I had only _____ black-and-white photos of haenyeo who _____ very _____.
A. looked   B. until   C. tired   D. seen

10 However, she _____ _____ even after she had _____ in the water for _____ five hours.
A. over   B. kept   C. been   D. laughing

11 I _____ then that I _____ _____ pictures of haenyeo.
A. should   B. realized   C. take

12 Q. You take beautiful pictures of them, but _____ _____ take pictures of haenyeo?
A. to   B. isn't   C. difficult   D. it

13 _____ first, they didn't understand _____ _____ to take their pictures.
A. wanted   B. why   C. I   D. at

14 They didn't think they _____ _____ _____ their _____.
A. pretty   B. wetsuits   C. looked   D. in

15 _____, I said to them, "You're _____ _____.
A. very   B. so   C. special

16 I want to _____ your _____ _____ the _____."
A. to   B. show   C. culture   D. world

17 They _____ _____ to me _____.
A. up   B. opened   C. then

18 Of course, I also promised them that I would _____ _____ _____ in my pictures.
A. them   B. beautiful   C. make   D. look

---

1   해녀, 한국의 여성 잠수부

2   지난 몇 년 동안, 수중 사진작가 Zin Kim은 제주 해녀 문화를 전 세계에 홍보해 왔다.

3   해녀는 어떤 호흡 장치도 사용하지 않고 해산물을 채취하는 한국의 여성 잠수부들이다.

4   그들의 문화는 2016년에 유네스코 무형문화유산에 등재되었다.

5   지난주 그녀의 작업실에서, Zin Kim과 해녀의 사진을 찍는 그녀의 경험에 대해 인터뷰를 했다.

6   Q. 어떻게 해녀의 사진을 찍는 것에 관심을 가지게 되었나요?

7   어느 날, 저는 우연히 한 해녀의 사진을 찍게 되었어요.

8   저는 그녀가 자신의 일을 즐겁게 하는 것을 보고 놀랐습니다.

9   그때까지, 저는 흑백 사진 속의 아주 지친 모습의 해녀만 봐 왔죠.

10   하지만, 그녀는 다섯 시간이 넘도록 물속에 있은 후에도 계속 웃었어요.

11   저는 그때 해녀의 사진을 찍어야겠다고 깨달았어요.

12   Q. 작가님은 아름다운 해녀 사진들을 찍으시는데, 그들의 사진을 찍는 것이 어렵진 않으신가요?

13   처음에, 그들은 제가 왜 자신들의 사진을 찍으려고 하는지 이해하지 못했어요.

14   그들은 잠수복을 입은 자신들의 모습이 예뻐 보인다고 생각하지 않았으니까요.

15   그래서, 제가 그들에게 말했죠, "여러분들은 아주 특별해요.

16   저는 여러분의 문화를 세계에 알리고 싶어요."

17   그들은 그때 제게 마음을 열었어요.

18   물론, 저 또한 그들에게 제 사진 속에서 그들을 아름답게 보이도록 하겠다고 약속했지요.

19 Q. Could you _____ _____ _____ haenyeo?
    A. more   B. tell   C. about   D. us

20 What's _____ _____ _____ them?
    A. special   B. about   C. so

21 I _____ _____ three _____.
    A. things   B. tell   C. you   D. can

22 First, haenyeo are a _____ of _____ _____.
    A. strong   B. symbol   C. women

23 Jejudo, which is a _____ island, is not _____ for _____, so many haenyeo have become the _____ for their families.
    A. suitable   B. breadwinners   C. farming   D. volcanic

24 Second, haenyeo _____ their _____ communities and help _____ _____.
    A. each   B. form   C. other   D. own

25 For _____, _____ haenyeo train _____ haenyeo.
    A. example   B. less-experienced   C. more-experienced

26 Third, because they _____ in the water _____ any _____ devices, haenyeo can't _____ a lot of seafood.
    A. without   B. stay   C. catch   D. breathing

27 This is _____ the _____.
    A. good   B. environment   C. for   D. underwater

28 Catching too much _____ life at one _____ in one _____ can _____ the ocean.
    A. destroy   B. marine   C. place   D. time

29 Q. Lastly, please tell us _____ you're _____ to _____ in the _____.
    A. what   B. future   C. planning   D. do

30 I once _____ an overseas _____ with a couple of haenyeo to give a _____ about their _____.
    A. talk   B. attended   C. lives   D. exhibition

31 When I _____ my talk, one of the haenyeo _____ my _____ _____.
    A. held   B. tightly   C. finished   D. hand

32 She _____ _____ me, "Thank you _____.
    A. much   B. so   C. to   D. said

33 I've never known in my whole life that I was _____ _____."
    A. special   B. a   C. person   D. such

34 She was _____ _____ _____.
    A. with   B. crying   C. happiness

35 Everyone in the audience _____ _____ _____.
    A. deeply   B. was   C. moved

36 I can _____ that _____, so I'll _____ to take pictures of haenyeo.
    A. continue   B. forget   C. never   D. moment

37 I want to tell _____ _____ _____ them to many more people in the world.
    A. beautiful   B. about   C. more   D. stories

---

19 Q. 해녀에 대해서 더 말씀해 주시겠어요?

20 그들은 무엇이 그렇게 특별한가요?

21 세 가지를 말씀 드릴게요.

22 첫 번째로, 해녀들은 강인한 여성의 상징이에요.

23 제주도는 화산섬이고, 이는 농사에 적합하지 않아서 많은 해녀들이 가족들의 생계비를 버는 가장이 되어 왔어요.

24 둘째로, 해녀들은 그들 자신의 공동체를 조직하고 서로 도와요.

25 예를 들어, 경험이 더 많은 해녀들이 경험이 적은 해녀들을 훈련시키지요.

26 세 번째로, 어떤 호흡 장치도 사용하지 않고 물속에 머물기 때문에, 해녀는 많은 해산물을 채취할 수가 없어요.

27 이것은 수중 환경에 좋은 것이지요.

28 한 번에 한 장소에서 너무 많은 해양생물을 채취하는 것은 바다를 파괴할 수 있으니까요.

29 Q. 마지막으로, 앞으로 계획하고 있는 것에 대해 말씀해 주세요.

30 예전에 두 명의 해녀들과 함께 그들의 삶에 대해 이야기하기 위해 해외에서 열리는 박람회에 참가한 적이 있어요.

31 제가 연설을 마쳤을 때, 해녀 중 한 분이 제 손을 꼭 잡았어요.

32 그분이 말했죠. "너무 고마워.

33 내 평생 내가 이렇게 특별한 사람이라는 걸 미처 알지 못했어."

34 그녀는 행복해서 울고 있었어요.

35 청중들 모두가 깊은 감동을 받았어요.

36 전 그 순간을 절대 잊을 수가 없기 때문에 해녀의 사진을 계속해서 찍을 거예요.

37 저는 그들에 대한 더 많은 아름다운 이야기들을 세계의 더 많은 사람들에게 알려 주고 싶어요.

※ 다음 우리말과 일치하도록 빈칸에 알맞은 말을 쓰시오.

1 Haenyeo, _____ _____ of Korea

2 For the past several years, the _____ _____ Zin Kim _____ _____ the culture of Jeju haenyeo _____.

3 Haenyeo are Korean _____ _____ who harvest seafood _____ _____ _____ _____ _____.

4 Their culture _____ _____ _____ _____ _____ _____ in 2016.

5 At her studio last week, Zin Kim _____ _____ about her _____ _____ _____ _____ of haenyeo.

6 Q. How did you _____ _____ _____ _____ photos of haenyeo?

7 _____ _____, I _____ _____ take pictures of a haenyeo.

8 I _____ _____ _____ that she _____ _____ her job.

9 _____ _____, I _____ _____ _____ black-and-white photos of haenyeo who _____ _____ _____.

10 However, she _____ _____ even after she had been in the water _____ _____ _____ _____ _____.

11 I _____ then that I _____ _____ _____ of haenyeo.

12 Q. You take beautiful pictures of them, but _____ _____ _____ _____ _____ _____ of haenyeo?

13 _____ _____, they didn't understand _____ _____ to take their pictures.

14 They didn't think they _____ _____ _____ _____ _____.

15 So, I said to them, "You're _____ _____.

16 I want to _____ your culture _____ the world."

17 They _____ _____ to me _____.

18 _____ _____, I also promised them that I would _____ _____ look _____ in my pictures.

1 해녀, 한국의 여성 잠수부

2 지난 몇 년 동안, 수중 사진작가 Zin Kim은 제주 해녀 문화를 전 세계에 홍보해 왔다.

3 해녀는 어떤 호흡 장치도 사용하지 않고 해산물을 채취하는 한국의 여성 잠수부들이다.

4 그들의 문화는 2016년에 유네스코 무형문화유산에 등재되었다.

5 지난주 그녀의 작업실에서, Zin Kim과 해녀의 사진을 찍는 그녀의 경험에 대해 인터뷰를 했다.

6 Q. 어떻게 해녀의 사진을 찍는 것에 관심을 가지게 되었나요?

7 어느 날, 저는 우연히 한 해녀의 사진을 찍게 되었어요.

8 저는 그녀가 자신의 일을 즐겁게 하는 것을 보고 놀랐습니다.

9 그때까지, 저는 흑백 사진 속의 아주 지친 모습의 해녀만 봐 왔죠.

10 하지만, 그녀는 다섯 시간이 넘도록 물속에 있은 후에도 계속 웃었어요.

11 저는 그때 해녀의 사진을 찍어야겠다고 깨달았어요.

12 Q. 작가님은 아름다운 해녀 사진들을 찍으시는데, 그들의 사진을 찍는 것이 어렵진 않으신가요?

13 처음에, 그들은 제가 왜 자신들의 사진을 찍으려고 하는지 이해하지 못했어요.

14 그들은 잠수복을 입은 자신들의 모습이 예뻐 보인다고 생각하지 않았으니까요.

15 그래서, 제가 그들에게 말했죠, "여러분들은 아주 특별해요.

16 저는 여러분의 문화를 세계에 알리고 싶어요."

17 그들은 그때 제게 마음을 열었어요.

18 물론, 저 또한 그들에게 제 사진 속에서 그들을 아름답게 보이도록 하겠다고 약속했지요.

19 Q. Could you tell us _____ _____ haenyeo?

20 What's _____ _____ about them?

21 I _____ _____ _____ three things.

22 First, haenyeo are a _____ _____ _____ _____ .

23 Jejudo, _____ is a volcanic island, _____ _____ _____ _____ farming, so many haenyeo _____ _____ _____ _____ _____ their families.

24 Second, haenyeo _____ their _____ _____ and help _____ _____ .

25 For example, _____ haenyeo train _____ haenyeo.

26 Third, _____ they stay in the water _____ any _____ _____ , haenyeo _____ _____ a lot of seafood.

27 This _____ _____ _____ the _____ _____ .

28 _____ too much marine life _____ _____ _____ _____ _____ _____ _____ the ocean.

29 Q. Lastly, please tell us _____ you're _____ _____ _____ in the future.

30 I once _____ an _____ _____ with a couple of haenyeo to _____ _____ _____ about their lives.

31 When I finished my talk, one of the haenyeo _____ _____ _____ _____ .

32 She said to me, "Thank you _____ _____ .

33 I've never known in my _____ _____ that I was _____ _____ _____ _____ ."

34 She was _____ _____ _____ .

35 Everyone in the audience _____ _____ _____ _____ .

36 I _____ _____ that moment, so I'll _____ _____ _____ pictures of haenyeo.

37 I want to tell _____ _____ _____ _____ _____ _____ to many more people in the world.

19 Q. 해녀에 대해서 더 말씀해 주시겠어요?

20 그들은 무엇이 그렇게 특별한가요?

21 세 가지를 말씀 드릴게요.

22 첫 번째로, 해녀들은 강인한 여성의 상징이에요.

23 제주도는 화산섬이고, 이는 농사에 적합하지 않아서 많은 해녀들이 가족들의 생계비를 버는 가장이 되어 왔어요.

24 둘째로, 해녀들은 그들 자신의 공동체를 조직하고 서로 도와요.

25 예를 들어, 경험이 더 많은 해녀들이 경험이 적은 해녀들을 훈련시키지요.

26 세 번째로, 어떤 호흡 장치도 사용하지 않고 물속에 머물기 때문에, 해녀는 많은 해산물을 채취할 수가 없어요.

27 이것은 수중 환경에 좋은 것이지요.

28 한 번에 한 장소에서 너무 많은 해양생물을 채취하는 것은 바다를 파괴할 수 있으니까요.

29 Q. 마지막으로, 앞으로 계획하고 있는 것에 대해 말씀해 주세요.

30 예전에 두 명의 해녀들과 함께 그들의 삶에 대해 이야기하기 위해 해외에서 열리는 박람회에 참가한 적이 있어요.

31 제가 연설을 마쳤을 때, 해녀 중 한 분이 제 손을 꼭 잡았어요.

32 그분이 말했죠, "너무 고마워.

33 내 평생 내가 이렇게 특별한 사람이라는 걸 미처 알지 못했어."

34 그녀는 행복해서 울고 있었어요.

35 청중들 모두가 깊은 감동을 받았어요.

36 전 그 순간을 절대 잊을 수가 없기 때문에 해녀의 사진을 계속해서 찍을 거예요.

37 저는 그들에 대한 더 많은 아름다운 이야기들을 세계의 더 많은 사람들에게 알려 주고 싶어요.

※ 다음 문장을 우리말로 쓰시오.

1 Haenyeo, Female Divers of Korea

➡ _____

2 For the past several years, the underwater photographer Zin Kim has promoted the culture of Jeju haenyeo worldwide.

➡ _____

3 Haenyeo are Korean female divers who harvest seafood without any breathing devices.

➡ _____

4 Their culture made UNESCO's Intangible Cultural Heritage list in 2016.

➡ _____

5 At her studio last week, Zin Kim was interviewed about her experience of taking pictures of haenyeo.

➡ _____

6 Q. How did you become interested in taking photos of haenyeo?

➡ _____

7 One day, I happened to take pictures of a haenyeo.

➡ _____

8 I was surprised to find that she was enjoying her job.

➡ _____

9 Until then, I had only seen black-and-white photos of haenyeo who looked very tired.

➡ _____

10 However, she kept laughing even after she had been in the water for over five hours.

➡ _____

11 I realized then that I should take pictures of haenyeo.

➡ _____

12 Q. You take beautiful pictures of them, but isn't it difficult to take pictures of haenyeo?

➡ _____

13 At first, they didn't understand why I wanted to take their pictures.

➡ _____

14 They didn't think they looked pretty in their wetsuits.

➡ _____

15 So, I said to them, "You're very special.

➡ _____

16 I want to show your culture to the world."

➡ _____

17 They opened up to me then.

➡ _____

18 Of course, I also promised them that I would make them look beautiful in my pictures.

➡ _____

19 Q. Could you tell us more about haenyeo?w

➡ _____

20 What's so special about them?

➡ _____

21 I can tell you three things.

➡ _____

22 First, haenyeo are a symbol of strong women.

➡ _____

23 Jejudo, which is a volcanic island, is not suitable for farming, so many haenyeo have become the breadwinners for their families.

➡ _____

24 Second, haenyeo form their own communities and help each other.

➡ _____

25 For example, more-experienced haenyeo train less-experienced haenyeo.

➡ _____

26 Third, because they stay in the water without any breathing devices, haenyeo can't catch a lot of seafood.

➡ _____

27 This is good for the underwater environment.

➡ _____

28 Catching too much marine life at one time in one place can destroy the ocean.

➡ _____

29 Q. Lastly, please tell us what you're planning to do in the future.

➡ _____

30 I once attended an overseas exhibition with a couple of haenyeo to give a talk about their lives.

➡ _____

31 When I finished my talk, one of the haenyeo held my hand tightly.

➡ _____

32 She said to me, "Thank you so much.

➡ _____

33 I've never known in my whole life that I was such a special person."

➡ _____

34 She was crying with happiness.

➡ _____

35 Everyone in the audience was deeply moved.

➡ _____

36 I can never forget that moment, so I'll continue to take pictures of haenyeo.

➡ _____

37 I want to tell more beautiful stories about them to many more people in the world.

➡ _____

※ 다음 괄호 안의 단어들을 우리말에 맞도록 바르게 배열하시오.

1 (Female / Haenyeo, / of / Divers / Korea)
➡ _____

2 (the / for / past / years, / several / underwater / the / Zin / photographer / Kim / promoted / has / culture / the / Jeju / of / worldwide. / haenyeo)
➡ _____
_____

3 (are / haenyeo / Korean / divers / female / harvest / who / without / seafood / breathing / any / devices.)
➡ _____
_____

4 (culture / their / UNESCO's / made / Cultural / Intangible / Heritage / in / list / 2016.)
➡ _____

5 (her / at / last / studio / week, / Kim / Zin / interviewed / was / her / about / of / experience / taking / of / pictures / haenyeo.)
➡ _____

6 (Q. / did / how / become / you / in / interested / photos / taking / haenyeo? / of)
➡ _____

7 (day, / one / happened / I / take / to / of / pictures / haenyeo. / a)
➡ _____

8 (was / I / to / surprised / find / she / that / enjoying / was / job. / her)
➡ _____

9 (then, / until / had / I / seen / only / photos / black-and-white / haenyeo / of / looked / who / tired. / very)
➡ _____

10 (she / however, / laughing / kept / after / even / she / been / had / the / in / water / over / for / hours. / five)
➡ _____
_____

11 (realized / I / that / then / should / I / pictures / take / haenyeo. / of)
➡ _____

12 (Q. / take / you / pictures / beautiful / them, / of / isn't / but / difficult / it / take / to / of / pictures / haenyeo?)
➡ _____
_____

---

1 해녀, 한국의 여성 잠수부

2 지난 몇 년 동안, 수중 사진작가 Zin Kim은 제주 해녀 문화를 전 세계에 홍보해 왔다.

3 해녀는 어떤 호흡 장치도 사용하지 않고 해산물을 채취하는 한국의 여성 잠수부들이다.

4 그들의 문화는 2016년에 유네스코 무형문화유산에 등재되었다.

5 지난주 그녀의 작업실에서, Zin Kim과 해녀의 사진을 찍는 그녀의 경험에 대해 인터뷰를 했다.

6 Q. 어떻게 해녀의 사진을 찍는 것에 관심을 가지게 되었나요?

7 어느 날, 저는 우연히 한 해녀의 사진을 찍게 되었어요.

8 저는 그녀가 자신의 일을 즐겁게 하는 것을 보고 놀랐습니다.

9 그때까지, 저는 흑백 사진 속의 아주 지친 모습의 해녀만 봐 왔죠.

10 하지만, 그녀는 다섯 시간이 넘도록 물속에 있은 후에도 계속 웃었어요.

11 저는 그때 해녀의 사진을 찍어야겠다고 깨달았어요.

12 Q. 작가님은 아름다운 해녀 사진들을 찍으시는데, 그들의 사진을 찍는 것이 어렵진 않으신가요?

13 (first, / at / didn't / they / why / understand / wanted / I / take / to / pictures. / their)

⇒ _____

14 (didn't / they / they / think / pretty / looked / their / in / wetsuits.)

⇒ _____

15 (I / so, / said / them, / to / very / "you're / special.)

⇒ _____

16 (want / I / show / to / culture / your / the / to / world.")

⇒ _____

17 (opened / they / to / up / then. / me)

⇒ _____

18 (course, / of / also / I / them / promised / I / that / make / would / look / them / in / beautiful / pictures. / my)

⇒ _____

_____

19 (Q. / you / could / us / tell / about / more / haenyeo?)

⇒ _____

20 (so / what's / about / special / them?)

⇒ _____

21 (can / I / you / tell / things. / three)

⇒ _____

22 (haenyeo / first, / a / are / of / symbol / women. / strong)

⇒ _____

23 (which / Jejudo, / is / volcanic / a / island, / not / is / for / suitable / farming, / many / so / have / haenyeo / the / become / breadwinners / their / for / families.)

⇒ _____

_____

24 (haenyeo / second, / their / form / communities / own / and / each / help / other.)

⇒ _____

25 (example, / for / haenyeo / more-experienced / less-experienced / train / haenyeo.)

⇒ _____

---

13 처음에, 그들은 제가 왜 자신들의 사진을 찍으려고 하는지 이해하지 못했어요.

14 그들은 잠수복을 입은 자신들의 모습이 예뻐 보인다고 생각하지 않았으니까요.

15 그래서, 제가 그들에게 말했죠, "여러분들은 아주 특별해요.

16 저는 여러분의 문화를 세계에 알리고 싶어요."

17 그들은 그때 제게 마음을 열었어요.

18 물론, 저 또한 그들에게 제 사진 속에서 그들을 아름답게 보이도록 하겠다고 약속했지요.

19 Q. 해녀에 대해서 더 말씀해 주시겠어요?

20 그들은 무엇이 그렇게 특별한가요?

21 세 가지를 말씀 드릴게요.

22 첫 번째로, 해녀들은 강인한 여성의 상징이에요.

23 제주도는 화산섬이고, 이는 농사에 적합하지 않아서 많은 해녀들이 가족들의 생계비를 버는 가장이 되어 왔어요.

24 둘째로, 해녀들은 그들 자신의 공동체를 조직하고 서로 도와요.

25 예를 들어, 경험이 더 많은 해녀들이 경험이 적은 해녀들을 훈련시키지요.

26 (because / third, / stay / they / the / in / without / water / breathing / any / devices, / can't / haenyeo / a / catch / of / lot / seafood.)

➡ _____

➡ _____

27 (is / this / for / good / underwater / the / environment.)

➡ _____

28 (too / catching / much / life / marine / one / at / time / one / in / place / destroy / can / ocean. / the)

➡ _____

29 (Q. / please / lastly, / us / tell / you're / what / to / planning / do / the / in / future.)

➡ _____

30 (once / I / an / attneded / overseas / with / exhibition / a / of / couple / haenyeo / a / give / to / talk / their / lives. / about)

➡ _____

➡ _____

31 (I / when / my / finished / talk, / of / one / haenyeo / the / my / held / tightly. / hand)

➡ _____

32 (said / she / me, / to / you / "thank / much. / so)

➡ _____

33 (never / I've / in / known / whole / my / that / life / was / I / a / such / person." / special)

➡ _____

34 (was / she / with / crying / happiness.)

➡ _____

35 (in / everyone / audience / the / was / moved. / deeply)

➡ _____

36 (can / I / forget / never / moment, / that / I'll / so / to / continue / take / of / haenyeo / pictures)

➡ _____

37 (want / I / to / more / tell / stories / beautiful / about / to / them / more / many / people / the / in / world.)

➡ _____

➡ _____

26 세 번째로, 어떤 호흡 장치도 사용하지 않고 물속에 머물기 때문에, 해녀는 많은 해산물을 채취할 수가 없어요.

27 이것은 수중 환경에 좋은 것이지요.

28 한 번에 한 장소에서 너무 많은 해양생물을 채취하는 것은 바다를 파괴할 수 있으니까요.

29 Q. 마지막으로, 앞으로 계획하고 있는 것에 대해 말씀해 주세요.

30 예전에 두 명의 해녀들과 함께 그들의 삶에 대해 이야기하기 위해 해외에서 열리는 박람회에 참가한 적이 있어요.

31 제가 연설을 마쳤을 때, 해녀 중 한 분이 제 손을 꼭 잡았어요.

32 그분이 말했죠. "너무 고마워.

33 내 평생 내가 이렇게 특별한 사람이라는 걸 미처 알지 못했어."

34 그녀는 행복해서 울고 있었어요.

35 청중들 모두가 깊은 감동을 받았어요.

36 전 그 순간을 절대 잊을 수가 없기 때문에 해녀의 사진을 계속해서 찍을 거예요.

37 저는 그들에 대한 더 많은 아름다운 이야기들을 세계의 더 많은 사람들에게 알려 주고 싶어요.

※ 다음 우리말을 영어로 쓰시오.

1 해녀, 한국의 여성 잠수부
➡ _____

2 지난 몇 년 동안, 수중 사진작가 Zin Kim은 제주 해녀 문화를 전 세계에 홍보해 왔다.
➡ _____
_____

3 해녀는 어떤 호흡 장치도 사용하지 않고 해산물을 채취하는 한국의 여성 잠수부들이다.
➡ _____

4 그들의 문화는 2016년에 유네스코 무형문화유산에 등재되었다.
➡ _____

5 지난주 그녀의 작업실에서, Zin Kim과 해녀의 사진을 찍는 그녀의 경험에 대해 인터뷰를 했다.
➡ _____

6 Q. 어떻게 해녀의 사진을 찍는 것에 관심을 가지게 되었나요?
➡ _____

7 어느 날, 저는 우연히 한 해녀의 사진을 찍게 되었어요.
➡ _____

8 저는 그녀가 자신의 일을 즐겁게 하는 것을 보고 놀랐습니다.
➡ _____

9 그때까지, 저는 흑백 사진 속의 아주 지친 모습의 해녀만 봐 왔죠.
➡ _____

10 하지만, 그녀는 다섯 시간이 넘도록 물속에 있은 후에도 계속 웃었어요.
➡ _____

11 저는 그때 해녀의 사진을 찍어야겠다고 깨달았어요.
➡ _____

12 Q. 작가님은 아름다운 해녀 사진들을 찍으시는데, 그들의 사진을 찍는 것이 어렵진 않으신가요?
➡ _____

13 처음에, 그들은 제가 왜 자신들의 사진을 찍으려고 하는지 이해하지 못했어요.
➡ _____

14 그들은 잠수복을 입은 자신들의 모습이 예뻐 보인다고 생각하지 않았으니까요.
➡ _____

15 그래서, 제가 그들에게 말했죠, "여러분들은 아주 특별해요.
➡ _____

16 저는 여러분의 문화를 세계에 알리고 싶어요."
➡ _____

17 그들은 그때 제게 마음을 열었어요.
➡ _____

18 물론, 저 또한 그들에게 제 사진 속에서 그들을 아름답게 보이도록 하겠다고 약속했지요.
➡ _____

19 Q. 해녀에 대해서 더 말씀해 주시겠어요?
➡ _____

20 그들은 무엇이 그렇게 특별한가요?

➡ _____

21 세 가지를 말씀 드릴게요.

➡ _____

22 첫 번째로, 해녀들은 강인한 여성의 상징이에요.

➡ _____

23 제주도는 화산섬이고, 이는 농사에 적합하지 않아서 많은 해녀들이 가족들의 생계비를 버는 가장이 되어 왔어요.

➡ _____

_____

24 둘째로, 해녀들은 그들 자신의 공동체를 조직하고 서로 도와요.

➡ _____

25 예를 들어, 경험이 더 많은 해녀들이 경험이 적은 해녀들을 훈련시키지요.

➡ _____

26 세 번째로, 어떤 호흡 장치도 사용하지 않고 물속에 머물기 때문에, 해녀는 많은 해산물을 채취할 수가 없어요.

➡ _____

_____

27 이것은 수중 환경에 좋은 것이지요.

➡ _____

28 한 번에 한 장소에서 너무 많은 해양생물을 채취하는 것은 바다를 파괴할 수 있으니까요.

➡ _____

29 Q. 마지막으로, 앞으로 계획하고 있는 것에 대해 말씀해 주세요.

➡ _____

30 예전에 두 명의 해녀들과 함께 그들의 삶에 대해 이야기하기 위해 해외에서 열리는 박람회에 참가한 적이 있어요.

➡ _____

31 제가 연설을 마쳤을 때, 해녀 중 한 분이 제 손을 꼭 잡았어요.

➡ _____

32 그분이 말했죠, "너무 고마워.

➡ _____

33 내 평생 내가 이렇게 특별한 사람이라는 걸 미처 알지 못했어."

➡ _____

34 그녀는 행복해서 울고 있었어요.

➡ _____

35 청중들 모두가 깊은 감동을 받았어요.

➡ _____

36 전 그 순간을 절대 잊을 수가 없기 때문에 해녀의 사진을 계속해서 찍을 거예요.

➡ _____

37 저는 그들에 대한 더 많은 아름다운 이야기들을 세계의 더 많은 사람들에게 알려 주고 싶어요.

➡ _____

※ 다음 우리말과 일치하도록 빈칸에 알맞은 말을 쓰시오.

Communicate – B Talk and Play

1. A: I wonder _____ _____ _____ .

2. B: They're _____ _____ .

3. A: Could you _____ _____ _____ them?

4. B: They're _____ _____ _____ _____ .

1. A: 나는 이것들이 무엇인지 궁금해.
2. B: 그것들은 송편이라고 불려.
3. A: 이것에 대해 좀 더 설명해 줄래?
4. B: 그것들은 전통적인 한국 떡이야.

After You Read A

1. A _____ _____ _____ Haenyeo

2. Zin Kim, _____ _____ _____ , _____ _____ the culture of Jeju haenyeo _____ .

3. She _____ _____ _____ of them _____ _____ _____ a haenyeo _____ _____ _____ her job.

4. _____ was not _____ _____ their pictures _____ _____ .

5. _____ , when she told them _____ she wanted to show _____ _____ _____ , the haenyeo _____ _____ _____ _____ .

6. _____ _____ _____ , she _____ _____ _____ about the lives of haenyeo.

7. After her speech, _____ _____ the haenyeo _____ _____ _____ _____ .

8. Zin Kim said that she _____ _____ _____ _____ pictures of haenyeo.

1. 해녀를 사랑하는 사진작가
2. 수중 사진작가 김진은 전 세계에 제주의 해녀 문화를 홍보해 왔다.
3. 그녀는 자신의 일을 즐기고 있었던 한 해녀를 만났을 때, 그들의 사진을 찍기로 결심했다.
4. 처음에는 그들의 사진을 찍는 것이 쉽지 않았다.
5. 그러나, 그녀가 세상 사람들에게 그들의 문화를 보여주고 싶다고 그들에게 말했을 때, 마침내 해녀들은 마음을 열었다.
6. 한 해외 전시회에서 그녀는 해녀들의 삶에 대해 강연했다.
7. 그녀의 연설이 끝나자 해녀들 중 한 사람은 기쁨의 눈물을 흘렸다.
8. 김진은 앞으로도 해녀들의 사진 찍는 일을 계속할 것이라고 말했다.

Write

1. Kim Minho is a barista. He _____ _____ _____ _____ _____ .

2. He _____ _____ _____ after he _____ _____ _____ _____ _____ for coffee.

3. _____ _____ _____ _____ _____ his job is _____ _____ _____ hot milk and _____ his customers _____ it.

4. He is _____ _____ _____ his own coffee shop.

1. 김민호는 바리스타이다. 그의 직업은 커피 음료를 만드는 것이다.
2. 그는 커피에 대한 그의 열정을 발견한 후에 바리스타가 되었다.
3. 그의 직업에서 그가 가장 좋아하는 부분은 뜨거운 우유로 커피를 장식하고 그의 손님들이 그것을 즐기는 것을 보는 것이다.
4. 그는 자신의 커피점을 열 계획이다.

※ 다음 우리말을 영어로 쓰시오.

Communicate – B Talk and Play

1. A: 나는 이것들이 무엇인지 궁금해.
➡ _____

2. B: 그것들은 송편이라고 불려.
➡ _____

3. A: 이것에 대해 좀 더 설명해 줄래?
➡ _____

4. B: 그것들은 전통적인 한국 떡이야.
➡ _____

After You Read A

1. 해녀를 사랑하는 사진작가
➡ _____

2. 수중 사진작가 김진은 전 세계에 제주의 해녀 문화를 홍보해 왔다.
➡ _____

3. 그녀는 자신의 일을 즐기고 있었던 한 해녀를 만났을 때, 그들의 사진을 찍기로 결심했다.
➡ _____

4. 처음에는 그들의 사진을 찍는 것이 쉽지 않았다.
➡ _____

5. 그러나, 그녀가 세상 사람들에게 그들의 문화를 보여주고 싶다고 그들에게 말했을 때, 마침내 해녀들은 마음을 열었다.
➡ _____
➡ _____

6. 한 해외 전시회에서 그녀는 해녀들의 삶에 대해 강연했다.
➡ _____

7. 그녀의 연설이 끝나자 해녀들 중 한 사람은 기쁨의 눈물을 흘렸다.
➡ _____

8. 김진은 앞으로도 해녀들의 사진 찍는 일을 계속할 것이라고 말했다.
➡ _____

Write

1. 김민호는 바리스타이다. 그의 직업은 커피 음료를 만드는 것이다.
➡ _____

2. 그는 커피에 대한 그의 열정을 발견한 후에 바리스타가 되었다.
➡ _____

3. 그의 직업에서 그가 가장 좋아하는 부분은 뜨거운 우유로 커피를 장식하고 그의 손님들이 그것을 즐기는 것을 보는 것이다.
➡ _____

4. 그는 자신의 커피점을 열 계획이다.
➡ _____

※ 다음 영어를 우리말로 쓰시오.

01	seafood	22	psychologist
02	anxious	23	carefully
03	competition	24	political
04	enemy	25	supporter
05	relax	26	apart
06	graduate	27	chew
07	actually	28	presentation
08	helpless	29	solution
09	professional	30	convenient
10	instead	31	rare
11	judge	32	rival
12	stranger	33	stressful
13	lucky	34	psychology
14	relieved	35	get off
15	famously	36	make a presentation
16	prepare	37	stop by
17	mind	38	not ~ at all
18	nervous	39	by oneself
19	confident	40	come up with
20	behavior	41	make a reservation
21	unique	42	turn A into B
		43	not only A but also B

※ 다음 우리말을 영어로 쓰시오.

01	졸업하다		22	경쟁, 대회
02	행동		23	대신에
03	자신감 있는		24	이어달리기
04	해결책		25	발표
05	결심하다		26	판단하다
06	적		27	편리한
07	(음식을) 씹다		28	경쟁자
08	유명하게		29	낯선 사람
09	전문적인		30	독특한
10	실제로		31	행운인, 운이 좋은
11	심리학자		32	준비하다
12	드문, 희귀한		33	빌려주다
13	스트레스가 많은		34	추측하다
14	휴식을 취하다		35	~에 따르면
15	지원자		36	A를 B로 바꾸다
16	해산물, 해물		37	발표하다
17	정치적인		38	A뿐만 아니라 B도
18	안도하는		39	혼자서
19	무력한		40	(해답 등을) 찾아내다, 내놓다
20	조심스럽게		41	결코 ~가 아닌
21	심리학		42	예약하다
			43	더 이상 ~가 아닌

※ 다음 영영풀이에 알맞은 단어를 <보기>에서 골라 쓴 후, 우리말 뜻을 쓰시오.

1 _____ : not common: _____

2 _____ : to cook something using dry heat, in an oven: _____

3 _____ : someone who hates you and wants to harm you: _____

4 _____ : someone that you do not know: _____

5 _____ : to bite food several times before swallowing it: _____

6 _____ : someone who supports a particular person, group, or plan: _____

7 _____ : unable to look after yourself or to do anything to help yourself: _____

8 _____ : useful to you because it saves you time: _____

9 _____ : to complete your education at a college, school, etc.: _____

10 _____ : an event at which you describe or explain a new product or idea: _____

11 _____ : feeling happy because you are no longer worried about something: _____

12 _____ : the study of the mind and how it influences people's behavior: _____

13 _____ : to let someone borrow money or something that belongs to you for a short time: _____

14 _____ : to rest or do something that is enjoyable, especially after you have been working: _____

15 _____ : sure that something will happen in the way that you want or expect: _____

16 _____ : a person, group, or organization that you compete with in sport, business, a fight, etc. : _____

보기			
rival	chew	helpless	convenient
graduate	lend	stranger	rare
relax	relieved	psychology	presentation
supporter	confident	bake	enemy

※ 다음 우리말과 일치하도록 빈칸에 알맞은 말을 쓰시오.

Listen & Speak 1 A-1

G: What _____ _____ your shoes? _____ they new?

B: Yes, but my dog _____ them. He does it _____ _____ _____. I'm _____ _____ him.

G: He was probably _____. _____ _____ _____ _____ him more often?

B: O.K., I will. I _____ he will _____ _____ my shoes.

Listen & Speak 1 A-2

B: You look a bit _____.

G: I'm _____ _____ my _____ _____ this Saturday.

B: Don't _____. You're such a good swimmer. Just _____ and _____ yourself!

G: Thanks. I feel _____ _____ now.

Listen & Speak 2 A-1

B: Mom, _____ _____ are we going to _____ _____ tomorrow morning?

W: _____ 8 a.m. I'm going to _____ _____ for her before we go.

B: Then, should I _____ _____ _____ to help you?

W: You _____ _____ _____. Your dad will help me.

B: O.K, then. Good night, Mom!

Listen & Speak 2 A-2

W: _____ _____ _____ that new Mexican restaurant tomorrow?

M: _____ not? I'll _____ the restaurant to _____ _____ _____ for us.

W: You _____ _____ _____ call them. You can do it _____.

M: Oh, I see. _____ _____!

G: 신발이 왜 그래? 새것 아니었어?
B: 맞는데, 내 개가 씹어 버렸어. 항상 그렇게 해. 그 개가 걱정돼.
G: 아마 심심했었을 거야. 개와 더 자주 놀아 주는 게 어때?
B: 알겠어, 그럴게. 그 개가 내 신발 씹는 걸 그만두면 좋겠네.

B: 너 좀 긴장한 것 같아 보이는데.
G: 이번 토요일에 있는 수영 대회가 걱정돼.
B: 걱정 마. 너는 수영을 아주 잘 하잖아. 그냥 긴장을 풀고 즐겨!
G: 고마워. 기분이 훨씬 괜찮아졌어.

B: 엄마, 우리 내일 아침 몇 시에 할머니 댁에 가나요?
W: 8시쯤에. 가기 전에 할머니를 위해 쿠키를 구울 거란다.
B: 그럼, 제가 일찍 일어나서 도와드릴까요?
W: 그럴 필요 없단다. 아빠가 도와주실 거야.
B: 알겠어요, 그럼. 안녕히 주무세요, 엄마!

W: 우리 내일 새로 생긴 멕시코 레스토랑에 가 볼까요?
M: 좋죠! 레스토랑에 전화해서 예약해 둘게요.
W: 전화할 필요 없어요. 온라인으로 할 수 있거든요.
M: 오, 그렇군요. 정말 편리하네요!

Communicate A

Yuri: Hi, Jaden. Sports Day is next Friday. I _____ _____!

Jaden: Really? I'm _____ _____ about it.

Yuri: Why? _____ you _____ _____ sports?

Jaden: Yes, I am, but I'm _____ about the 800-meter _____.

Yuri: _____ do you _____?

Jaden: I'm the _____ _____. _____ _____ our team loses _____ _____ me?

Yuri: I think you're _____ _____ _____ _____ _____ yourself.

Jaden: Really? Don't you think I should _____ every day?

Yuri: No, you _____ _____ _____ _____ that. It's just a school race. It's not about _____ or _____.

Jaden: I guess you're _____, Yuri. I'm _____ to have a friend _____ you.

유리: 안녕, Jaden. 운동회가 다음 주 금요일이야. 너무 기다려져!
Jaden: 정말? 난 사실 걱정돼.
유리: 왜? 너 운동 잘하지 않아?
Jaden: 응, 그렇긴 하지만, 800미터 릴레이가 걱정돼.
유리: 무슨 뜻이니?
Jaden: 내가 마지막 주자거든. 나 때문에 우리 팀이 지면 어쩌지?
유리: 넌 네 스스로에게 너무 많은 압박을 주고 있는 것 같아.
Jaden: 그래? 내가 매일 연습해야 한다고 생각하지 않니?
유리: 아니, 그럴 필요 없어. 그냥 학교 경기일 뿐인걸. 이기고 지고에 관한 게 아냐.
Jaden: 네 말이 맞는 것 같다, 유리야. 너 같은 친구를 둬서 다행이야.

Progress Check 1

B: You look a bit _____.

G: Well, I'm _____ _____ my _____ in _____ _____.

B: Don't worry. You've _____ _____ _____. You'll _____ a great _____.

G: Thanks. I _____ _____ _____ now.

B: 너 좀 긴장한 것 같다.
G: 그게, 역사 수업 시간에 내가 할 발표가 걱정돼.
B: 걱정 마. 많이 준비했잖아. 잘할 거야.
G: 고마워. 기분이 훨씬 나아졌어.

Progress Check 2

M: Shall we have _____ _____ for dinner?

W: Sure. I'll _____ _____ the store _____ _____ _____ home.

M: _____ _____ _____ _____ do that. We already have _____ we _____.

W: Oh, I see. Then, I'll be _____ _____ _____ 6 to _____ you _____.

M: 우리 저녁으로 해물 스파게티를 먹을까요?
W: 좋아요. 집에 오는 길에 가게에 들를게요.
M: 그럴 필요 없어요. 필요한 건 이미 가지고 있거든요.
W: 오, 그렇군요. 그럼, 6시까지 돌아와서 요리하는 걸 도울게요.

※ 다음 우리말에 맞도록 대화를 영어로 쓰시오.

Listen & Speak 1 A-1

G: _____

B: _____

G: _____

B: _____

G: 신발이 왜 그래? 새것 아니었어?
B: 맞는데, 내 개가 씹어 버렸어. 항상 그렇게 해. 그 개가 걱정돼.
G: 아마 심심했었을 거야. 개와 더 자주 놀아 주는 게 어때?
B: 알겠어, 그럴게. 그 개가 내 신발 씹는 걸 그만두면 좋겠네.

Listen & Speak 1 A-2

B: _____

G: _____

B: _____

G: _____

B: 너 좀 긴장한 것 같아 보이는데.
G: 이번 토요일에 있는 수영 대회가 걱정돼.
B: 걱정 마. 너는 수영을 아주 잘 하잖아. 그냥 긴장을 풀고 즐겨!
G: 고마워. 기분이 훨씬 괜찮아졌어.

Listen & Speak 2 A-1

B: _____

W: _____

B: _____

W: _____

B: _____

B: 엄마, 우리 내일 아침 몇 시에 할머니 댁에 가나요?
W: 8시쯤에. 가기 전에 할머니를 위해 쿠키를 구울 거란다.
B: 그럼, 제가 일찍 일어나서 도와드릴까요?
W: 그럴 필요 없단다. 아빠가 도와주실 거야.
B: 알겠어요, 그럼. 안녕히 주무세요, 엄마!

Listen & Speak 2 A-2

W: _____

M: _____

W: _____

M: _____

W: 우리 내일 새로 생긴 멕시코 레스토랑에 가 볼까요?
M: 좋죠! 레스토랑에 전화해서 예약해 둘게요.
W: 전화할 필요 없어요. 온라인으로 할 수 있거든요.
M: 오, 그렇군요. 정말 편리하네요!

Communicate A

Yuri: _____

Jaden: _____

Yuri: _____

Jaden: _____

Yuri: _____

Jaden: _____

Yuri: _____

Jaden: _____

Yuri: _____

Jaden: _____

유리: 안녕, Jaden. 운동회가 다음 주 금요일이야. 너무 기다려져!

Jaden: 정말? 난 사실 걱정돼.

유리: 왜? 너 운동 잘하지 않아?

Jaden: 응, 그렇긴 하지만, 800미터 릴레이가 걱정돼.

유리: 무슨 뜻이니?

Jaden: 내가 마지막 주자거든. 나 때문에 우리 팀이 지면 어쩌지?

유리: 넌 네 스스로에게 너무 많은 압박을 주고 있는 것 같아.

Jaden: 그래? 내가 매일 연습해야 한다고 생각하지 않니?

유리: 아니, 그럴 필요 없어. 그냥 학교 경기일 뿐인걸. 이기고 지고에 관한 게 아냐.

Jaden: 네 말이 맞는 것 같다, 유리야. 너 같은 친구를 둬서 다행이야.

Progress Check 1

B: _____

G: _____

B: _____

G: _____

B: 너 좀 긴장한 것 같다.

G: 그게, 역사 수업 시간에 내가 할 발표가 걱정돼.

B: 걱정 마. 많이 준비했잖아. 잘할 거야.

G: 고마워. 기분이 훨씬 나아졌어.

Progress Check 2

M: _____

W: _____

M: _____

W: _____

M: 우리 저녁으로 해물 스파게티를 먹을까요?

W: 좋아요. 집에 오는 길에 가게에 들를게요.

M: 그럴 필요 없어요. 필요한 건 이미 가지고 있거든요.

W: 오, 그렇군요. 그럼, 6시까지 돌아와서 요리하는 걸 도울게요.

※ 다음 우리말과 일치하도록 빈칸에 알맞은 것을 골라 쓰시오.

1 _____ _____ Your _____
A. Answers   B. Questions   C. Psychology

2 Do you _____ you _____ a _____ problem?
A. unique   B. have   C. think

3 _____ are that _____ _____ people have the _____ problem.
A. same   B. chances   C. other   D. many

4 Psychology is the study of the _____ _____ and _____, so it can help you find a _____ to your problem.
A. behavior   B. solution   C. mind   D. human

5 How do I _____ _____ _____?
A. less   B. become   C. nervous

6 It was five minutes before Jisu's big _____ in _____ of the _____.
A. class   B. presentation   C. whole   D. front

7 _____, Jisu was _____ her notes in her chair.
A. carefully   B. feeling   C. studying   D. nervous

8 Then, her teacher _____ _____ and told her to _____ _____ like Wonder Woman.
A. over   B. came   C. tall   D. stand

9 After _____ _____ for a few minutes, Jisu did _____ feel nervous _____.
A. anymore   B. tall   C. not   D. standing

10 _____ _____, she was _____ that she would make a great _____.
A. fact   B. presentation   C. in   D. confident

11 _____ to Amy Cuddy, a famous psychologist, we can become more confident just by _____ for two minutes before _____ events.
A. stressful   B. standing   C. according   D. tall

12 Our _____ change our _____, and our minds can _____ our _____.
A. behavior   B. bodies   C. minds   D. change

13 Do you _____ _____ _____ _____?
A. confident   B. to   C. feel   D. want

14 Stand _____ your feet _____, and _____ your hands _____ your hips.
A. place   B. apart   C. with   D. on

15 You will _____ only feel _____ about yourself _____ also look _____ to other people.
A. but   B. not   C. confident   D. sure

16 Who can _____ me _____ _____?
A. feel   B. help   C. better

17 When he _____ high school next year, Taeho wants to _____ a _____ farmer.
A. from   B. professional   C. graduates   D. become

18 _____, he _____ anyone about it.
A. never   B. however   C. told   D. has

1 심리학이 당신의 물음에 답하다

2 여러분은 당신만의 유일무이한 고민을 가지고 있다고 생각하는가?

3 아마 많은 다른 사람들이 여러분과 똑같은 고민을 가지고 있을 것이다.

4 심리학은 인간의 마음과 행동에 관한 연구이며, 따라서 여러분이 문제에 대한 해결책을 찾는 데 도움을 줄 수 있다.

5 어떻게 하면 긴장을 덜 할 수 있나요?

6 지수가 반 전체 앞에서 발표를 하기 5분 전이었다.

7 지수는 긴장이 되어, 의자에 앉아 자신의 필기를 열심히 들여다보고 있었다.

8 그때 선생님이 다가와서는 원더우먼처럼 꼿꼿이 서 있어 보라고 말했다.

9 그렇게 몇 분을 우뚝 선 후에, 지수는 더 이상 긴장되지 않았다.

10 사실, 그녀는 발표를 멋있게 할 수 있을 것이라는 자신감이 생겼다.

11 유명한 심리학자인 Amy Cuddy에 의하면, 우리는 스트레스를 받는 상황 이전에 2분 정도 꼿꼿이 서 있는 것만으로도 자신감이 더 생길 수 있다고 한다.

12 우리의 몸은 마음을 바꾸고, 마음은 우리의 행동을 바꿀 수 있다.

13 자신감이 생기기를 원하는가?

14 양발을 벌리고, 허리께에 손을 올려 보아라.

15 자신에 대한 확신이 생길 뿐만 아니라 다른 사람이 보기에도 자신감에 차 보인다.

16 누가 내 기분을 낫게 해 줄 수 있나요?

17 내년에 고등학교를 졸업한 이후에 태호는 전문적인 농부가 되고 싶어 한다.

18 하지만, 누구에게도 그것에 대해 한 번도 말하지 않았다.

19 He is _____ _____ his parents or his friends _____ not _____.

A. understand   B. worried   C. will   D. that

20 _____ to _____ his mind, Taeho decided to take a day trip on a train _____ _____.

A. himself   B. wanting   C. by   D. clear

21 On the train, he told a _____ _____ _____ _____ him about his problem.

A. sitting   B. complete   C. beside   D. stranger

22 He had no idea _____ _____ _____ _____.

A. he   B. why   C. it   D. did

23 However, he _____ _____ _____ _____ when he got _____ the train.

A. off   B. much   C. felt   D. better

24 _____ _____, we often tell _____ about our problems just _____ Taeho.

A. enough   B. strangely   C. like   D. strangers

25 That is _____ we do not have to worry about _____ _____ or _____ them again.

A. being   B. because   C. seeing   D. judged

26 If you have a problem that you cannot _____ _____ your family or friends, _____ _____ to a stranger.

A. with   B. talking   C. share   D. try

27 You will _____ _____ _____.

A. much   B. feel   C. better

28 How do I _____ a _____ a friend?

A. rival   B. turn   C. into

29 Benjamin Franklin once had a _____ rival who did _____ like him _____ _____.

A. not   B. political   C. all   D. at

30 Franklin wanted to become _____ _____ him, so he _____ _____ with a plan.

A. came   B. friends   C. with   D. up

31 His _____ had a _____ _____.

A. rival   B. rare   C. book

32 Franklin asked his rival _____ _____ him the book _____ a _____ days.

A. few   B. lend   C. for   D. to

33 When Franklin _____ the book, he _____ him _____.

A. thanked   B. returned   C. deeply

34 _____ that day, his rival became not _____ a political _____ but _____ a good friend.

A. only   B. also   C. since   D. supporter

35 Franklin _____ said, "_____ who do you one _____ will want to do _____."

A. favor   B. famously   C. more   D. enemies

36 If you want to _____ a rival _____ a friend, don't do your _____ a _____.

A. into   B. rival   C. turn   D. favor

37 _____, ask your _____ to _____ you a _____.

A. rival   B. favor   C. instead   D. do

19 그는 부모님이나 친구들이 이해하지 못할까 걱정이 된다.

20 마음을 정리하기 위해서, 태호는 혼자 하루 기차 여행을 떠나기로 결심했다.

21 기차에서, 그는 옆에 앉은 전혀 모르는 사람에게 자신의 고민에 대해서 말했다.

22 그는 자신이 왜 그랬는지 알 수 없었다.

23 그러나, 기차에서 내릴 때 기분이 훨씬 좋아졌다.

24 정말 이상하게도, 우리는 태호처럼 우리의 문제에 대해 낯선 사람에게 말할 때가 있다.

25 그것은 우리가 평가받거나 그 사람을 다시 볼 것이라는 걱정을 할 필요가 없기 때문이다.

26 만약 가족이나 친구들과도 나눌 수 없는 고민이 있다면, 낯선 이에게 말해 보아라.

27 기분이 훨씬 나아질 것이다.

28 라이벌을 어떻게 친구로 만들 수 있을까요?

29 Benjamin Franklin에게는 한때 그를 전혀 좋아하지 않는 정치적 경쟁자가 있었다.

30 Franklin은 그와 친구가 되고 싶어서, 계획을 세웠다.

31 그의 경쟁자는 희귀한 책을 가지고 있었다.

32 Franklin은 그의 정적에게 그 책을 며칠 동안 빌려달라고 부탁했다.

33 Franklin이 그 책을 돌려줄 때, 그는 그에게 진심으로 감사를 표했다.

34 그날 이후로, 그의 경쟁자는 정치적인 후원자뿐만 아니라 좋은 친구가 되었다.

35 Franklin은 "당신을 한 번 도운 적은 더 돕고 싶어 하게 된다."라는 유명한 말을 했다.

36 여러분이 경쟁자를 친구로 만들고 싶다면, 경쟁자의 부탁을 들어주지 마라.

37 대신, 경쟁자에게 부탁을 해 보아라.

※ 다음 우리말과 일치하도록 빈칸에 알맞은 것을 골라 쓰시오.

1 _____ _____ Your _____

2 Do you think you have a _____ _____?

3 _____ _____ that many other people have the same problem.

4 Psychology is the study of the _____ _____ and _____, _____ it can _____ you _____ a solution _____ your problem.

5 How do I _____ _____ _____?

6 It was five minutes before Jisu's _____ in _____ of the _____ _____.

7 _____ _____, Jisu was _____ _____ her notes in her chair.

8 Then, her teacher _____ _____ and told her _____ _____ _____ _____ Wonder Woman.

9 After _____ _____ for _____ _____ minutes, Jisu did _____ feel nervous _____.

10 _____ _____, she was _____ _____ she would _____ a great _____.

11 _____ _____ Amy Cuddy, a famous psychologist, we can _____ more confident just _____ _____ _____ _____ two minutes before _____ _____.

12 Our _____ change our _____, and our _____ can change our _____.

13 Do you want to _____ _____?

14 Stand with your _____ _____, and _____ your hands _____ your hips.

15 You will _____ _____ _____ _____ about yourself _____ _____ to _____ _____.

16 Who can help me _____ _____?

17 When he _____ _____ high school _____ _____, Taeho wants to become a _____ farmer.

18 _____, he _____ _____ _____ anyone about it.

---

1 심리학이 당신의 물음에 답하다

2 여러분은 당신만의 유일무이한 고민을 가지고 있다고 생각하는가?

3 아마 많은 다른 사람들이 여러분과 똑같은 고민을 가지고 있을 것이다.

4 심리학은 인간의 마음과 행동에 관한 연구이며, 따라서 여러분이 문제에 대한 해결책을 찾는 데 도움을 줄 수 있다.

5 어떻게 하면 긴장을 덜 할 수 있나요?

6 지수가 반 전체 앞에서 발표를 하기 5분 전이었다.

7 지수는 긴장이 되어, 의자에 앉아 자신의 필기를 열심히 들여다보고 있었다.

8 그때 선생님이 다가와서는 원더 우먼처럼 꼿꼿이 서 있어 보라고 말했다.

9 그렇게 몇 분을 우뚝 선 후에, 지수는 더 이상 긴장되지 않았다.

10 사실, 그녀는 발표를 멋있게 할 수 있을 것이라는 자신감이 생겼다.

11 유명한 심리학자인 Amy Cuddy에 의하면, 우리는 스트레스를 받는 상황 이전에 2분 정도 꼿꼿이 서 있는 것만으로도 자신감이 더 생길 수 있다고 한다.

12 우리의 몸은 마음을 바꾸고, 마음은 우리의 행동을 바꿀 수 있다.

13 자신감이 생기기를 원하는가?

14 양발을 벌리고, 허리께에 손을 올려 보아라.

15 자신에 대한 확신이 생길 뿐만 아니라 다른 사람이 보기에도 자신감에 차 보인다.

16 누가 내 기분을 낮게 해 줄 수 있나요?

17 내년에 고등학교를 졸업한 이후에 태호는 전문적인 농부가 되고 싶어 한다.

18 하지만, 누구에게도 그것에 대해 한 번도 말하지 않았다.

19 He is _____ _____ his parents or his friends _____ _____ _____.

20 _____ to _____ _____ _____ _____, Taeho _____ _____ _____ a day trip on a train _____ _____.

21 On the train, he told a _____ stranger _____ _____ him about his problem.

22 He had no idea _____ _____ _____ _____ _____.

23 _____, he _____ _____ _____ when he _____ _____ the train.

24 _____ _____, we _____ _____ _____ about our problems just like Taeho.

25 That is _____ we do _____ _____ _____ worry about _____ _____ or _____ them again.

26 If you have a problem _____ you cannot _____ _____ your family or friends, try _____ to a _____.

27 You will _____ _____ _____.

28 How do I _____ a _____ _____ a friend?

29 Benjamin Franklin once had a _____ _____ _____ did _____ like him _____ _____.

30 Franklin wanted to _____ _____ _____ him, so he _____ _____ _____ a plan.

31 His rival had a _____ book.

32 Franklin asked his rival _____ _____ him the book for _____ _____ _____.

33 When Franklin returned the book, he thanked him _____.

34 _____ that day, his rival became _____ _____ a political supporter _____ _____ a good friend.

35 Franklin _____ said, "Enemies _____ _____ _____ _____ _____ will want to do more."

36 If you want to _____ a rival _____ a friend, don't _____ _____ _____ _____ _____.

37 _____, ask your rival _____ _____ you a _____.

---

19 그는 부모님이나 친구들이 이해하지 못할까 걱정이 된다.

20 마음을 정리하기 위해서, 태호는 혼자 하루 기차 여행을 떠나기로 결심했다.

21 기차에서, 그는 옆에 앉은 전혀 모르는 사람에게 자신의 고민에 대해서 말했다.

22 그는 자신이 왜 그랬는지 알 수 없었다.

23 그러나, 기차에서 내릴 때 기분이 훨씬 좋아졌다.

24 정말 이상하게도, 우리는 태호처럼 우리의 문제에 대해 낯선 사람에게 말할 때가 있다.

25 그것은 우리가 평가받거나 그 사람을 다시 볼 것이라는 걱정을 할 필요가 없기 때문이다.

26 만약 가족이나 친구들과도 나눌 수 없는 고민이 있다면, 낯선 이에게 말해 보아라.

27 기분이 훨씬 나아질 것이다.

28 라이벌을 어떻게 친구로 만들 수 있을까요?

29 Benjamin Franklin에게는 한때 그를 전혀 좋아하지 않는 정치적 경쟁자가 있었다.

30 Franklin은 그와 친구가 되고 싶어서, 계획을 세웠다.

31 그의 경쟁자는 희귀한 책을 가지고 있었다.

32 Franklin은 그의 정적에게 그 책을 며칠 동안 빌려달라고 부탁했다.

33 Franklin이 그 책을 돌려줄 때, 그는 그에게 진심으로 감사를 표했다.

34 그날 이후로, 그의 경쟁자는 정치적인 후원자뿐만 아니라 좋은 친구가 되었다.

35 Franklin은 "당신을 한 번 도운 적은 더 돕고 싶어 하게 된다."라는 유명한 말을 했다.

36 여러분이 경쟁자를 친구로 만들고 싶다면, 경쟁자의 부탁을 들어주지 마라.

37 대신, 경쟁자에게 부탁을 해 보아라.

※ 다음 문장을 우리말로 쓰시오.

1 Psychology Answers Your Questions
➡ _____

2 Do you think you have a unique problem?
➡ _____

3 Chances are that many other people have the same problem.
➡ _____

4 Psychology is the study of the human mind and behavior, so it can help you find a solution to your problem.
➡ _____

5 How do I become less nervous?
➡ _____

6 It was five minutes before Jisu's big presentation in front of the whole class.
➡ _____

7 Feeling nervous, Jisu was carefully studying her notes in her chair.
➡ _____

8 Then, her teacher came over and told her to stand tall like Wonder Woman.
➡ _____

9 After standing tall for a few minutes, Jisu did not feel nervous anymore.
➡ _____

10 In fact, she was confident that she would make a great presentation.
➡ _____

11 According to Amy Cuddy, a famous psychologist, we can become more confident just by standing tall for two minutes before stressful events.
➡ _____

12 Our bodies change our minds, and our minds can change our behavior.
➡ _____

13 Do you want to feel confident?
➡ _____

14 Stand with your feet apart, and place your hands on your hips.
➡ _____

15 You will not only feel sure about yourself but also look confident to other people.
➡ _____

16 Who can help me feel better?
➡ _____

17 When he graduates from high school next year, Taeho wants to become a professional farmer.
➡ _____

18 However, he has never told anyone about it.

➡ _____

19 He is worried that his parents or his friends will not understand.

➡ _____

20 Wanting to clear his mind, Taeho decided to take a day trip on a train by himself.

➡ _____

21 On the train, he told a complete stranger sitting beside him about his problem.

➡ _____

22 He had no idea why he did it.

➡ _____

23 However, he felt much better when he got off the train.

➡ _____

24 Strangely enough, we often tell strangers about our problems just like Taeho.

➡ _____

25 That is because we do not have to worry about being judged or seeing them again.

➡ _____

26 If you have a problem that you cannot share with your family or friends, try talking to a stranger.

➡ _____

27 You will feel much better.

➡ _____

28 How do I turn a rival into a friend?

➡ _____

29 Benjamin Franklin once had a political rival who did not like him at all.

➡ _____

30 Franklin wanted to become friends with him, so he came up with a plan.

➡ _____

31 His rival had a rare book.

➡ _____

32 Franklin asked his rival to lend him the book for a few days.

➡ _____

33 When Franklin returned the book, he thanked him deeply.

➡ _____

34 Since that day, his rival became not only a political supporter but also a good friend.

➡ _____

35 Franklin famously said, "Enemies who do you one favor will want to do more."

➡ _____

36 If you want to turn a rival into a friend, don't do your rival a favor.

➡ _____

37 Instead, ask your rival to do you a favor.

➡ _____

Step4

※ 다음 괄호 안의 단어들을 우리말에 맞도록 바르게 배열하시오.

1 (Answers / Psychology / Questions / Your)
➡ _____

2 (you / do / you / think / a / have / problem? / unique)
➡ _____

3 (are / chances / many / that / people / other / the / have / problem. / same)
➡ _____

4 (is / psychology / the / of / study / the / mind / human / and / so / behavior, / it / help / can / you / a / find / to / solution / problem. / your)
➡ _____

5 (do / how / become / I / nervous? / less)
➡ _____

6 (was / it / minutes / five / Jisu's / before / presentation / big / front / in / the / of / class. / whole)
➡ _____

7 (nervous, / feeling / was / Jisu / carefully / her / studying / notes / her / in / chair.)
➡ _____

8 (her / then, / teacher / over / came / and / her / told / to / tall / stand / Wonder / like / Woman.)
➡ _____

9 (standing / after / for / tall / few / a / minutes, / did / Jisu / feel / not / anymore. / nervous)
➡ _____

10 (fact, / in / was / she / that / confident / would / she / a / make / presentation. / great)
➡ _____

11 (to / according / Cuddy, / Amy / a / psychologist, / famous / can / we / more / become / just / confident / by / tall / standing / two / for / before / minutes / events. / stressful)
➡ _____

12 (bodies / our / change / minds, / our / and / minds / our / change / can / behavior. / our)
➡ _____

13 (you / do / to / want / confident? / feel)
➡ _____

14 (with / stand / feet / your / apart, / place / and / hands / your / on / hips. / your)
➡ _____

15 (will / you / only / not / sure / feel / yourself / about / also / but / confident / look / other / to / people.)
➡ _____

16 (can / who / me / help / better? / feel)
➡ _____

17 (he / when / graduates / high / from / school / year, / next / wants / Taeho / to / a / become / farmer. / professional)
➡ _____

18 (he / however, / never / has / anyone / told / it. / about)
➡ _____

1 심리학이 당신의 물음에 답하다

2 여러분은 당신만의 유일무이한 고민을 가지고 있다고 생각하는가?

3 아마 많은 다른 사람들이 여러분과 똑같은 고민을 가지고 있을 것이다.

4 심리학은 인간의 마음과 행동에 관한 연구이며, 따라서 여러분이 문제에 대한 해결책을 찾는 데 도움을 줄 수 있다.

5 어떻게 하면 긴장을 덜 할 수 있나요?

6 지수가 반 전체 앞에서 발표를 하기 5분 전이었다.

7 지수는 긴장이 되어, 의자에 앉아 자신의 필기를 열심히 들여다보고 있었다.

8 그때 선생님이 다가와서는 원더 우먼처럼 꼿꼿이 서 있어 보라고 말했다.

9 그렇게 몇 분을 우뚝 선 후에, 지수는 더 이상 긴장되지 않았다.

10 사실, 그녀는 발표를 멋지게 할 수 있을 것이라는 자신감이 생겼다.

11 유명한 심리학자인 Amy Cuddy에 의하면, 우리는 스트레스를 받는 상황 이전에 2분 정도 꼿꼿이 서 있는 것만으로도 자신감이 더 생길 수 있다고 한다.

12 우리의 몸은 마음을 바꾸고, 마음은 우리의 행동을 바꿀 수 있다.

13 자신감이 생기기를 원하는가?

14 양발을 벌리고, 허리께에 손을 올려 보아라.

15 자신에 대한 확신이 생길 뿐만 아니라 다른 사람이 보기에도 자신감에 차 보인다.

16 누가 내 기분을 낫게 해 줄 수 있나요?

17 내년에 고등학교를 졸업한 이후에 태호는 전문적인 농부가 되고 싶어 한다.

18 하지만, 누구에게도 그것에 대해 한 번도 말하지 않았다.

19 (is / he / that / worried / parents / his / or / friends / his / not / will / understand.)
➡ _____

20 (to / wanting / his / clear / mind, / decided / Taeho / take / to / day / a / trip / a / on / train / himself. / by)
➡ _____

21 (the / on / train, / told / he / complete / a / stranger / beside / sitting / about / him / problem. / his)
➡ _____

22 (had / he / idea / no / he / why / it. / did)
➡ _____

23 (he / however, / felt / better / much / he / when / off / got / train. / the)
➡ _____

24 (enough, / strangely / often / we / strangers / tell / our / about / problems / like / Taeho. / just)
➡ _____

25 (is / that / we / because / not / do / to / have / worry / being / about / or / judged / them / seeing / again.)
➡ _____

26 (you / if / a / have / problem / you / that / share / cannot / with / family / your / friends, / or / talking / try / a / to / stranger.)
➡ _____

27 (will / you / much / feel / better.)
➡ _____

28 (do / how / turn / I / into / rival / friend? / a)
➡ _____

29 (Franklin / Benjamin / had / once / a / rival / political / did / who / like / not / at / him / all.)
➡ _____

30 (wanted / Franklin / become / to / with / friends / him, / he / so / up / came / a / with / plan.)
➡ _____

31 (rival / his / a / had / book. / rare)
➡ _____

32 (asked / Franklin / rival / his / lend / to / the / him / for / book / few / a / days.)
➡ _____

33 (Franklin / when / the / returned / book, / thanked / he / deeply. / him)
➡ _____

34 (that / since / day, / rival / his / not / became / only / political / a / but / supporter / a / also / friend. / good)
➡ _____

35 (Franklin / said, / famously / who / "enemies / you / do / favor / one / want / will / do / to / more.")
➡ _____

36 (you / if / to / want / turn / rival / a / into / friend, / a / do / don't / rival / your / favor. / a)
➡ _____

37 (ask / instead, / rival / your / do / to / you / favor. / a)
➡ _____

19 그는 부모님이나 친구들이 이해하지 못할까 걱정이 된다.

20 마음을 정리하기 위해서, 태호는 혼자 하루 기차 여행을 떠나기로 결심했다.

21 기차에서, 그는 옆에 앉은 전혀 모르는 사람에게 자신의 고민에 대해서 말했다.

22 그는 자신이 왜 그랬는지 알 수 없었다.

23 그러나, 기차에서 내릴 때 기분이 훨씬 좋아졌다.

24 정말 이상하게도, 우리는 태호처럼 우리의 문제에 대해 낯선 사람에게 말할 때가 있다.

25 그것은 우리가 평가받거나 그 사람을 다시 볼 것이라는 걱정을 할 필요가 없기 때문이다.

26 만약 가족이나 친구들과도 나눌 수 없는 고민이 있다면, 낯선 이에게 말해 보아라.

27 기분이 훨씬 나아질 것이다.

28 라이벌을 어떻게 친구로 만들 수 있을까요?

29 Benjamin Franklin에게는 한때 그를 전혀 좋아하지 않는 정치적 경쟁자가 있었다.

30 Franklin은 그와 친구가 되고 싶어서, 계획을 세웠다.

31 그의 경쟁자는 희귀한 책을 가지고 있었다.

32 Franklin은 그의 정적에게 그 책을 며칠 동안 빌려달라고 부탁했다.

33 Franklin이 그 책을 돌려줄 때, 그는 그에게 진심으로 감사를 표했다.

34 그날 이후로, 그의 경쟁자는 정치적인 후원자뿐만 아니라 좋은 친구가 되었다.

35 Franklin은 "당신을 한 번 도운 적은 더 돕고 싶어 하게 된다." 라는 유명한 말을 했다.

36 여러분이 경쟁자를 친구로 만들고 싶다면, 경쟁자의 부탁을 들어주지 마라.

37 대신, 경쟁자에게 부탁을 해 보아라.

※ 다음 우리말을 영어로 쓰시오.

1 심리학이 당신의 물음에 답하다

➡ _____

2 여러분은 당신만의 유일무이한 고민을 가지고 있다고 생각하는가?

➡ _____

3 아마 많은 다른 사람들이 여러분과 똑같은 고민을 가지고 있을 것이다.

➡ _____

4 심리학은 인간의 마음과 행동에 관한 연구이며, 따라서 여러분이 문제에 대한 해결책을 찾는 데 도움을 줄 수 있다.

➡ _____

_____

5 어떻게 하면 긴장을 덜 할 수 있나요?

➡ _____

6 지수가 반 전체 앞에서 발표를 하기 5분 전이었다.

➡ _____

7 지수는 긴장이 되어, 의자에 앉아 자신의 필기를 열심히 들여다보고 있었다.

➡ _____

8 그때 선생님이 다가와서는 원더우먼처럼 꼿꼿이 서 있어 보라고 말했다.

➡ _____

9 그렇게 몇 분을 우뚝 선 후에, 지수는 더 이상 긴장되지 않았다.

➡ _____

10 사실, 그녀는 발표를 멋있게 할 수 있을 것이라는 자신감이 생겼다.

➡ _____

11 유명한 심리학자인 Amy Cuddy에 의하면, 우리는 스트레스를 받는 상황 이전에 2분 정도 꼿꼿이 서 있는 것만으로도 자신감이 더 생길 수 있다고 한다.

➡ _____

_____

12 우리의 몸은 마음을 바꾸고, 마음은 우리의 행동을 바꿀 수 있다.

➡ _____

13 자신감이 생기기를 원하는가?

➡ _____

14 양발을 벌리고, 허리께에 손을 올려 보아라.

➡ _____

15 자신에 대한 확신이 생길 뿐만 아니라 다른 사람이 보기에도 자신감에 차 보인다.

➡ _____

16 누가 내 기분을 낫게 해 줄 수 있나요?

➡ _____

17 내년에 고등학교를 졸업한 이후에 태호는 전문적인 농부가 되고 싶어 한다.

➡ _____

18 하지만, 누구에게도 그것에 대해 한 번도 말하지 않았다.
➡ _____

19 그는 부모님이나 친구들이 이해하지 못할까 걱정이 된다.
➡ _____

20 마음을 정리하기 위해서, 태호는 혼자 하루 기차 여행을 떠나기로 결심했다.
➡ _____

21 기차에서, 그는 옆에 앉은 전혀 모르는 사람에게 자신의 고민에 대해서 말했다.
➡ _____

22 그는 자신이 왜 그랬는지 알 수 없었다.
➡ _____

23 그러나, 기차에서 내릴 때 기분이 훨씬 좋아졌다.
➡ _____

24 정말 이상하게도, 우리는 태호처럼 우리의 문제에 대해 낯선 사람에게 말할 때가 있다.
➡ _____

25 그것은 우리가 평가받거나 그 사람을 다시 볼 것이라는 걱정을 할 필요가 없기 때문이다.
➡ _____

26 만약 가족이나 친구들과도 나눌 수 없는 고민이 있다면, 낯선 이에게 말해 보아라.
➡ _____

27 기분이 훨씬 나아질 것이다.
➡ _____

28 라이벌을 어떻게 친구로 만들 수 있을까요?
➡ _____

29 Benjamin Franklin에게는 한때 그를 전혀 좋아하지 않는 정치적 경쟁자가 있었다.
➡ _____

30 Franklin은 그와 친구가 되고 싶어서, 계획을 세웠다.
➡ _____

31 그의 경쟁자는 희귀한 책을 가지고 있었다.
➡ _____

32 Franklin은 그의 정적에게 그 책을 며칠 동안 빌려달라고 부탁했다.
➡ _____

33 Franklin이 그 책을 돌려줄 때, 그는 그에게 진심으로 감사를 표했다.
➡ _____

34 그날 이후로, 그의 경쟁자는 정치적인 후원자뿐만 아니라 좋은 친구가 되었다.
➡ _____

35 Franklin은 "당신을 한 번 도운 적은 더 돕고 싶어 하게 된다."라는 유명한 말을 했다.
➡ _____

36 여러분이 경쟁자를 친구로 만들고 싶다면, 경쟁자의 부탁을 들어주지 마라.
➡ _____

37 대신, 경쟁자에게 부탁을 해 보아라.
➡ _____

※ 다음 우리말과 일치하도록 빈칸에 알맞은 말을 쓰시오.

Listen & Speak 2 - Think and Talk

1. A: What _____ I _____ _____ _____ on Stress-Free Day?

2. B: You _____ _____ _____ _____ the classroom.

3. C: You _____ _____ _____ _____ _____ _____ 8:30.

1. A: 스트레스가 없는 날에 무엇을 할 필요가 없을까?
2. B: 너는 교실 청소를 할 필요가 없어.
3. C: 너는 8:30분까지 학교에 올 필요가 없어.

Link

1. _____ _____ do you _____ _____ _____ ?

2. _____ _____ _____ the answer to this question, we _____ _____ _____ about confidence.

3. Thirty students _____ _____ _____ . The _____ was nine.

4. Eighteen students _____ _____ _____ _____ _____ .

5. _____ , sixty percent of the students _____ _____ _____ _____ _____ .

1. 당신은 스스로에 대해 얼마나 확신이 있나요?
2. 질문에 대한 답을 찾고 싶어, 우리는 자신감에 대한 검사지를 만들었습니다.
3. 30명의 학생들이 검사를 했습니다. 평균적인 점수는 9점이었습니다.
4. 18명의 학생들이 평균 점수를 넘었습니다.
5. 따라서, 학생들의 60%가 그들 스스로에 대해 꽤 자신감을 갖고 있습니다.

Write

1. _____ _____ _____ in my life

2. The _____ _____ _____ _____ _____ _____ was when my grandmother _____ _____ five years _____ .

3. When I was _____ , she _____ _____ _____ me _____ _____ the time.

4. _____ _____ _____ _____ _____ , I _____ _____ and _____ .

5. _____ _____ , I _____ my grandmother's diary.

6. She _____ _____ _____ _____ _____ about her memories _____ _____ _____ that I would lead a happy life.

7. _____ _____ _____ , I _____ _____ that I should _____ _____ _____ just _____ _____ _____ .

1. 내 삶에서 가장 힘들었던 순간
2. 내 삶에서 가장 힘들었던 순간은 5년 전 할머니께서 돌아가셨을 때였다.
3. 내가 더 어렸을 때, 그녀는 대부분의 시간 동안 나를 돌봐 주셨다.
4. 그녀가 곁에 없어서, 나는 슬프고 외로웠다.
5. 어느 날, 나는 할머니의 일기장을 발견했다.
6. 그녀는 그녀의 기억에 대해 많이 적었을 뿐만 아니라, 내가 행복한 삶을 살기를 바랐다.
7. 이 경험을 통해, 나는 그녀가 원했던 것처럼 행복해지려고 노력해야 한다는 것을 배웠다.

※ 다음 우리말을 영어로 쓰시오.

Listen & Speak 2 - Think and Talk

1. A: 스트레스가 없는 날에 무엇을 할 필요가 없을까?

  ➡ _____

2. B: 너는 교실 청소를 할 필요가 없어.

  ➡ _____

3. C: 너는 8:30분까지 학교에 올 필요가 없어.

  ➡ _____

Link

1. 당신은 스스로에 대해 얼마나 확신이 있나요?

  ➡ _____

2. 질문에 대한 답을 찾고 싶어, 우리는 자신감에 대한 검사지를 만들었습니다.

  ➡ _____

3. 30명의 학생들이 검사를 했습니다. 평균적인 점수는 9점이었습니다.

  ➡ _____

4. 18명의 학생들이 평균 점수를 넘었습니다.

  ➡ _____

5. 따라서, 학생들의 60%가 그들 스스로에 대해 꽤 자신감을 갖고 있습니다.

  ➡ _____

Write

1. 내 삶에서 가장 힘들었던 순간

  ➡ _____

2. 내 삶에서 가장 힘들었던 순간은 5년 전 할머니께서 돌아가셨을 때였다.

  ➡ _____

3. 내가 더 어렸을 때, 그녀는 대부분의 시간 동안 나를 돌봐 주셨다.

  ➡ _____

4. 그녀가 곁에 없어서, 나는 슬프고 외로웠다.

  ➡ _____

5. 어느 날, 나는 할머니의 일기장을 발견했다.

  ➡ _____

6. 그녀는 그녀의 기억에 대해 많이 적었을 뿐만 아니라, 내가 행복한 삶을 살기를 바랐다.

  ➡ _____

7. 이 경험을 통해, 나는 그녀가 원했던 것처럼 행복해지려고 노력해야 한다는 것을 배웠다.

  ➡ _____

※ 다음 영어를 우리말로 쓰시오.

01 uniquely

02 check

03 crush

04 unfortunately

05 surely

06 appreciate

07 fantastic

08 fix

09 grand

10 happen

11 completely

12 inconvenience

13 pursue

14 customer

15 inventor

16 reason

17 creative

18 role

19 real

20 rare

21 satisfied

22 honestly

23 complain

24 passion

25 finish

26 pay

27 innovative

28 throughout

29 provide

30 form

31 slice

32 fresh

33 gladly

34 successful

35 fill out

36 scare away

37 now that

38 as a result

39 of all time

40 put up

41 be used to

42 do one's best

43 take charge of

※ 다음 우리말을 영어로 쓰시오.

01 열정, 흥미 _____

02 진가를 알아보다, 고마워하다 _____

03 계산서 _____

04 ~ 동안 내내 _____

05 덜 익은, 살짝 익힌 _____

06 지불하다, 지급하다 _____

07 수리하다 _____

08 서류 _____

09 확실히, 분명히 _____

10 불편, 애로 _____

11 완전하게 _____

12 기꺼이 _____

13 추구하다, 추진하다 _____

14 이유 _____

15 역할, 배역 _____

16 일어나다 _____

17 불평하다 _____

18 장식하다, 꾸미다 _____

19 환상적인 _____

20 식사 _____

21 신선한 _____

22 솔직하게, 솔직히 _____

23 창의적인, 창조적인 _____

24 으깨다 _____

25 획기적인 _____

26 한 조각, 일부 _____

27 성공적인 _____

28 불행하게도 _____

29 웅장한, 위대한 _____

30 고객, 소비자 _____

31 독특하게 _____

32 만찬, 저녁 식사 _____

33 제공하다 _____

34 만족한 _____

35 ~에 익숙하다 _____

36 작성하다 _____

37 더 이상 아니다 _____

38 결과적으로 _____

39 역대, 지금껏 _____

40 최선을 다하다 _____

41 ~할 마음이 나다 _____

42 내붙이다, 게시하다 _____

43 겁주어 쫓아내다 _____

※ 다음 영영풀이에 알맞은 단어를 <보기>에서 골라 쓴 후, 우리말 뜻을 쓰시오.

1 _____ : the character played by an actor: _____

2 _____ : cooked a short time; still red inside: _____

3 _____ : the foods eaten or prepared for eating at one time: _____

4 _____ : to supply something that is wanted or needed: _____

5 _____ : an informal meal that people eat in the evening: _____

6 _____ : during the whole period of time of something: _____

7 _____ : a bill for the food and drinks that are served in a restaurant: _____

8 _____ : to like something because one recognizes its good qualities: _____

9 _____ : to press something so hard that it breaks or is damaged: _____

10 _____ : someone who buys goods or services from a shop, company, etc.: _____

11 _____ : to make something look more nice by putting something pretty on it:

_____

12 _____ : to repair something that is broken or not working properly: _____

13 _____ : an official document with spaces where you write information:

_____

14 _____ : a person who has invented something or whose job is inventing things:

_____

15 _____ : to say that you are annoyed, not satisfied, or unhappy about something or

someone: _____

16 _____ : to make efforts to achieve a particular aim or result, often over a long

period of time: _____

보기			
complain	inventor	meal	throughout
crush	decorate	check	rare
pursue	form	provide	role
fix	customer	supper	appreciate

※ 다음 우리말과 일치하도록 빈칸에 알맞은 말을 쓰시오.

Listen & Speak 1 A-1

B: Wow! Did you _____ this?

G: I _____. Do you like _____?

B: Yes, the bread and the milk _____ _____ _____ . I _____ _____ _____ _____ _____ _____ the bread.

G: Thanks, but _____ _____ _____ _____ it. It's not _____.

B: I don't think _____. I think it's a _____ _____.

B: 우와! 이거 네가 그린 거야?
G: 내가 그렸어. 마음에 들어?
B: 응, 빵이랑 우유가 정말 진짜 같아. 빵을 한 입 먹고 싶어지는데.
G: 고마워, 하지만 이건 만족스럽진 않아. 독창적이지 않아.
B: 난 그렇게 생각 안 해. 정말 멋진 그림인 것 같아.

Listen & Speak 1 A-2

M: Hello, ma'am. _____ _____ I _____ you?

W: I _____ this phone _____ _____ _____ _____, but it _____ _____ _____ _____ _____.

M: Oh, I see. May I _____ _____ _____ _____ it? (Pause) We're sorry for the _____. It'll _____ a _____ _____ _____ _____ it.

W: _____ _____ _____ _____ _____ the phone. I'd _____ a new _____.

M: Of _____. I just need to _____ _____ this _____.

M: 안녕하세요, 고객님. 무엇을 도와드릴까요?
W: 이 휴대전화를 겨우 일주일 전에 샀는데, 가끔 저절로 꺼져요.
M: 오, 그렇군요. 제가 좀 봐도 될까요? 불편을 드려 죄송합니다. 고치는 데 몇 시간 정도 걸릴 거예요.
W: 그 휴대전화가 만족스럽지 않아요. 새것을 원해요.
M: 물론이죠. 이 서류만 작성하면 됩니다.

Listen & Speak 2 A-1

G: Wow, I like this blueberry jam. Where _____ you _____ it?

B: I made it _____.

G: Really? This is _____ _____ _____ _____ _____ I've ever had. You _____ _____ _____.

B: Do you think people _____ want _____ _____ this?

G: Of course. _____ _____ _____ _____ your first customer.

G: 우와, 이 블루베리 잼 마음에 든다. 어디서 샀어?
B: 직접 만든 거야.
G: 정말? 내가 지금껏 먹어본 잼 중에 제일 좋아. 팔아도 되겠어.
B: 사람들이 이걸 사길 원할 거라고 생각해?
G: 물론이지. 내가 너의 첫 손님이 되겠다고 약속할게.

Listen & Speak 2 A-2

B: Mom, I want to go to an arts high school. I want to become an actor.

W: What? I _____ you _____ _____ _____ science.

B: I was but _____ _____ . I _____ _____ _____ _____ a movie star.

W: _____ you _____ you want to be an actor?

B: Yes, I'll learn _____ _____ _____ . _____ _____ _____ _____ _____ _____.

B: 엄마, 저 예술 고등학교에 가고 싶어요. 배우가 되고 싶어요.
W: 뭐라고? 네가 과학에 관심이 있다고 생각했는데.
B: 그랬었는데 더는 아니에요. 저는 영화배우가 되고 싶어요.
W: 배우가 되고 싶은 게 확실하니?
B: 네, 연기하는 방법을 배울 거예요. 최선을 다하겠다고 약속할게요.

Communicate A

Man: Are you enjoying _____ _____?

Woman: Well, the bread was _____, and the salad was _____.

Man: How _____ your steak?

Woman: Honestly, _____ _____ _____ _____ the steak. It's too _____ for me.

Man: I'm sorry. _____ you _____ me _____ _____ you _____ _____?

Woman: That's O.K. I need to _____ _____. Let me just _____ the _____, please.

Man: I'm really sorry. You _____ _____ _____ the steak.

Woman: O.K. Thanks.

Man: _____ _____ _____ _____ you _____ a better _____ next time you visit.

남자: 식사가 마음에 드십니까?
여자: 음, 빵은 괜찮았고, 샐러드도 신선했어요.
남자: 스테이크는 어떠세요?
여자: 솔직히, 스테이크는 만족스럽지 않아요. 제겐 너무 덜 익었어요.
남자: 죄송합니다. 다른 것으로 가져다 드릴까요?
여자: 괜찮아요. 가봐야 해서요. 그냥 계산서 좀 갖다주세요.
남자: 정말 죄송합니다. 스테이크 값은 지불하지 않으셔도 됩니다.
여자: 알겠습니다. 감사해요.
남자: 다음에 방문하실 때는 더 좋은 경험을 드릴 것을 약속드릴게요.

Progress Check 1

M: Hello, ma'am. _____ _____ _____ help you?

W: I _____ this hat _____ a gift yesterday, but _____ _____ _____ _____ the color.

M: Oh, I see. We have this hat _____ _____ _____.

W: Do you have _____ _____ _____?

M: Yes, we _____. I'll _____ _____ for you.

W: Thanks.

M: 안녕하세요, 고객님. 무엇을 도와드릴까요?
W: 어제 이 모자를 선물 받았는데, 색상이 마음에 들지 않아요.
M: 오, 그렇군요. 이 모자로 다른 색상도 있습니다.
W: 파란 것도 있나요?
M: 네, 있습니다. 하나 가져다 드릴게요.
W: 고맙습니다.

Progress Check 2

B: Mom, I want to _____ cooking _____.

W: What? I thought you were _____ _____ sports.

B: I was but _____ _____. I want to become a _____.

W: Are you sure? Cooking is _____ _____.

B: Don't _____. _____ _____ _____ _____ _____ my best.

W: O.K., _____.

B: 엄마, 저 요리 수업을 듣고 싶어요.
W: 뭐? 네가 스포츠에 관심이 있다고 생각했는데.
B: 그랬는데 더는 아니에요. 저는 요리사가 되고 싶어요.
W: 정말이니? 요리는 힘든 일이란다.
B: 걱정하지 마세요. 최선을 다하겠다고 약속할게요.
W: 그래, 그럼.

Progress Check 3

G: Dad, I want to watch a movie _____ TV now.

M: _____ you _____ your homework?

G: No, but _____ _____ _____ _____ it after I watch TV.

G: 아빠, 저 지금 TV에서 영화를 보고 싶어요.
M: 숙제는 끝냈니?
G: 아니요, 하지만 TV를 보고 나서 끝낼 것을 약속드릴게요.

※ 다음 우리말에 맞도록 대화를 영어로 쓰시오.

Listen & Speak 1 A-1

B: _____

G: _____

B: _____

G: _____

B: _____

B: 우와! 이거 네가 그린 거야?
G: 내가 그렸어. 마음에 들어?
B: 응, 빵이랑 우유가 정말 진짜 같아. 빵을 한 입 먹고 싶어지는데.
G: 고마워. 하지만 이건 만족스럽진 않아. 독창적이지 않아.
B: 난 그렇게 생각 안 해. 정말 멋진 그림인 것 같아.

Listen & Speak 1 A-2

M: _____

W: _____

M: _____

W: _____

M: _____

M: 안녕하세요, 고객님. 무엇을 도와드릴까요?
W: 이 휴대전화를 겨우 일주일 전에 샀는데, 가끔 저절로 꺼져요.
M: 오, 그렇군요. 제가 좀 봐도 될까요? 불편을 드려 죄송합니다. 고치는 데 몇 시간 정도 걸릴 거예요.
W: 그 휴대전화가 만족스럽지 않아요. 새것을 원해요.
M: 물론이죠. 이 서류만 작성하면 됩니다.

Listen & Speak 2 A-1

G: _____

B: _____

G: _____

B: _____

G: _____

G: 우와, 이 블루베리 잼 마음에 든다. 어디서 샀어?
B: 직접 만든 거야.
G: 정말? 내가 지금껏 먹어본 잼 중에 제일 좋아. 팔아도 되겠어.
B: 사람들이 이걸 사길 원할 거라고 생각해?
G: 물론이지. 내가 너의 첫 손님이 되겠다고 약속할게.

Listen & Speak 2 A-2

B: _____

W: _____

B: _____

W: _____

B: _____

B: 엄마, 저 예술 고등학교에 가고 싶어요. 배우가 되고 싶어요.
W: 뭐라고? 네가 과학에 관심이 있다고 생각했는데.
B: 그랬었는데 더는 아니에요. 저는 영화 배우가 되고 싶어요.
W: 배우가 되고 싶은 게 확실하니?
B: 네, 연기하는 방법을 배울 거예요. 최선을 다하겠다고 약속할게요.

Communicate A

Man: _____

Woman: _____

Man: _____

Woman: _____

Man: _____

Woman: _____

Man: _____

Woman: _____

Man: _____

남자: 식사가 마음에 드십니까?
여자: 음, 빵은 괜찮았고, 샐러드도 신선했어요.
남자: 스테이크는 어떠세요?
여자: 솔직히, 스테이크는 만족스럽지 않아요. 제겐 너무 덜 익었어요.
남자: 죄송합니다. 다른 것으로 가져다 드릴까요?
여자: 괜찮아요. 가봐야 해서요. 그냥 계산서 좀 갖다주세요.
남자: 정말 죄송합니다. 스테이크 값은 지불하지 않으셔도 됩니다.
여자: 알겠습니다. 감사해요.
남자: 다음에 방문하실 때는 더 좋은 경험을 드릴 것을 약속드릴게요.

Progress Check 1

M: _____

W: _____

M: _____

W: _____

M: _____

W: _____

M: 안녕하세요, 고객님. 무엇을 도와드릴까요?
W: 어제 이 모자를 선물 받았는데, 색상이 마음에 들지 않아요.
M: 오, 그렇군요. 이 모자로 다른 색상도 있습니다.
W: 파란 것도 있나요?
M: 네, 있습니다. 하나 가져다 드릴게요.
W: 고맙습니다.

Progress Check 2

B: _____

W: _____

B: _____

W: _____

B: _____

W: _____

B: 엄마, 저 요리 수업을 듣고 싶어요.
W: 뭐? 네가 스포츠에 관심이 있다고 생각했는데.
B: 그랬는데 더는 아니에요. 저는 요리사가 되고 싶어요.
W: 정말이니? 요리는 힘든 일이란다.
B: 걱정하지 마세요. 최선을 다하겠다고 약속할게요.
W: 그래, 그럼.

Progress Check 3

G: _____

M: _____

G: _____

G: 아빠, 저 지금 TV에서 영화를 보고 싶어요.
M: 숙제는 끝냈니?
G: 아니요, 하지만 TV를 보고 나서 끝낼 것을 약속드릴게요.

대화문 Test **47**

※ 다음 우리말과 일치하도록 빈칸에 알맞은 것을 골라 쓰시오.

1 Da _____ _____ _____
A. Cook   B. the   C. Vinci

2 Leonardo da Vinci is _____ _____ one of the _____ painters of all _____.
A. time   B. known   C. greatest   D. as

3 He was _____ a great _____, scientist, and _____.
A. inventor   B. musician   C. also

4 Very _____ people, _____, know _____ da Vinci was also a _____ cook.
A. creative   B. however   C. few   D. that

5 _____ 1473, twenty-year-old da Vinci _____ _____ a cook _____ a restaurant in Florence, Italy.
A. as   B. in   C. worked   D. at

6 When he _____ _____ of the kitchen, da Vinci _____ the menu _____.
A. changed   B. charge   C. completely   D. took

7 He made _____ but _____ dishes _____ fish with a few carrot _____.
A. slices   B. simple   C. like   D. artistic

8 Some _____ were _____ _____ _____ flowers.
A. decorated   B. dishes   C. with   D. even

9 Customers, however, were unhappy _____ they were _____ to dishes _____ big _____ of meat.
A. servings   B. used   C. with   D. because

10 _____ a _____, da Vinci _____ his _____.
A. lost   B. as   C. job   D. result

11 A _____ years _____, da Vinci _____ a restaurant _____ his friend Sandro Botticelli.
A. opened   B. later   C. few   D. with

12 He wanted to _____ a place _____ people could _____ his _____ food.
A. innovative   B. create   C. try   D. where

13 They _____ _____ a beautifully painted sign and made a _____ _____ menu.
A. uniquely   B. up   C. written   D. put

14 Da Vinci _____ that people would soon _____ his _____ _____.
A. appreciate   B. believed   C. cooking   D. creative

15 _____, that _____ _____.
A. happened   B. unfortunately   C. never

---

1 요리사 다빈치

2 레오나르도 다빈치는 역대 가장 위대한 화가들 중의 한 명으로 알려져 있다.

3 그는 또한 위대한 발명가, 과학자, 그리고 음악가였다.

4 하지만, 극히 소수의 사람들만이 또한 그가 창의적인 요리사였다는 것을 안다.

5 1473년, 스무 살의 레오나르도 다빈치는 이탈리아 플로렌스에 있는 음식점에서 요리사로 일했다.

6 그가 부엌을 책임지게 되었을 때, 다빈치는 메뉴를 완전히 바꿔 버렸다.

7 그는 약간의 당근 조각을 곁들인 생선과 같이 간단하지만 예술적인 음식을 만들었다.

8 몇몇 음식들은 심지어 꽃으로 장식되었다.

9 하지만, 손님들은 많은 양의 고기 요리에 익숙했었기 때문에 불만족스러워했다.

10 그 결과, 다빈치는 그의 직업을 잃었다.

11 몇 년 후, 다빈치는 그의 친구인 산드로 보티첼리와 함께 음식점을 열었다.

12 그는 사람들이 그의 획기적인 음식을 먹어 볼 수 있는 장소로 만들기를 원했다.

13 그들은 아름답게 그려진 간판을 내걸었고 독특하게 써진 메뉴를 만들었다.

14 다빈치는 사람들이 곧 그의 창의적인 요리의 진가를 알아볼 것이라고 믿었다.

15 불행히도, 그런 일은 결코 일어나지 않았다.

16 _____ the _____ 1480s, da Vinci began to _____ _____ Ludovico Sforza in Milan.

A. work　　　B. early　　　C. for　　　D. in

17 He was given many _____ _____, _____ _____ a musician, a painter, and an engineer.

A. as　　　B. different　　　C. such　　　D. roles

18 He was also _____ _____ _____ the kitchen.

A. of　　　B. put　　　C. charge　　　D. in

19 He was happy to be given _____ _____ to _____ his _____ for cooking.

A. pursue　　　B. passion　　　C. chance　　　D. another

20 Da Vinci did not _____ _____ _____ _____ dishes.

A. creative　　　B. stop　　　C. cooking　　　D. at

21 He wanted to cook _____ _____ _____ and _____.

A. easily　　　B. more　　　C. much　　　D. quickly

22 _____, he _____ new _____ for his kitchen.

A. machines　　　B. invented　　　C. thus

23 He _____ machines that could _____ _____ and _____ spaghetti.

A. crush　　　B. created　　　C. pull　　　D. vegetables

24 He even made a _____ that could _____ frogs _____ _____ the water tank.

A. from　　　B. scare　　　C. device　　　D. away

25 Surely, they were all very _____, but _____ of them were too big or _____ difficult _____ use.

A. too　　　B. innovative　　　C. most　　　D. to

26 In 1495, Sforza asked da Vinci to make a _____ painting, which was _____ _____ the last supper of Jesus, on the _____ of a church in Milan.

A. based　　　B. wall　　　C. grand　　　D. on

27 Da Vinci gladly _____ on the project _____ he had always _____ _____ in food.

A. interested　　　B. took　　　C. been　　　D. because

28 He _____ a lot of time cooking all _____ of food to decide _____ to _____ on the table in his picture.

A. kinds　　　B. what　　　C. spent　　　D. put

29 "Da Vinci has _____ his time in the kitchen for _____ a year. That's the _____ why he hasn't finished the painting yet," _____ the people from the church to Sforza.

A. over　　　B. complained　　　C. reason　　　D. wasted

30 _____ da Vinci never became a _____ cook, he showed great _____ in cooking _____ his life.

A. throughout　　　B. successful　　　C. interest　　　D. although

31 He was _____ _____ a great painter _____ _____ a creative cook.

A. also　　　B. not　　　C. but　　　D. only

32 Now _____ you know all about his _____ passion for cooking, you will never look at *The Last Supper* the _____ _____.

A. same　　　B. secret　　　C. that　　　D. way

16 1480년대 초반에, 다빈치는 밀라노에서 루도비코 스포르차를 위해 일하기 시작했다.

17 그는 음악가, 화가, 그리고 공학자와 같은 많은 역할들을 부여받았다.

18 그는 또한 주방을 책임지게 되었다.

19 그는 요리를 향한 그의 열정을 추구할 또 다른 기회를 얻게 되어 행복했다.

20 다빈치는 창의적인 요리를 만드는 것에 멈추지 않았다.

21 그는 훨씬 더 빠르고 쉽게 요리하고 싶어했다.

22 따라서, 그는 그의 주방에서 사용할 새로운 기계들을 발명하였다.

23 그는 채소를 으깨고 스파게티를 뽑는 기계들을 만들었다.

24 그는 심지어 개구리를 겁주어 물탱크에서 쫓아낼 수 있는 기구도 만들었다.

25 확실히 그것들은 모두 매우 획기적이었지만, 그것들 중 대부분은 사용하기에 너무 크거나 너무 어려웠다.

26 1495년, 스포르차는 다빈치에게 웅장한 그림을 밀라노에 있는 교회의 벽에 그려 달라고 부탁했는데, 그것은 예수의 최후의 만찬을 바탕으로 한 것이었다.

27 다빈치는 기꺼이 그 작업을 맡았는데, 그가 항상 음식에 흥미를 가졌기 때문이었다.

28 그는 그림 속 식탁 위에 어떤 음식을 올릴지 결정하기 위해 모든 종류의 음식을 요리하느라 많은 시간을 썼다.

29 "다빈치는 1년 넘게 부엌에서 시간을 낭비해 오고 있습니다. 그것이 그가 아직도 그림을 끝내지 못한 이유입니다."라고 교회 사람들이 스포르차에게 불평을 했다.

30 다빈치는 결코 성공적인 요리사는 되지 못했지만 그는 그의 생애 내내 요리에 대한 큰 흥미를 보여 주었다.

31 그는 훌륭한 화가일 뿐만 아니라 창의적인 요리사였다.

32 이제 여러분은 요리에 대한 그의 비밀스런 열정을 모두 알게 되었기 때문에 〈최후의 만찬〉을 절대 같은 식으로는 보지 않을 것이다.

※ 다음 우리말과 일치하도록 빈칸에 알맞은 것을 골라 쓰시오.

1 Da Vinci _____ _____

2 Leonardo da Vinci _____ _____ _____ one of the _____ _____ _____ _____ _____.

3 He was _____ a great _____, _____, and musician.

4 Very _____ people, _____, know that da Vinci was also a _____ _____.

5 In 1473, _____ da Vinci worked _____ _____ _____ at a restaurant in Florence, Italy.

6 When he _____ _____ _____ the kitchen, da Vinci _____ the menu _____.

7 He made simple _____ artistic dishes _____ fish with _____ _____ _____ _____.

8 Some dishes _____ _____ _____ _____ flowers.

9 Customers, _____, were unhappy because they _____ _____ _____ dishes _____ big _____ of meat.

10 _____ _____ _____, da Vinci lost his job.

11 _____ _____ years _____, da Vinci opened a restaurant with his friend Sandro Botticelli.

12 He wanted _____ _____ a place _____ people could try his _____ food.

13 They _____ _____ a _____ _____ sign and made a _____ _____ menu.

14 Da Vinci believed that people _____ soon _____ his _____ cooking.

15 _____, that never _____.

1 요리사 다빈치

2 레오나르도 다빈치는 역대 가장 위대한 화가들 중의 한 명으로 알려져 있다.

3 그는 또한 위대한 발명가, 과학자, 그리고 음악가였다.

4 하지만, 극히 소수의 사람들만이 또한 그가 창의적인 요리사였다는 것을 안다.

5 1473년, 스무 살의 레오나르도 다빈치는 이탈리아 플로렌스에 있는 음식점에서 요리사로 일했다.

6 그가 부엌을 책임지게 되었을 때, 다빈치는 메뉴를 완전히 바꿔 버렸다.

7 그는 약간의 당근 조각을 곁들인 생선과 같이 간단하지만 예술적인 음식을 만들었다.

8 몇몇 음식들은 심지어 꽃으로 장식되었다.

9 하지만, 손님들은 많은 양의 고기 요리에 익숙했었기 때문에 불만족스러워했다.

10 그 결과, 다빈치는 그의 직업을 잃었다.

11 몇 년 후, 다빈치는 그의 친구인 산드로 보티첼리와 함께 음식점을 열었다.

12 그는 사람들이 그의 획기적인 음식을 먹어 볼 수 있는 장소로 만들기를 원했다.

13 그들은 아름답게 그려진 간판을 내걸었고 독특하게 써진 메뉴를 만들었다.

14 다빈치는 사람들이 곧 그의 창의적인 요리의 진가를 알아볼 것이라고 믿었다.

15 불행히도, 그런 일은 결코 일어나지 않았다.

16 In the _____ 1480s, da Vinci began _____ _____ for Ludovico Sforza in Milan.

17 He _____ _____ many different _____, _____ _____ _____ a musician, a painter, and an engineer.

18 He _____ also _____ _____ _____ _____ _____ the kitchen.

19 He was happy _____ _____ _____ _____ chance _____ _____ his _____ for cooking.

20 Da Vinci did not _____ _____ cooking creative dishes.

21 He wanted to cook _____ _____ quickly and easily.

22 _____, he _____ new machines for his kitchen.

23 He created machines _____ could _____ vegetables and pull spaghetti.

24 He even made a device _____ could _____ frogs _____ the water tank.

25 Surely, they were all very innovative, but most of them _____ _____ big or _____ difficult _____ _____.

26 In 1495, Sforza asked da Vinci _____ _____ a grand painting, _____ _____ _____ the last supper of Jesus, on the wall of a church in Milan.

27 Da Vinci gladly _____ _____ the project because he _____ always _____ _____ _____ food.

28 He spent _____ _____ _____ time _____ all kinds of food to decide _____ _____ _____ on the table in his picture.

29 "Da Vinci has wasted his time in the kitchen _____ _____ a year. That's the reason _____ he hasn't finished the painting yet," complained the people from the church _____ Sforza.

30 _____ da Vinci never became a successful cook, he showed great _____ _____ cooking _____ his life.

31 He was _____ _____ a great painter _____ _____ _____ a _____ _____.

32 _____ _____ you know all about his _____ _____ for cooking, you will never look at *The Last Supper* _____ _____ _____.

(Korean translations 16–32 in right column)

※ 다음 문장을 우리말로 쓰시오.

1 Da Vinci the Cook

➡ _____

2 Leonardo da Vinci is known as one of the greatest painters of all time.

➡ _____

3 He was also a great inventor, scientist, and musician.

➡ _____

4 Very few people, however, know that da Vinci was also a creative cook.

➡ _____

5 In 1473, twenty-year-old da Vinci worked as a cook at a restaurant in Florence, Italy.

➡ _____

6 When he took charge of the kitchen, da Vinci changed the menu completely.

➡ _____

7 He made simple but artistic dishes like fish with a few carrot slices.

➡ _____

8 Some dishes were even decorated with flowers.

➡ _____

9 Customers, however, were unhappy because they were used to dishes with big servings of meat.

➡ _____

10 As a result, da Vinci lost his job.

➡ _____

11 A few years later, da Vinci opened a restaurant with his friend Sandro Botticelli.

➡ _____

12 He wanted to create a place where people could try his innovative food.

➡ _____

13 They put up a beautifully painted sign and made a uniquely written menu.

➡ _____

14 Da Vinci believed that people would soon appreciate his creative cooking.

➡ _____

15 Unfortunately, that never happened.

➡ _____

16 In the early 1480s, da Vinci began to work for Ludovico Sforza in Milan.

➡ _____

17 He was given many different roles, such as a musician, a painter, and an engineer.

➡ _____

18 He was also put in charge of the kitchen.

➡ _____

19 He was happy to be given another chance to pursue his passion for cooking.

➡ _____

20 Da Vinci did not stop at cooking creative dishes.

➡ _____

21 He wanted to cook much more quickly and easily.

➡ _____

22 Thus, he invented new machines for his kitchen.

➡ _____

23 He created machines that could crush vegetables and pull spaghetti.

➡ _____

24 He even made a device that could scare frogs away from the water tank.

➡ _____

25 Surely, they were all very innovative, but most of them were too big or too difficult to use.

➡ _____

26 In 1495, Sforza asked da Vinci to make a grand painting, which was based on the last supper of Jesus, on the wall of a church in Milan.

➡ _____

_____

27 Da Vinci gladly took on the project because he had always been interested in food.

➡ _____

28 He spent a lot of time cooking all kinds of food to decide what to put on the table in his picture.

➡ _____

29 "Da Vinci has wasted his time in the kitchen for over a year. That's the reason why he hasn't finished the painting yet," complained the people from the church to Sforza.

➡ _____

_____

30 Although da Vinci never became a successful cook, he showed great interest in cooking throughout his life.

➡ _____

31 He was not only a great painter but also a creative cook.

➡ _____

32 Now that you know all about his secret passion for cooking, you will never look at *The Last Supper* the same way.

➡ _____

_____

※ 다음 괄호 안의 단어들을 우리말에 맞도록 바르게 배열하시오.

1 (Vinci / Da / Cook / the)
➡ _____

2 (da / Leonardo / Vinci / known / is / one / as / the / of / painters / greatest / all / of / time.)
➡ _____

3 (was / he / also / a / inventor, / great / musician. / and / scientist,)
➡ _____

4 (few / very / people, / know / however, / that / Vinci / da / also / was / a / cook. / creative)
➡ _____

5 (1473, / in / twenty-year-old / da / worked / Vinci / a / as / cook / a / at / restaurant / in / Italy. / Florence,)
➡ _____

6 (he / when / took / of / charge / kitchen, / the / Vinci / da / the / changed / completely. / menu)
➡ _____

7 (made / he / simple / artistic / but / like / dishes / with / fish / few / a / slices. / carrot)
➡ _____

8 (dishes / some / even / were / with / decorated / flowers.)
➡ _____

9 (however, / customers, / unhappy / were / they / because / were / used / dishes / to / big / with / of / servings / meat.)
➡ _____

10 (a / as / result, / Vinci / da / his / lost / job.)
➡ _____

11 (few / a / later, / years / Vinci / da / a / opened / restaurant / his / with / Sandro / friend / Botticelli.)
➡ _____

1 요리사 다빈치

2 레오나르도 다빈치는 역대 가장 위대한 화가들 중의 한 명으로 알려져 있다.

3 그는 또한 위대한 발명가, 과학자, 그리고 음악가였다.

4 하지만, 극히 소수의 사람들만이 또한 그가 창의적인 요리사였다는 것을 안다.

5 1473년, 스무 살의 레오나르도 다빈치는 이탈리아 플로렌스에 있는 음식점에서 요리사로 일했다.

6 그가 부엌을 책임지게 되었을 때, 다빈치는 메뉴를 완전히 바꿔 버렸다.

7 그는 약간의 당근 조각을 곁들인 생선과 같이 간단하지만 예술적인 음식을 만들었다.

8 몇몇 음식들은 심지어 꽃으로 장식되었다.

9 하지만, 손님들은 많은 양의 고기 요리에 익숙했었기 때문에 불만족스러워했다.

10 그 결과, 다빈치는 그의 직업을 잃었다.

11 몇 년 후, 다빈치는 그의 친구인 산드로 보티첼리와 함께 음식점을 열었다.

12 (wanted / he / create / to / place / a / where / could / people / his / try / food. / innovative)

➡ _____

_____

13 (put / they / up / beautifully / a / painted / and / sign / made / uniquely / a / menu. / written)

➡ _____

_____

14 (Vinci / da / believed / people / that / soon / would / appreciate / creative / his / cooking.)

➡ _____

_____

15 (that / unfortunately, / happened. / never)

➡ _____

16 (the / in / 1480s, / early / Vinci / da / to / began / for / work / Sforza / Ludovico / Milan. / in)

➡ _____

17 (was / he / many / given / roles, / different / as / such / musician, / a / painter, / a / and / engineer. / an)

➡ _____

_____

18 (was / he / put / also / charge / in / the / of / kitchen.)

➡ _____

19 (was / he / to / happy / given / be / chance / another / pursue / to / passion / his / cooking. / for)

➡ _____

_____

20 (Vinci / da / not / did / at / stop / creative / cooking / dishes.)

➡ _____

21 (wanted / he / cook / to / more / much / easily. / and / quickly)

➡ _____

12 그는 사람들이 그의 획기적인 음식을 먹어 볼 수 있는 장소로 만들기를 원했다.

13 그들은 아름답게 그려진 간판을 내걸었고 독특하게 써진 메뉴를 만들었다.

14 다빈치는 사람들이 곧 그의 창의적인 요리의 진가를 알아볼 것이라고 믿었다.

15 불행히도, 그런 일은 결코 일어나지 않았다.

16 1480년대 초반에, 다빈치는 밀라노에서 루도비코 스포르차를 위해 일하기 시작했다.

17 그는 음악가, 화가, 그리고 공학자와 같은 많은 역할들을 부여받았다.

18 그는 또한 주방을 책임지게 되었다.

19 그는 요리를 향한 그의 열정을 추구할 또 다른 기회를 얻게 되어 행복했다.

20 다빈치는 창의적인 요리를 만드는 것에 멈추지 않았다.

21 그는 훨씬 더 빠르고 쉽게 요리하고 싶어했다.

22 (he / thus, / iinvented / machines / new / his / for / kitchen.)
➡ _____

23 (created / he / that / machines / crush / could / vegetables / pull / and / spaghetti.)
➡ _____

24 (even / he / a / made / that / device / scare / could / away / frogs / the / from / tank. / water)
➡ _____
_____

25 (they / surely, / were / very / all / innovative, / of / but / most / them / too / were / big / too / or / difficult / use. / to)
➡ _____
_____

26 (1495, / in / asked / Sforza / Vinci / da / make / to / grand / a / painting, / was / which / on / based / the / supper / last / Jesus, / of / the / on / wall / a / of / in / church / Milan.)
➡ _____
_____

27 (Vinci / da / took / gladly / the / on / because / project / had / he / been / always / interested / food. / in)
➡ _____
_____

28 (spent / he / lot / a / of / cooking / time / all / of / kinds / to / food / what / decide / to / on / put / table / the / his / in / picture.)
➡ _____
_____

29 (Vinci / "da / wasted / has / time / his / the / in / for / kitchen / over / year. / a // the / that's / why / reason / hasn't / he / the / finished / yet," / painting / `complained / people / the / from / church / the / Sforza. / to)
➡ _____
_____

30 (da / although / Vinci / became / never / a / cook, / successful / showed / he / interest / great / cooking / in / his / throughout / life.)
➡ _____
_____

31 (was / he / only / not / great / a / but / painter / also / creative / a / cook.)
➡ _____

32 (that / now / know / you / about / all / secret / his / for / passion / cooking, / will / you / look / never / *The* / at / *Supper* / *Last* / same / the / way.)
➡ _____
_____

22 따라서, 그는 그의 주방에서 사용할 새로운 기계들을 발명하였다.

23 그는 채소를 으깨고 스파게티를 뽑는 기계들을 만들었다.

24 그는 심지어 개구리를 겁주어 물탱크에서 쫓아낼 수 있는 기구도 만들었다.

25 확실히 그것들은 모두 매우 획기적이었지만, 그것들 중 대부분은 사용하기에 너무 크거나 너무 어려웠다.

26 1495년, 스포르차는 다빈치에게 웅장한 그림을 밀라노에 있는 교회의 벽에 그려 달라고 부탁했는데, 그것은 예수의 최후의 만찬을 바탕으로 한 것이었다.

27 다빈치는 기꺼이 그 작업을 맡았는데, 그가 항상 음식에 흥미를 가졌기 때문이었다.

28 그는 그림 속 식탁 위에 어떤 음식을 올릴지 결정하기 위해 모든 종류의 음식을 요리하느라 많은 시간을 썼다.

29 "다빈치는 1년 넘게 부엌에서 시간을 낭비해 오고 있습니다. 그것이 그가 아직도 그림을 끝내지 못한 이유입니다."라고 교회 사람들이 스포르차에게 불평을 했다.

30 다빈치는 결코 성공적인 요리사는 되지 못했지만 그는 그의 생애 내내 요리에 대한 큰 흥미를 보여 주었다.

31 그는 훌륭한 화가일 뿐만 아니라 창의적인 요리사였다.

32 이제 여러분은 요리에 대한 그의 비밀스런 열정을 모두 알게 되었기 때문에 〈최후의 만찬〉을 절대 같은 식으로는 보지 않을 것이다.

※ **다음 우리말을 영어로 쓰시오.**

1 요리사 다빈치

➡ _____

2 레오나르도 다빈치는 역대 가장 위대한 화가들 중의 한 명으로 알려져 있다.

➡ _____

3 그는 또한 위대한 발명가, 과학자, 그리고 음악가였다.

➡ _____

4 하지만, 극히 소수의 사람들만이 또한 그가 창의적인 요리사였다는 것을 안다.

➡ _____

5 1473년, 스무 살의 레오나르도 다빈치는 이탈리아 플로렌스에 있는 음식점에서 요리사로 일했다.

➡ _____

6 그가 부엌을 책임지게 되었을 때, 다빈치는 메뉴를 완전히 바꿔 버렸다.

➡ _____

7 그는 약간의 당근 조각을 곁들인 생선과 같이 간단하지만 예술적인 음식을 만들었다.

➡ _____

8 몇몇 음식들은 심지어 꽃으로 장식되었다.

➡ _____

9 하지만, 손님들은 많은 양의 고기 요리에 익숙했었기 때문에 불만족스러워했다.

➡ _____

10 그 결과, 다빈치는 그의 직업을 잃었다.

➡ _____

11 몇 년 후, 다빈치는 그의 친구인 산드로 보티첼리와 함께 음식점을 열었다.

➡ _____

12 그는 사람들이 그의 획기적인 음식을 먹어 볼 수 있는 장소로 만들기를 원했다.

➡ _____

13 그들은 아름답게 그려진 간판을 내걸었고 독특하게 써진 메뉴를 만들었다.

➡ _____

14 다빈치는 사람들이 곧 그의 창의적인 요리의 진가를 알아볼 것이라고 믿었다.

➡ _____

15 불행히도, 그런 일은 결코 일어나지 않았다.

➡ _____

16 1480년대 초반에, 다빈치는 밀라노에서 루도비코 스포르차를 위해 일하기 시작했다.

➡ _____

17 그는 음악가, 화가, 그리고 공학자와 같은 많은 역할들을 부여받았다.

➡ _____

18 그는 또한 주방을 책임지게 되었다.

➡ _____

19 그는 요리를 향한 그의 열정을 추구할 또 다른 기회를 얻게 되어 행복했다.

➡ _____

20 다빈치는 창의적인 요리를 만드는 것에 멈추지 않았다.

➡ _____

21 그는 훨씬 더 빠르고 쉽게 요리하고 싶어했다.

➡ _____

22 따라서, 그는 그의 주방에서 사용할 새로운 기계들을 발명하였다.

➡ _____

23 그는 채소를 으깨고 스파게티를 뽑는 기계들을 만들었다.

➡ _____

24 그는 심지어 개구리를 겁주어 물탱크에서 쫓아낼 수 있는 기구도 만들었다.

➡ _____

25 확실히 그것들은 모두 매우 획기적이었지만, 그것들 중 대부분은 사용하기에 너무 크거나 너무 어려웠다.

➡ _____

26 1495년, 스포르차는 다빈치에게 웅장한 그림을 밀라노에 있는 교회의 벽에 그려 달라고 부탁했는데, 그것은 예수의 최후의 만찬을 바탕으로 한 것이었다.

➡ _____

_____

27 다빈치는 기꺼이 그 작업을 맡았는데, 그가 항상 음식에 흥미를 가졌기 때문이었다.

➡ _____

28 그는 그림 속 식탁 위에 어떤 음식을 올릴지 결정하기 위해 모든 종류의 음식을 요리하느라 많은 시간을 썼다.

➡ _____

29 "다빈치는 1년 넘게 부엌에서 시간을 낭비해 오고 있습니다. 그것이 그가 아직도 그림을 끝내지 못한 이유입니다."라고 교회 사람들이 스포르차에게 불평을 했다.

➡ _____

_____

30 다빈치는 결코 성공적인 요리사는 되지 못했지만 그는 그의 생애 내내 요리에 대한 큰 흥미를 보여 주었다.

➡ _____

31 그는 훌륭한 화가일 뿐만 아니라 창의적인 요리사였다.

➡ _____

32 이제 여러분은 요리에 대한 그의 비밀스런 열정을 모두 알게 되었기 때문에 〈최후의 만찬〉을 절대 같은 식으로는 보지 않을 것이다.

➡ _____

_____

※ 다음 우리말과 일치하도록 빈칸에 알맞은 말을 쓰시오.

Write

1. My name is Kim Jieun. I am _____ _____ _____ _____ _____.

2. There was a _____ _____ when I _____ _____ _____ to be.

3. _____ _____ 2030, I made a _____ _____ _____.

4. It was a _____ _____ _____ _____ about _____ _____ for arts.

5. Thus, I _____ _____ go to a _____ _____ _____.

6. _____ I _____ _____ high school, I _____ Korea Art College and _____ more about _____ and _____.

7. _____ _____, I _____ my first _____.

8. I _____ very _____ _____ my life.

1. 내 이름은 김지은이다. 나는 기술을 사용하는 예술가다.
2. 내가 예술가가 되기로 결심했을 때 특별한 순간이 있었다.
3. 2030년에, 나는 기술을 사용해 작은 동상을 만들었다.
4. 그것은 예술을 위한 기술을 배우는 데에 아주 좋은 기회였다.
5. 따라서, 나는 기술 고등학교에 진학하기로 결심했다.
6. 고등학교를 졸업한 뒤, 나는 한국 예술 대학에 입학해서 예술과 기술에 대해 더 배웠다.
7. 올해, 나는 내 첫 전시회를 열었다.
8. 나는 내 인생에 매우 만족한다.

Link

1. Some people think creativity is _____ _____ _____ _____ when they _____ _____ _____.

2. They like to _____ _____ _____ new ideas and _____ _____ _____.

3. Thus, they want to _____ _____ _____ _____ they can _____ _____ _____.

1. 어떤 사람들은 직업을 선택할 때 고려해야 할 가장 중요한 것은 창의력이라고 생각한다.
2. 그들은 새로운 아이디어를 떠올리고 새로운 것들을 구상하기를 좋아한다.
3. 따라서, 그들은 그들의 창의력을 발휘할 수 있는 곳에서 일하기를 원한다.

Watch and Think Share

1. Winston Churchill _____ _____ _____ _____ the Prime Minister of the United Kingdom _____ World War II.

2. Very _____ _____, _____, know that he was also a _____, a _____, and a _____.

3. He even _____ the _____ _____ _____ _____ in 1953.

1. Winston Churchill은 제 2차 세계대전 중 영국의 수상이었던 것으로 알려져 있다.
2. 하지만, 극소수의 사람들은 그가 또한 사학자이며, 화가이자, 작가임을 알고 있다.
3. 심지어 그는 1953년에 노벨 문학상을 수상하기도 했다.

※ 다음 우리말을 영어로 쓰시오.

Write

1. 내 이름은 김지은이다. 나는 기술을 사용하는 예술가다.

   ➡ _____

2. 내가 예술가가 되기로 결심했을 때 특별한 순간이 있었다.

   ➡ _____

3. 2030년에, 나는 기술을 사용해 작은 동상을 만들었다.

   ➡ _____

4. 그것은 예술을 위한 기술을 배우는 데에 아주 좋은 기회였다.

   ➡ _____

5. 따라서, 나는 기술 고등학교에 진학하기로 결심했다.

   ➡ _____

6. 고등학교를 졸업한 뒤, 나는 한국 예술 대학에 입학해서 예술과 기술에 대해 더 배웠다.

   ➡ _____

   _____

7. 올해, 나는 내 첫 전시회를 열었다.

   ➡ _____

8. 나는 내 인생에 매우 만족한다.

   ➡ _____

Link

1. 어떤 사람들은 직업을 선택할 때 고려해야 할 가장 중요한 것은 창의력이라고 생각한다.

   ➡ _____

2. 그들은 새로운 아이디어를 떠올리고 새로운 것들을 구상하기를 좋아한다.

   ➡ _____

3. 따라서, 그들은 그들의 창의력을 발휘할 수 있는 곳에서 일하기를 원한다.

   ➡ _____

Watch and Think Share

1. Winston Churchill은 제 2차 세계대전 중 영국의 수상이었던 것으로 알려져 있다.

   ➡ _____

2. 하지만, 극소수의 사람들은 그가 또한 사학자이며, 화가이자, 작가임을 알고 있다.

   ➡ _____

3. 심지어 그는 1953년에 노벨 문학상을 수상하기도 했다.

   ➡ _____

MEMO

MEMO

영어 기출 문제집

적중100

2학기

정답 및 해설

미래 | 최연희

중 3

적중100

영어 기출 문제집

적중100

2학기

정답 및 해설

미래 | 최연희

중 3

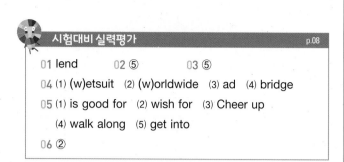

This Is Korea

시험대비 실력평가
p.08

01 lend   **02** ⑤   **03** ⑤

04 (1) (w)etsuit (2) (w)orldwide (3) ad (4) bridge

05 (1) is good for (2) wish for (3) Cheer up

    (4) walk along (5) get into

06 ②

01 주어진 단어는 반의어 관계이다. lend: 빌려주다, borrow: 빌리다

02 '가치가 있지만 물리적으로 존재하지는 않는'을 의미하는 말은 intangible(무형의)이다.

03 experience: 경험

04 wetsuit: 잠수복, worldwide: 세계적으로, ad: 광고, bridge: 다리

05 cheer up: 격려하다, wish for: 기원하다, get into: ~에 들어가다, be good for: ~에 유익하다, walk along: ~을 따라 걷다

06 주어진 문장에서 press는 '누르다'를 의미하며 이와 같은 의미로 쓰인 것은 ②번이다. 나머지는 모두 '신문, 언론'을 뜻한다.

서술형 시험대비
p.09

01 past

02 (1) (p)ath (2) community (3) (p)romote

    (4) jellyfish

03 (1) We had a good harvest last year.

    (2) Money does not always bring happiness.

    (3) Our national heritage was destroyed by the fire.

04 (1) We walked along the street for an hour.

    (2) This book is suitable for elementary school students.

    (3) Let's make double-sided copies to save paper.

05 (1) promote (2) realize (3) several

    (4) underwater (5) volcanic

01 주어진 단어는 반의어 관계이다. future: 미래, past: 과거

02 path: 길, community: 지역 공동체, promote: 홍보하다, jellyfish: 해파리

03 good harvest: 풍년, happiness: 행복, heritage: 유산

04 walk along: ~을 따라 걷다, be suitable for: ~에 적절하다, make double-sided copies: 양면 복사를 하다

05 realize: 깨닫다, promote: 홍보하다, underwater: 물속의, 수중의, volcanic: 화산의, several: 몇몇의

Conversation

핵심 Check
p.10~11

1 I wonder where the photo was taken.

2 (C) → (B) → (A)

교과서 대화문 익히기

Check(√) True or False
p.12

1 T **2** T **3** T **4** F

교과서 확인학습
p.14~15

Listen & Speak 1 A-1

bridge, ad, where the photo was taken / How / with, last summer

Listen & Speak 1 A-2

I wonder why, waiting in line / get into / famous / on / try

Listen & Speak 2 A-1

I'd like to borrow / explain how to use it / Press, what to do

Listen & Speak 2 A-2

somewhere / walk along / Could you explain / long hiking path / enjoy your trip

Communicate A

I wonder where / check it out / strong beat, traditional / community / Could you explain / traditionally, cheer up, good harvest / rhythm / completes / Why not

Progress Check 1

I wonder why there are so many cars / going on vacation / why don't we

copy machine / how to make double-sided copies /
Press, press

시험대비 기본평가　p.16

01 I wonder where the photo was taken.
02 How do you know that?
03 Could you tell me what that is?　04 ⑤

01 간접의문문 어순으로 '의문사+주어+동사'의 어순이 알맞다.
04 Tom이 구체적으로 제주 올레길에 대한 설명을 요청한 것으로
보아 Tom이 이미 올레길에 대해 잘 알고 있다는 설명은 일치하
지 않는다.

시험대비 실력평가　p.17~18

01 (E) → (C) → (B) → (D) → (A)　02 ⑤
03 ⓑ → was taken　04 ⑤　05 ⑤
06 ⑤　07 (C) → (B) → (D) → (E) → (A)
08 ④
09 Dancing together completes the music.
10 ⑤

01 (E) 궁금함에 대한 대답 → (C) 유명한지 질문→ (B) 대답 및
이유 설명 → (D) 제안 → (A) 동의
02 ⑤번을 제외한 나머지는 모두 설명을 요청하는 표현이다.
03 사진이 찍혔으므로 수동태가 알맞다.
04 소녀가 다리 사진을 찍고 싶다는 내용은 대화를 통해 알 수 없다.
05 (A)는 진행을 나타내는 현재분사 waiting, (B) get into: 들어
가다, get out: 나가다, (C) TV에 나왔음을 나타내는 on이 적
절하다.
06 Brian과 수진은 줄을 서 있는 사람들을 보고 있다.
07 (C) 하고 싶은 일 부탁 → (B) 허락 → (D) 양면 복사 방법 질
문 → (E) 대답 → (A) 감사 표현
08 궁금함을 나타내는 표현으로 ④번으로 바꾸어 쓸 수 있다.
09 complete: 완성하다
10 궁금한 것을 알고 싶다는 말에 노력에 감사하다는 대답은 어색
하다.

서술형 시험대비　p.19

01 Could you explain how to use it?
02 She gets to know what she should do.
03 (A) waiting in line　(B) the new bakery
　　(C) get into　(D) it was on a TV program

04 (1) band　(2) strong　(3) farmers　(4) harvest
05 They are going to join some people dancing to
　the rhythm.

02 버튼을 누르면 여자는 무엇을 해야 하는지 알 수 있다.
03 Brian과 Sujin은 새로 생긴 제과점 앞에 줄을 서 있는 많은 사
람들을 보았다. 사람들은 그곳에 들어가고 싶어 했다. 새로 생긴
제과점은 매우 인기가 있었다. 왜냐하면 TV 프로그램에 나왔었
기 때문이다. Brian과 Sujin은 함께 그곳의 빵을 먹어보고 싶
어 했다.
05 Jaden과 유리는 대화 후 춤추는 사람들과 함께 할 것이다.

교과서 Grammar

핵심 Check　p.20~21

1 (1) had　(2) visited
2 (1) will she make → she will make
　(2) was Sarah → Sarah was

시험대비 기본평가　p.22

01 ⑤　02 ③　03 ④
04 (1) asked how she became interested
　(2) tell us what is so special

01 기준이 되는 시점이 과거이고, 그 이전에 일어난 동작이므로 과
거완료시제를 찾는다.
02 의문사가 없는 의문문의 간접의문문은 if 또는 whether가 접속
사 역할을 한다.
03 ① '지금까지'이므로 현재완료시제로 써야 한다. had lived →
has lived, ② has → had ③ had found → found, ⑤ 과거
시점 이전에 일어난 일이므로 had gone이 적절하다.
04 간접의문문을 만들 때, 의문사는 접속사 역할을 하고 '의문사+주
어+동사'의 어순이 된다. 시제와 수에 유의하여, 동사를 적절히
쓴다. 의문사가 주어일 때는 순서가 바뀌지 않는 것도 주의한다.

시험대비 실력평가　p.23~25

01 ③　02 ⑤　03 ④　04 ④
05 ⑤　06 had been → has been　07 ⑤
08 ⑤　09 ②　10 ④　11 ③
12 ⑤

01 ③ 과거시점(Lucy asked) 이전에 발생한 일이다. has broken → had broken이 적절하다.

02 간접의문문의 어순은 '의문사+주어+동사'이다. 원래의 의문문 'What is that?'에서 What은 주어로 쓰인 것이 아님에 유의하여 'what that is' 어순으로 배열한 정답을 찾는다.

03 '의문사+be+there+주어'는 간접의문문이 될 때, '의문사+there+be+주어'의 어순이 된다.

04 ① had read → has read ② 'San Francisco로 이사를 하기 전에 New York에서 살았다'는 문장이므로 'William lived[had lived] in New York before he moved to San Francisco.'가 적절하다. ③ '민수가 보고서를 완성해야 한다고 요구'한 것이므로 had completed → (should) complete ⑤ had not eaten → have not eaten

05 ① what so special is → what is so special ② do I like → I like ③ Do you imagine how old → How old do you imagine ④ what is your favorite food → what your favorite food is

06 과거의 특정 시점 이전에 발생한 일을 과거완료시제로 표현해야 한다. 종속절이 'since+과거시제'이므로, 주절은 과거완료가 아니라 현재완료시제로 표현하는 것이 적절하다.

07 간접의문문의 접속사 역할을 하는 who가 주어로 사용되었으므로, 어순을 바꿀 필요가 없다. 'who took away her kids' toys' 원래 어순 그대로 쓰는 것이 적절하다.

08 <보기>의 had found는 과거완료시제 중 '완료' 용법으로 쓰였다. ①, ③, ④는 '계속', ②는 '경험' 용법이다.

09 <보기> if는 조건의 '부사절' 접속사이며, ②도 그렇다. 나머지는 모두 '의문사 없는 간접의문문을 이끄는 접속사'이다.

10 본동사가 think일 때, 간접의문문의 의문사는 문두로 보내고 어순은 '주어+동사' 순으로 한다.

11 ① 내용상 '내가 사준 것'이 '그녀가 목걸이를 잃어버린 것'보다 먼저이기 때문에 'Cecilia lost the necklace which I had bought for her.'가 적절하다. ② had melted → melted ④ have → had ⑤ has → had

12 ① Do you think where → Where do you think ② what did your action mean → what your action meant ③ did anyone see → anyone saw ④ how the writer of these books old → how old the writer of these books is

13 과거완료시제(had spent)와, 'spend+시간+V-ing'를 활용하

14 간접의문문을 활용하는 문제이다. 생각 동사 think, believe, imagine 등이 주절에 올 때, 간접의문문의 의문사를 문두로 보내는 것에 유의한다.

15 (1) 의문사 why를 간접의문문으로 활용한 문장이다. '지호는 누나에게 왜 사람이 하늘을 날 수 없는지 물어봤다.' (2) 과거완료시제를 이용하여, 어구를 배열하는 문장이다. 'Pooh는 그의 친구에게 그 날 아침에 벌집을 건드렸다고 말했다.'

서술형 시험대비

01 (1) collected many Korean treasures that some French had stolen before
   (2) wonders how she can promote the haenyeo worldwide
   (3) he found someone had broken into his house
   (4) Can you guess where the photographer took

02 (1) how they could get to the meeting on time
   (2) which boy the girl next to Jane chose at the blind date
   (3) if(또는 whether) Shrek hasn't learned German yet
   (4) where Alex found the baby tiger
   (5) the new employee looks

03 had only seen black-and-white photos of haenyeo who

04 (1) Can you tell me where the magician was when he disappeared?
   (2) Does the young student know how far the hotel is?
   (3) Do you know if[whether] I could take pictures of haenyeo?
   (4) They didn't understand why the girl wanted to take their pictures.
   (5) Tell me what Zin Kim promised the haenyeo.
   (6) I wonder why Jejudo isn't suitable for farming.

05 The haenyeo had not thought that she was pretty until the photographer took her picture twelve years ago.

06 (1) Tom wondered how haenyeo could stay in the water for so long without any breathing devices.
   (2) They are studying how catching too much marine life can destroy the ocean.
   (3) The witch asked the mirror who the most beautiful woman in the world was.
   (4) The mother goat did not know when the babies opened the door to the wolf.

01 (1), (3) 과거의 특정 시점 이전에 일어난 일은 '과거완료시제'로 쓰는 것에 유의한다. (2), (4) '간접의문문'의 어순은 '의문사+주어+동사'이다. 특히, (4)번에서 guess라는 생각 동사가 오지만, yes나 no로 대답이 가능한 의문문의 경우 의문사가 앞으로 가지 않는 것에 유의한다.

02 '간접의문문'의 어순은 '의문사+주어+동사'이다. 어순이 바뀔 때는 수와 시제에 유의해야 한다. (5)번에서 think와 같은 생각 동사가 있을 때는 의문사가 문두로 와야 한다.

03 only see를 과거완료시제로 표현하면 had only seen이다. 빈칸 뒤의 looked가 동사이므로 주어 역할의 관계대명사 who를 마지막에 쓴다.

04 (1) was the magician → the magician was (2) how the hotel is far → how far the hotel is (3) could I → if(또는 whether) I could (4) did the girl want → the girl wanted (5) did Zin Kim promise → Zin Kim promised (6) why is Jejudo not → why Jejudo isn't

05 과거의 어느 특정 시점을 기준으로 그 전의 동작은 과거완료시제로 표현한다. 12년 전에 사진작가가 사진을 찍기까지는 자신을 예쁘다고 생각하지 않았으므로, 부정의 과거완료시제를 사용해서 표현하면, 'had not thought that she was pretty'가 적절하다.

06 주어진 단어들 중 동사의 수와 시제에 유의하여, 간접의문문의 어순과 내용에 알맞게 적절한 문장을 영작한다.

Reading

[교과서]

확인문제   p.28

1 T 2 F 3 F 4 T 5 F

확인문제   p.29

1 T 2 F 3 T 4 F 5 T

교과서 확인학습 A   p.30~31

01 Female Divers
02 underwater photographer, has promoted
03 without any breathing devices
04 made UNESCO's Intangible Cultural Heritage list
05 was interviewed   06 become interested in
07 happened to   08 was surprised to find
09 looked very tired   10 kept laughing
11 should take   12 isn't it difficult

13 why I wanted   14 in their wetsuits
15 very special   16 show, to
17 opened up   18 make them, beautiful
19 more about   20 so special
21 can tell you   22 strong women
23 is not suitable for, the breadwinners for
24 form, each other
25 more-experienced, less-experienced
26 without, can't catch   27 is good for
28 at one time in one place 29 planning to do
30 attended, give a talk   31 held my hand
32 so much
33 such a special person   34 with happiness
35 was deeply moved   36 can never forget
37 more beautiful stories about them

교과서 확인학습 B   p.32~33

1 Haenyeo, Female Divers of Korea
2 For the past several years, the underwater photographer Zin Kim has promoted the culture of Jeju haenyeo worldwide.
3 Haenyeo are Korean female divers who harvest seafood without any breathing devices.
4 Their culture made UNESCO's Intangible Cultural Heritage list in 2016.
5 At her studio last week, Zin Kim was interviewed about her experience of taking pictures of haenyeo.
6 Q. How did you become interested in taking photos of haenyeo?
7 One day, I happened to take pictures of a haenyeo.
8 I was surprised to find that she was enjoying her job.
9 Until then, I had only seen black-and-white photos of haenyeo who looked very tired.
10 However, she kept laughing even after she had been in the water for over five hours.
11 I realized then that I should take pictures of haenyeo.
12 Q. You take beautiful pictures of them, but isn't it difficult to take pictures of haenyeo?
13 At first, they didn't understand why I wanted to take their pictures.
14 They didn't think they looked pretty in their wetsuits.

5

15 So, I said to them, "You're very special.

16 I want to show your culture to the world."

17 They opened up to me then.

18 Of course, I also promised them that I would make them look beautiful in my pictures.

19 Q. Could you tell us more about haenyeo?

20 What's so special about them?

21 I can tell you three things.

22 First, haenyeo are a symbol of strong women.

23 Jejudo, which is a volcanic island, is not suitable for farming, so many haenyeo have become the breadwinners for their families.

24 Second, haenyeo form their own communities and help each other.

25 For example, more-experienced haenyeo train less-experienced haenyeo.

26 Third, because they stay in the water without any breathing devices, haenyeo can't catch a lot of seafood.

27 This is good for the underwater environment.

28 Catching too much marine life at one time in one place can destroy the ocean.

29 Q. Lastly, please tell us what you're planning to do in the future.

30 I once attended an overseas exhibition with a couple of haenyeo to give a talk about their lives.

31 When I finished my talk, one of the haenyeo held my hand tightly.

32 She said to me, "Thank you so much.

33 I've never known in my whole life that I was such a special person."

34 She was crying with happiness.

35 Everyone in the audience was deeply moved.

36 I can never forget that moment, so I'll continue to take pictures of haenyeo.

37 I want to tell more beautiful stories about them to many more people in the world.

시험대비 실력평가
p.34~37

01 ②, ④　　02 ⑤　　03 ④　　04 ③
05 laughing　06 ④　　07 ⑤　　08 ②
09 they didn't understand why I wanted to take their pictures
10 (A) attended　(B) such　(C) so
11 ⑤　　12 ④　　13 ②, ③
14 breadwinners　　15 that → which

16 because they stay in the water without any breathing devices, haenyeo can't catch a lot of seafood

17 ②　　18 ③　　19 ①
20 looking → look　21 ④　　22 ③
23 suitable → not suitable 또는 unsuitable
24 ①, ⑤　　25 to catch

01 주격 관계대명사 who와 that이 적절하다.

02 ⓑ와 ⑤: ~이 되다, ~의 지위를 얻다; ~으로 승진[승격]하다, 존스는 5년 만에 교수가 되었다. ① 만들다[제작/제조하다], ② (~로 하여금 …하게) 만들다[하다], ③ 선출[임명/지명]하다, ④ (억지로 무엇을 하게) 만들다[시키다]

03 해녀는 어떤 호흡 장치도 '사용하지 않고' 해산물을 채취하는 한국의 여성 잠수부들이다.

04 대답에서 해녀의 사진을 찍는 것에 관심을 가지게 된 이유를 설명하고 있으므로, 빈칸에 들어갈 질문으로는 ③번 '어떻게 해녀의 사진을 찍는 것에 관심을 가지게 되었나요?'가 적절하다.

05 keep -ing: 계속 ~하다

06 (B)와 ②: 계속 용법, ①, ④: 완료 용법, ③: 결과 용법, ⑤: 경험 용법

07 주어진 문장의 then에 주목한다. 그들이 '그때' 제게 마음을 열었다고 했을 때의 '그때'는 ⑤번 앞 문장에서 말한 "여러분들은 아주 특별해요. 저는 여러분의 문화를 세계에 알리고 싶어요."라고 말한 때를 가리키므로 ⑤번이 적절하다.

08 이 글은 '글쓴이가 해녀들을 설득하여 그들의 사진을 찍게 된 과정'을 설명하는 글이므로, 제목으로는 ②번 '와! 해녀들은 내가 사진을 통해 그들의 문화를 알리도록 허락해 주었어!'가 적절하다.

09 why는 의문문의 문두에 쓰이는 의문사이지만 간접의문문에서는 문장 안에 쓰인다. 이때는 보통 주어가 동사 앞에 와서 '의문사+주어+동사'의 순서로 쓰인다.

10 (A) 박람회에 '참가한' 적이 있다고 해야 하므로 attended가 옳다. attend to: ~을 돌보다, 시중들다, (B) 'such+a+형용사+명사'의 순서로 써야 하므로 such가 옳다. 'so+형용사+a+명사', (C) '그 순간을 절대 잊을 수가 없기 때문에 해녀의 사진을 계속해서 찍을 것'이라고 해야 하므로 so가 옳다.

11 중반부의 'She was crying with happiness. Everyone in the audience was deeply moved.'를 통해 'touching'을 찾을 수 있다. touching: 감동적인, ① 혼란스러운, ② 재미있는, 흥미로운, ③ 우울하게 만드는, 우울한, ④ 지루한

12 Zin Kim이 얼마나 오랫동안 해녀들의 사진을 찍어 왔는지는 대답할 수 없다. ① With a couple of haenyeo. ② To give a talk about haenyeo's lives. ③ She said, "Thank you so much. I've never known in my whole life that I was such a special person." ⑤ She wants to tell more

beautiful stories about haenyeo.

13 ⓐ와 ②, ③: 경험 용법, ① 완료 용법, ④ 완료 용법, ⑤ 계속 용법

14 필수적인 것들을 위해 가족이 필요한 돈을 버는 사람들, breadwinner: (집안의) 생계비를 버는 사람, 가장

15 관계대명사 that은 계속적 용법으로 쓸 수 없으므로 which로 바꾸는 것이 적절하다.

16 앞 문장의 내용을 가리킨다.

17 이 글은 '해녀에 대해 무엇이 특별한지'를 설명하는 글이므로, 주제로는 ②번 '해녀에 대한 특별한 점들'이 적절하다. ① subject: (그림·사진 등의) 대상[소재]

18 ⓐ in: '착용'을 나타내는 전치사, ⓑ show는 3형식으로 고칠 때 전치사 to를 사용한다.

19 ①은 Zin Kim을 가리키고, 나머지는 다 '해녀들'을 가리킨다.

20 사역동사 make의 목적격보어이므로 동사원형으로 고치는 것이 적절하다.

21 전반부의 'they didn't understand why I wanted to take their pictures'를 통해 'puzzled'를, 중반부의 'They opened up to me then.'을 통해 'consenting'을 찾을 수 있다. puzzled: 어리둥절해하는, 얼떨떨한, consenting: 동의[승낙]하는, ① nervous: 초조한, ② delighted: 아주 기뻐하는, upset: 속상한, ③ agreeing: 동의하는, ⑤ confused: 혼란스러워 하는, disappointed: 실망한

22 앞의 내용의 예가 나오고 있으므로 For example이 가장 적절하다. ① 그러므로, ④ 게다가, ⑤ 그 결과

23 제주도는 화산섬이라서 농사에 '적합하지 않다'로 고치는 것이 적절하다.

24 (B)와 ②, ③, ④: 동명사(목적, 용도), ①, ⑤: 현재분사(동작의 진행)

25 to부정사를 진주어로 하여 고치는 것이 적절하다.

서술형 시험대비   p.38~39

01 by chance (또는 by accident)

02 have → had

03 (A) enjoying   (B) laughing

04 (A) For   (B) any   (C) Intangible

05 Haenyeo 또는 haenyeo

06 two thousand (and) sixteen 또는 twenty sixteen

07 marine

08 (A) breathing devices   (B) can't catch

09 (1) 해녀들은 강인한 여성의 상징이다.
　(2) 해녀들은 그들 자신의 공동체를 조직하고 서로 돕는다.
　(3) 어떤 호흡 장치도 사용하지 않고 물속에 머물기 때문에, 해녀는 많은 해산물을 채취할 수가 없다.

---

10 what you're planning to do in the future

11 me   12 touched

13 (A) take pictures   (B) more beautiful stories

---

01 by chance = by accident = accidentally: 우연히, 뜻밖에, happen to do it = do it by chance[by accident]: 우연히 ~하다

02 Until then이 있으므로 과거완료로 고치는 것이 적절하다.

03 Zin Kim이 우연히 한 해녀의 사진을 찍게 되었을 때, 그녀는 자신의 직업을 '즐겼고 '다섯 시간이 넘도록 물속에 있은 후에도 계속 '웃었다'. Zin Kim은 그것에 놀라서 해녀의 사진을 찍어야겠다고 결심했다.

04 (A) '지난 몇 년 동안'이라고 해야 하므로 For가 옳다. during은 뒤에 기간을 나타내는 명사를 써서, 특정 기간 중의 어느 한 시점을 가리키고, for는 'how long?'에 대한 답을 나타낸다. (B) 부정의 뜻을 가지는 without이 있으므로 any가 옳다. (C) '무형문화유산'이라고 해야 하므로 Intangible이 옳다. tangible: 유형의

05 haenyeo를 복수로 취급했고, 한 명의 해녀는 a haenyeo라고 하는 것이 적절하다.

06 2001년부터 2009년까지는 two thousand (and) ~로 읽는 것이 적절하다.

07 바다 혹은 바다에서 사는 동식물들과 관련된, marine: 바다의, 해양의

08 해녀는 어떤 '호흡 장치'도 사용하지 않고 물속에 머물러서, 많은 해산물을 '채취할 수가 없기' 때문이다.

09 인터뷰 질문에 대한 답 세 가지를 쓰는 것이 적절하다.

10 간접의문문의 순서(의문사+주어+동사)로 쓰는 것이 적절하다.

11 소유격+신체의 일부를 나타내는 명사 = 목적격+전치사+the+신체의 일부를 나타내는 명사

12 moved = touched: 감동한

13 Zin Kim은 해녀 중 한 분이 그녀에게 감사를 표했던 순간을 절대 잊을 수가 없기 때문에 해녀의 '사진을 계속해서 찍을' 것이다. 그녀는 그들에 대한 '더 많은 아름다운 이야기들을' 세계의 더 많은 사람들에게 알려 주고 싶어 한다.

영역별 핵심문제   p.41~46

01 happiness   02 ②   03 ⑤

04 (1) go on (a) vacation   (2) a couple of
　(3) cheer up   (4) Give, a call

05 (1) overwork   (2) greenhouse   (3) breathe
　(4) device   (5) heritage

06 He wants to make double-sided copies.

07 He will press the button for double-sided copies.

08 ③   09 ⑤   10 ⓐ → check it out

11 beat   12 ⑤   13 had eaten

14 ①, ②   15 ③, ④

16 (1) thinking about which university he should go
       to

   (2) wondering when the rain will stop

17 (1) had pulled   (2) was killed

   (3) had already gone   (4) had been

   (5) had seen   (6) appeared

18 (1) what time the store opens

   (2) how we can contact the store manager

   (3) where the store is located

   (4) if[whether] there is any subway station near the
       store

19 (1) ⓑ   (2) ⓒ   (3) ⓐ   (4) ⓒ   (5) ⓐ   (6) ⓓ   (7) ⓑ

   (8) ⓓ

20 (1) Vanessa had cleaned the windows and (had)
       washed the dishes

   (2) Sally had given the dog some food and (had)
       watered the plant

21 (1) why she had to learn how to cook in another
       country

   (2) if there are any seats left on the plane

22 ③   23 ①, ④   24 ⑤   25 ②

26 ③   27 ⑤   28 ④   29 ②

01 주어진 단어는 형용사와 명사의 관계이다.

02 '가족을 부양하려고 돈을 버는 가족 구성원'을 나타내는 말은
   breadwinner(생계를 책임지는 사람, 가장)이다.

03 path: 오솔길, 작은 길

04 go on (a) vacation: 휴가가다, a couple of: 두 서너 개의,
   cheer up: 힘을 북돋아 주다, 격려하다, give (someone) a
   call: 전화를 걸다

05 heritage: 유산, greenhouse: 온실, device: 장치, breathe:
   호흡하다, overwork: 과로

06 Jack은 양면 복사를 하고 싶다.

07 Jack은 시작 버튼을 누르기 전에 양면 복사 버튼을 누를 것이
   다.

08 주어진 문장은 구체적인 설명을 요청하는 것이므로 이어지는 문
   장에서 구체적인 제주 올레길에 대한 설명이 이어지는 (C)에 들
   어가는 것이 적절하다.

09 Tom이 제주도에서 무엇을 하고 싶은지는 대화를 통해 알 수 없
   다.

10 '동사+부사'로 이루어진 구동사의 목적어가 인칭대명사일 때 목
   적어가 동사 바로 뒤에 위치한다.

11 '일련의 규칙적인 움직임 또는 치는 동작 중의 하나'를 가리키는
   말은 beat(소리)이다.

12 유리는 함께 춤추는 것이 음악을 완성한다고 설명한다.

13 대학 졸업 전에 처음 치즈 퐁듀를 먹었다고 했으므로, 과거완료
   시제이다. before와 같이 명백한 전후 관계를 알 수 있는 접속
   사가 있을 때는 과거시제로 써도 괜찮다. 그러나 빈칸이 두 개이
   므로 과거완료시제를 쓰는 것이 적절하다.

14 ① where the monsters are from ② why 뒤에는 완전한
   문장 구조가 와야 한다. in 뒤에 특정한 명사를 덧붙이거나 why
   대신 의문대명사 who, which, what 등을 써야 한다.

15 간접의문문에서는 '의문사+주어+동사' 구조를 잘 이해하고,
   think 동사 등의 예외에 주의해야 한다. ③ when did he
   leave → when he left ④ Do you think when → When
   do you think

16 (1) 준호는 어느 대학에 갈지 생각 중이다. (2) 예은이는 비가
   언제 그칠지 궁금해 하고 있다.

17 (1), (3), (4), (5) 과거의 어느 특정 시점을 기준으로 그 이전에
   시작된 일은 과거완료시제로 표현한다. (2) '역사적 사실'은 주
   절의 동사 시제와 상관없이 과거시제를 쓴다. (6) when은 '시
   점'을 표현하기 때문에 의문문 또는 간접의문문에서 완료시제로
   표현할 수 없다.

18 의문문이 간접의문문이 될 때는 '의문사+주어+동사'의 어순이
   된다. 의문사가 없을 경우 if 또는 whether를 써서 접속사 역할
   을 하도록 한다.

19 과거완료시제는 완료, 경험, 결과, 계속 등의 용법으로 구분할
   수 있으며, 해석을 정확하게 하는 것이 중요하다.

20 우리말에 맞게 과거완료시제를 사용하여 쓴다.

21 (1) 간접의문문의 어순은 '의문사+주어+동사'이다. (2) '의문사
   가 없는 간접의문문'은 if또는 whether가 접속사 역할을 한다.

22 ⓐ be suitable for: ~에 적합하다, ⓑ the breadwinners
   for their families: 가족들의 생계비를 버는 가장

23 ⓒ와 ①, ④: 동명사, ②, ③, ⑤: 현재분사

24 어떤 호흡 장치도 사용하지 않고 물속에 머물기 때문에, 해녀는
   한 번에 많은 해산물을 채취할 수가 '없다.'

25 ⓐ와 ②: 감동시키다, ① (몸 등을) 움직이다, ③ (집, 근무지
   등을) 옮기다[이사하다], ④ (차·배 따위가) 나아가다, 전진하
   다, ⑤ (안건 등을) 제안[제출]하다

26 이 글은 'Zin Kim이 앞으로 계획하고 있는 것'을 설명하는 글
   이므로, 주제로는 ③번 'Zin Kim의 앞으로의 계획'이 적절하
   다.

27 앞에 나오는 내용과 상반되는 내용이 뒤에 이어지므로
   However가 가장 적절하다. ① 즉[말하자면], ② 게다가, 더욱
   이, ③ 따라서, 그러므로

28 위 글은 '기사문'이다. ① (책·연극·영화 등에 대한) 논평[비평],
   감상문, ② 독후감, ⑤ 자서전

29 Zin Kim이 어떻게 해녀들의 사진을 찍었는지는 대답할 수 없
   다. ① She is an underwater photographer. ③ When
   she met a haenyeo who was enjoying her job. ④ No.
   ⑤ Haenyeo's culture.

01 ①   02 (D) → (C) → (A) → (B)   03 ②

04 ⑤

05 She wants to borrow an audio guide.

06 She should press the button.

07 I wonder why there are so many cars on the road.

08 how about going somewhere, too?

09 (D) → (B) → (A) → (C)

10 Could you explain how to make double-sided copies?

11 ⑤   12 ①

13 (1) After Susan had learned the importance of recycling, she promised her teacher not to throw away used batteries.

     (2) Before Sunwoo lay in his room all day long, he had sprained his ankle during the basketball game.

14 ⓐ when the shopping mall closes

     ⓒ what kind of movie she was watching

     ⓓ what she usually does on Sundays

     ⓕ what time the show begins

15 ④, ⑤

16 how much he weighed, he had already gained, had often eaten

17 ④   18 ④   19 ③

20 She had only seen black-and-white photos of haenyeo who looked very tired.

21 ⑤   22 ②   23 ①   24 ④

25 ②   26 for   27 barista

28 It's decorating coffee with hot milk and watching his customers enjoying it.

---

01 give a presentation: 발표하다, give a hand: 돕다, give a call: 전화를 걸다

02 (D) 궁금한 점 말하기 → (C) 궁금한 점에 대한 답변 → (A) 제안 → (B) 수락

03 농악을 소개하는 문장으로 그것은 한국의 전통 음악인지 묻는 대답으로 적절하므로 (B)가 적절하다.

04 대화를 통해 어떤 종류의 춤이 음악을 완성하는지 알 수 없다.

05 여자는 음성 가이드를 빌리고 싶다.

06 여자는 음성 가이드를 사용하기 위해 버튼을 눌러야 한다.

08 'Why don't we ~?'는 '~하는 게 어때?'라고 제안하는 표현으로 'How about ~?'으로 바꾸어 쓸 수 있다.

09 (D) 궁금한 것 말하기 → (B) 궁금한 것에 대한 설명 → (A) 어떻게 알게 되었는지 질문 → (C) 대답

10 double-sided: 양면의

11 Jack은 양면 복사 버튼을 먼저 누르고 시작 버튼을 눌러야 한

12 'Do you suppose?'와 'What music is Paul listening to?'를 한 문장으로 합칠 때 간접의문의 의문사를 문두로 보내고 '주어+동사'의 어순으로 정리하면 ①과 같다.

13 과거의 특정 시점을 기준으로 전에 일어난 동작이나 상태를 과거완료로 표현한다. before나 after와 같이 '명확한 전후 관계'를 알 수 있는 경우 과거완료를 쓰지 않아도 되지만, 문제의 조건에 맞게 과거완료를 사용하도록 한다.

14 간접의문문의 어순은 '의문사+주어+동사'이다. 시제와 인칭에 맞게 동사의 형태에 유의한다.

15 과거 이전에 발생한 일은 과거완료시제로 표현한다. ① '그의 가족은 Brian이 전날 열심히 일했지만 결국 병원에 실려갔다는 사실을 우연히 알게 되었다' has worked → had worked ② '우리가 경기장에 도착했을 때, 전반전이 벌써 시작되었다'는 The first half of the match had already started when we arrived at the stadium.이 적절하다. ③ '대부분의 아시아인들은 봉감독이 칸 영화제에서 대상을 수상한 것을 자랑스럽게 느꼈다.' has won → had won 또는 felt → feel로 고쳐도 된다.

16 '불독은 몸무게가 얼마나 될지 알고 싶었다. 그는 저울에 오르기 전에 이미 살이 쪘다는 사실을 알게 되어 놀랐다. 그는 자기 전에 간식을 자주 먹었던 것을 후회했다.'

17 간접의문문 앞에 think, believe, imagine, guess 등 생각, 추측 등의 동사가 있을 때는 의문사를 문두로 보낸다. How old do you guess she is?가 적절하다.

18 앞에 나오는 내용과 상반되는 내용이 뒤에 이어지므로 however가 가장 적절하다. ① 게다가, ③ 즉, ⑤ 그러므로

19 이 글은 '어떻게 Zin Kim이 해녀의 사진을 찍는 것에 관심을 가지게 되었는지'를 설명하는 글이므로, 주제로는 ③번 'Zin Kim이 해녀의 사진을 찍는 것에 관심을 가지게 된 이유'가 적절하다.

20 Zin Kim이 우연히 한 해녀의 사진을 찍었을 때까지, '그녀는 흑백 사진 속의 아주 지친 모습의 해녀만 봐 왔다.'

21 ⓐ와 ⑤: 가주어, ① 가목적어, ② 비인칭 주어, ③ 'It is … that'의 구문으로 문장의 주어·목적어·부사어구를 강조하는 대명사, ④ 그것(앞에 이미 언급되었거나 현재 이야기되고 있는 사물·동물을 가리킴)

22 처음에, 해녀들은 왜 Zin Kim이 자신들의 사진을 찍으려고 하는지 이해하지 못했다.

23 주어진 문장의 my talk에 주목한다. ①번 앞 문장의 a talk를 받고 있으므로 ①번이 적절하다.

24 lastly = finally: (여러 개를 언급할 때) 마지막으로, ① 결국, 마침내, ② 즉시, ③ 극도로, 극히, ⑤ 마침내[드디어]

25 ⓐ와 ①, ③, ④: 부사적 용법, ②: 형용사적 용법, ⑤: 명사적 용법

26 ⓐ for a living: 밥벌이로, 생계 수단으로, ⓑ passion for: ~

9

에 대한 열정

27 barista: 바리스타, 커피 내리는 사람

28 '뜨거운 우유로 커피를 장식하고 그의 손님들이 그것을 즐기는 것을 보는 것'이다.

01 They are waiting to get into the new bakery.

02 Because it was on a TV program.

03 He wants to try the new bakery's bread.

04 ① The film director was tired because he spoke[had spoken] in front of so many people.

05 ④ Where do you think the police officer caught the thief?

06 (1) Because Mary had learned taekwondo before, she fought off a strange man's attack.

(2) Until Kevin saw a video of himself being a heavy drinker, he had never thought of quitting drinking.

07 prettily → pretty

08 I would make them look beautiful in my pictures.

09 (A) very special   (B) show their culture

10 (A) without   (B) for   (C) destroy

11 (A) Less-experienced   (B) more-experienced

12 Because they stay in the water without any breathing devices.

01 많은 사람들이 새로 생긴 제과점에 들어가려고 줄을 서서 기다리고 있다.

02 새로 생긴 제과점이 TV에 나왔었기 때문이다.

03 Brian은 새로 생긴 제과점의 빵을 먹어 보고 싶어 한다.

04 영화감독이 피곤한 것은 너무나 많은 사람들 앞에서 연설했기 때문이다. 피곤한 상황이 과거완료가 되어서는 전후 관계가 뒤바뀌므로 적절하지 않다.

05 간접의문문 앞에 think, believe, imagine, guess 등 생각, 추측 등의 동사가 있을 때 의문사가 문두에 와야 한다.

06 (1) 'Mary는 전에 태권도를 배웠기 때문에 낯선 남자의 공격을 물리쳤' (2) 'Kevin이 본인의 주정뱅이 모습을 보기 전까지는 술을 끊는 것을 생각해 본 적이 없었다.'

07 감각동사 looked의 보어로 형용사를 써야 하므로 pretty로 고치는 것이 적절하다.

08 사역동사 make+목적어+목적격보어(동사원형)의 순서로 쓰는 것이 적절하다.

09 해녀들은 '아주 특별하고', 세계에 '그들의 문화를 알리고' 싶었기 때문이다.

10 (A) 어떤 호흡 장치도 '사용하지 않고'라고 해야 하므로 without이 옳다. (B) 이것은 수중 환경에 '좋은' 것이라고 해야

하므로 for가 옳다. be good at: ~을 잘하다, be good for: ~에 좋다, (C) 한 번에 한 장소에서 너무 많은 해양생물을 채취하는 것은 바다를 '파괴할 수 있다'고 해야 하므로 destroy가 옳다. protect: ~을 보호하다

11 '경험이 적은 해녀들'은 '경험이 더 많은 해녀들'에 의해 훈련을 받는다.

12 '어떤 호흡 장치도 사용하지 않고 물속에 머물기' 때문이다.

|모범답안|

01 (A) strong beat   (B) where the music came from
(C) nongak   (D) community band music
(E) cheer up farmers and wish for a good harvest

02 (1) He wants to know when I fed the puppy.

(2) Did you check whether the plant is dried?

(3) Tell me where I should empty the waste bin.

01 거리를 걷다가, 나는 강한 비트가 있는 음악을 들었다. 나는 음악이 어디서 오는 것인지 알고 싶었다. 유리와 나는 그것이 농악이라고 불리는 한국의 전통 음악이라는 것을 알게 되었다. 유리는 그것이 공동체 악단 음악의 한 종류로 전통적으로 농부들의 힘을 북돋아 주고 풍년을 기원하기 위해 사용되었다고 설명했다. 나는 몇몇 사람들이 리듬에 맞춰 춤을 추는 것이 인상 깊었다. 왜냐하면 함께 춤추는 것이 음악을 완성했기 때문이다. 유리와 나는 함께 했고 음악을 완성했다.

01 ①   02 ①

03 (1) I want to be a photographer.

(2) She was the most suitable candidate.

(3) He held my hand tightly.

(4) I'd like to borrow the novel.

04 ⑤

05 He visited Gwangandaegyo in Busan (with his family).

06 I wonder why there are so many people waiting in line.

07 ⑤   08 (C) → (D) → (E) → (A) → (B)

09 Because lots of people are going on vacation this weekend.

10 She suggested going somewhere.

11 ⑤   12 ②   13 ④   14 ⑤

15 if the woman had really put(또는 really had put) the fish

01 '사람들이 사도록 설득하려고 의도된 사진, 어구 또는 짧은 영상'을 가리키는 말은 advertisement(광고)이다.

02 주어진 문장에서 beat는 '리듬, 비트'를 가리키며 이와 같은 의미로 쓰인 것은 ①번이다. ②번은 '이기다', 나머지는 모두 '때리다, 두드리다'를 뜻한다.

03 photographer: 사진작가, suitable: 적절한, tightly: 단단히, 꽉, novel: 소설, borrow: 빌리다

04 ⑤번을 제외하고는 궁금한 점을 묻는 표현이다.

05 소년은 (그의 가족들과) 부산에 있는 광안대교를 방문했다.

07 위 대화를 통해 새로 생긴 제과점이 언제 TV에 방영되었는지는 알 수 없다.

08 (C) 이번 여름 계획 질문 → (D) 계획 설명 → (E) 올레길에 대한 설명 요청 → (A) 올레길에 대한 설명 → (B) 바람 표현

09 길 위에 많은 차들이 있는 것은 많은 사람들이 이번 주말에 휴가를 가려고 하기 때문이다.

10 Emma는 어딘가 갈 것을 제안했다.

11 궁금한 것을 묻는 질문에 이해가 가지 않는다는 말은 어색하다.

12 간접의문문의 어순은 '의문사+주어+동사'이다. 의문사를 문두로 보낼 이유가 없다.

13 그가 바이러스에 감염된 것은 그 질병의 중심지에서 3개월간 체류했던 것 때문이며, 과거보다 더 앞선 시점의 일이다. 과거완료 시제를 활용하는 것이 적절하다.

14 모두 '명사절로 사용된 간접의문문'인데, ⑤번만 '관계대명사가 이끄는 형용사절'로 쓰였다.

15 James는 그 여자가 붕어빵에 정말로 붕어를 넣었는지 궁금했다. 부사 really는 'had+p.p'의 중간에 와도 좋고, had 앞에 위치해도 괜찮다.

16 (A) Yori는 WeTube에서 그녀의 첫 비디오가 2만 개의 조회수를 얻었을 때 콘텐츠 창작자가 되었다. (B) 그녀가 자신의 직업에서 가장 좋아하는 부분은 한국 음식의 어떤 점이 특별한지 세계의 많은 사람들과 공유하는 것이다.

17 ⓐ와 ①, ③: 부사적 용법, ②, ⑤: 명사적 용법, ④: 형용사적 용법

18 Zin Kim이 우연히 한 해녀의 사진을 찍기 전에 그녀는 '흑백 사진 속의' 아주 지친 모습의 해녀만 봐 왔다.

19 이 글은 '해녀에 대해 무엇이 특별한지'를 설명하는 글이므로, 빈칸에 들어갈 질문으로는 ①번 '그들은 무엇이 그렇게 특별한가요?'가 적절하다. ④ hold one's breath: 숨을 참다

20 주어진 문장의 This에 주목한다. ④번 앞 문장의 내용을 받고 있으므로 ④번이 적절하다.

21 '되어 왔어요'를 현재완료 시제로 쓰는 것이 적절하다.

22 twenty thousands로 읽지 않도록 조심해야 한다.

23 what 다음의 동사가 is이므로, the things which[that]는 적절하지 않다.

24 Yori가 WeTube의 그녀의 첫 번째 동영상에 대해 언제 20,000 뷰를 돌파했는지는 알 수 없다. ① She is a content creator about traditional Korean food. ② By getting 20,000 views on her first video clip on WeTube. ④ It is sharing what is special about Korean food with many people around the world. ⑤ She is planning to write a cookbook on Korean food.

05 professional: 전문적인, What if ~?: ~하면 어쩌지?, clear one's mind: 마음을 가다듬다 with one's feet apart: 양발을 벌린 채로

A Journey into Your Mind

시험대비 실력평가   p.62

01 (r)are   02 ②   03 ④   04 ⑤

05 ⑤

06 (1) apart (2) behavior (3) hips (4) invisible

01 주어진 단어는 반의어 관계이다. common: 흔한, rare: 드문, 귀한

02 사람의 마음과 그것이 행동에 영향을 미치는 방식을 연구하는 학문을 가리키는 말은 psychology(심리학)이다.

03 confident: 자신감 있는

04 주어진 문장에서 judge는 '판단하다'를 의미한다. ① 심사위원을 하다 ② 판사 ③ 추정하다 ④ 재판하다 ⑤ 판단하다

05 come back: 돌아오다, come up with: 떠올리다, come over: (장소에) 들르다

06 apart: 떨어진, behavior: 행동, hip: 엉덩이, 허리께, invisible: 눈에 보이지 않는

서술형 시험대비   p.63

01 careful 또는 careless

02 (1) Chances are that (2) Strangely enough
   (3) stand tall (4) by myself

03 (1) I want to become a professional psychologist.
   (2) Children get bored easily.
   (3) My dog often chews my shoes.
   (4) Believe in yourself, and be confident.

04 (1) judge (2) law (3) loudly (4) rivals (5) seat

05 (1) His drawing skills are almost professional.
   (2) What if she forgets to make a reservation?
   (3) I decided to take a walk to clear my mind.
   (4) Stand with your feet apart and your hands facing upwards.

01 주어진 단어는 명사와 형용사와의 관계를 나타낸다. careful: 주의 깊은, careless: 부주의한

02 chances are that: 아마 ~일 것이다, strangely enough: 매우 이상하게도, stand tall: 당당해 보이다, by oneself: 혼자서

03 professional: 전문적인, psychologist: 심리학자, bored: 지루해하는, chew: 씹다, confident: 자신감 있는

04 rival: 경쟁자, seat: 좌석, judge: 판단하다, loudly: 큰 소리

Conversation

핵심 Check   p.64~65

1 I'm worried about him.
2 No, you don't have to. / No, you don't need to.
3 (C) → (A) → (B)

교과서 대화문 익히기

Check(√) True or False   p.66

1 T 2 F 3 T 4 F

교과서 확인학습   p.68~69

Listen & Speak 1 A-1

happened to / chewed, all the time, worried about / bored . Why don't you / hope, chewing

Listen & Speak 1 A-2

nervous / swimming competition / worry, relax, enjoy / better

Listen & Speak 2 A-1

what time / bake cookies / get up / don't have to

Listen & Speak 2 A-2

Shall we try / Why, make a reservation / don't have to, online / convenient

Communicate A

wait / worried / good at / relay / What, mean / last runner, What if / putting too much pressure on / practice / don't have to do / winning, losing / right, lucky

Progress Check 1

nervous / presentation, history / prepared, do, job / feel much better

Progress Check 2

seafood spaghetti / stop by, on the way / You don't have to, what / back, help, cook

01 ⓔ → chewing   02 ②

03 She's worried about her swimming competition this Saturday.

04 He advises her to relax and enjoy herself.

01 stop+to부정사: ~하기 위해 멈추다, stop+~ing: ~하던 것을 멈추다. 개가 신발을 씹는 걸 그만두길 바란다는 내용이 이어져야 하므로 chewing이 적절하다.

02 Brian은 항상 개가 신발을 씹는다고 이야기했다.

03 소녀는 이번 주 토요일에 있는 수영대회에 대해 걱정한다.

04 소년은 소녀에게 긴장을 풀고 즐길 것을 조언한다.

01 ①, ③

02 How about playing with him more often?

03 ⑤   04 ⑤   05 ①

06 (E) → (C) → (B) → (D) → (A)

07 She suggests trying that new Mexican restaurant tomorrow.

08 Because he can do it online.

09 ②   10 ⑤   11 ⑤

01 걱정을 나타내는 표현으로 ①, ③번과 바꾸어 쓸 수 있다.

02 Why don't you ~? = How about ~ing?: ~하는 게 어때?

03 Brian이 언제 신발을 샀는지는 알 수 없다.

04 이어지는 대화에서 걱정하는 모습이 나타나므로 nervous가 적절하다.

05 수영대회에 대해 걱정했지만 기분이 나아졌으므로 ①번이 적절하다. relieved: 안도된, 안심한, lonely: 외로운

06 (E) 몇 시에 출발할지 질문 → (C) 대답 및 계획 설명 → (B) 일찍 일어나야 하는지 질문 → (D) 대답 → (A) 반응 및 인사

07 Emily는 새로운 멕시코 레스토랑에 가볼 것을 제안한다.

08 레스토랑 예약은 온라인으로 할 수 있기 때문에 Tom은 레스토랑에 전화할 필요가 없다.

09 (A) be concerned about: ~에 대해 걱정하다 (B) because+주어+동사, because of+명사(대명사), (C) 주어와 목적어가 일치하므로 재귀대명사 yourself가 적절하다.

10 대화를 통해 누가 800미터 릴레이에 첫 번째 주자인지는 알 수 없다.

11 영어 수업 시간에 할 발표에 긴장하고 있다는 말에 감사하다는 말은 어색하다.

01 (B) → (D) → (C) → (A)

02 He's going to go to his grandma's place.

03 She is going to bake cookies for her.

04 She doesn't need his help because his dad will help her.

05 (A) last runner

(B) my team might lose because of me

(C) much pressure   (D) I should practice

(E) winning or losing

01 (B) 긴장되어 보임을 언급 → (D) 걱정 표현 → (C) 격려 → (A) 감사 표현

02 Jack은 내일 할머니 댁에 갈 것이다.

03 엄마는 할머니를 위해 쿠키를 구울 것이다.

04 엄마는 아빠가 그녀를 도와줄 것이기 때문에 Jack의 도움이 필요하지 않다.

05 오늘 나는 운동회에 대해 매우 걱정했다. 나는 800미터 릴레이의 마지막 주자로 선정되었다. 모든 학급 친구들은 내가 잘할 수 있을 것이라고 믿었다. 하지만 나는 매우 부담이 되었다. 나는 만약 나 때문에 팀이 지게 될까봐 걱정되었다. 나는 이것에 대해 유리에게 이야기를 했고 그녀는 내가 스스로에게 너무 많은 부담을 주고 있다고 말했다. 사실, 나는 내가 매일 연습을 해야 할지 말지 생각 중이었다. 유리는 내게 하지 말라고 했다. 왜냐하면 이것은 단지 학교 경기일 뿐이며 이기고 지는 것에 관한 것이 아니기 때문이었다. 나는 그녀로 인해 많이 용기를 북돋게 되었으며 정말로 그녀에게 고마웠다.

교과서
Grammar

핵심 Check   p.74~75

1 (1) Feeling   (2) coming

2 (1) teach → teaches   (2) are → is

01 ⑤   02 ③   03 ④

04 (1) he listened to music   (2) she felt lonely

(3) Though[Although] he is small and weak

01 상관접속사 not only와 but also 뒤에는 문법적으로 같은 것이 들어가야 한다.

02 부사절을 분사구문으로 바꿀 때, 주어가 같으면 주어를 생략하

고 분사를 쓴다. ④의 완료분사구문은 종속절의 시제가 주절의 시제보다 앞설 때 써야 한다.

03 ④ 상관접속사 not only와 but also 뒤에는 문법적으로 같은 것이 들어가야 한다. 동사 writes가 오면, but also 뒤에도 dances가 와야 한다.

04 분사구문은 분사를 활용하여 부사절을 부사구로 줄인 표현이다. 대개 양보, 동시동작, 이유, 시간, 조건 등의 부사절이며, 절과 구의 전환시 동사의 시제 등에 유의해야 한다. (3)은 내용상 양보이므로 Though 외에도 Although, Even though 등의 접속사가 가능하다.

01 ①　　02 ⑤　　03 ④　　04 ③
05 ⑤　　06 Exhausting → Exhausted
07 ②　　08 ①　　09 ②　　10 ④
11 ③　　12 ⑤
13 Having been built of wood and dry grass
14 Not wanting to be late for the meeting
15 (1) standing tall like Wonder Woman for a few minutes
　　(2) not only late for school but also hit by

01 ① not only ~ but also에서는 but also 뒤의 명사에 동사의 수를 일치시킨다. have → has가 적절하다.

02 'with+목적어+분사' 구문은 '목적어의 능/수동' 여부가 중요하다. 눈이 '감겨진 것'이므로 closed가 적절하다.

03 부사절로 영작하면, 'Though he had bullied many people, Tom lived well off.'이다. 분사구문 Having bullied에 의미를 명확하게 하기 위해 접속사 Though를 추가한 문장이 ④이다.

04 ① both는 복수 주어(is → are) ② 'not only A but also B'는 B가 주어(have → has) ④ neither ~ nor는 부정문과 함께 쓸 수 없다(don't have → have 또는 neither ~ nor → either ~ or) ⑤ not only가 문두에 오면 주어와 동사를 도치시킨다.(I am → am I)

05 ① speak → speaks ② know → knows ③ is → are ④ she likes to go → where she likes to go

06 '고된 일로 지친 것'(수동)이므로 Being이 생략된 과거분사 형태가 문두에 오는 것이 적절하다.

07 ② Both A and B는 복수 동사를 써야 한다. listens → listen 이 적절하다.

08 <보기>와 ①은 '양보' 의미의 분사구문이다.

09 <보기>는 'Josh 뿐만 아니라 Mina도 음주 뿐 아니라 흡연을 좋아하지 않는다.'라는 뜻이다. ① 'Josh와 Mina 둘 다 흡연이 아닌 음주를 좋아한다.' ③ 'Josh 또는 Mina 둘 중 하나는 흡연

도 음주도 좋아하지 않는다.' ④ 문법적 오류 ⑤ 'Josh와 Mina 둘 다 흡연이 아닌 음주를 싫어한다.'

10 완료분사구문과 양보 의미의 부사구가 쓰였으므로, 접속사는 Though, 시제는 came이 적절하다.

11 ① and also → but also ② likes → like ④ the passengers were → were the passengers ⑤ only → not only

12 ① or → and ② nor → or ③ wonder → wonders ④ know → knows

13 종속절의 시제가 앞서 있고, 수동태이므로 완료분사구문의 수동형인 'Having been p.p.'를 활용하여 알맞게 배열한다.

14 분사구문의 부정은 분사 앞에 not이나 never를 쓴다.

15 (1) '몇 분간 원더우먼처럼 꼿꼿이 서 있고 나서, 지수는 더 이상 긴장되지 않았다.' (2) 'Jenny는 학교에 늦었을 뿐만 아니라 도로에서 물벼락까지 맞았다.' *splash: 물이 튐

01 (1) Wanting to clear his mind
　　(2) not only feel sure about yourself but also look confident
　　(3) Wanting to turn a rival into a friend
02 (1) When he graduates from high school next year
　　(2) Though I was sick all day long
　　(3) If you have a problem that you cannot share with your family or friends
　　(4) While he listened to the radio
　　(5) Because we do not have to worry about being judged
03 (1) Having no friends at school,
　　(2) She not only helped me but also became a good friend.
　　(3) Asking for help, you can make friends.
04 (1) Minju's mom is not only a good doctor but also a great cook.
　　(2) Harry not only speaks Spanish but also dances well.
　　(3) Seohyun is not only beautiful but also very kind.
　　(4) Not only Frank but also his parents are nice.
05 (1) study → studies　(2) is → are　(3) is → are
　　(4) stress → stressful　(5) is → are
06 (1) that its food is not only delicious[healthy] but also healthy[delicious]
　　(2) Having picked a huge carrot, the farmer donated it

01 (1), (3)은 분사구문을 활용하는 문제이다. 의미에 맞게 단어를 배열하도록 한다. *clear one's mind: 마음을 정리하다 *do one a favor: A에게 부탁을 들어주다[호의를 베풀다] (2)는 'not only A but also B' 구문이다.

02 문제에 쓰인 분사구문은 각각 시간, 양보, 조건, 동시동작, 이유 등의 의미로 쓰였다. (1) 내년에 고등학교를 졸업할 때, Tammy는 전문적인 농부가 되고 싶어 한다.(동사 시제를 현재형으로 쓰는 것에 유의할 것) (2) 비록 하루 종일 아팠지만, 나는 그 힘든 프로젝트를 완수할 수 있었다. (3) 가족이나 친구들과 나눌 수 없는 문제가 있다면, 낯선 이에게 얘기를 걸어보라. (4) 라디오를 들으면서, Henry는 자신의 기타들을 닦았다. (5) 우리가 평가받을 것에 대해 걱정할 필요가 없기 때문에, 우리는 종종 낯선 사람에게 우리 문제를 말한다.

03 (1) not ~ any를 no로 바꾸면, 'As I had no friends at school'이 된다. 분사구문으로 전환하면 'Having no friends at school'이다. (3) 부사절을 활용하면, 'If you ask for help'이며, 분사구문으로 바꾸면 'Asking for help'가 된다.

04 (1) 민주의 엄마는 좋은 의사일 뿐만 아니라 훌륭한 요리사이다. (2) Harry는 스페인어를 말할 뿐 아니라 춤도 잘 춘다. (3) 서현이는 예쁠 뿐만 아니라 매우 친절하다. (4) Frank뿐만 아니라 그의 부모님 또한 착하다.

05 (1) 그녀는 모든 시험에서 만점을 받아야 한다고 생각할 뿐만 아니라, 잠도 안 자고 공부한다. (2) Both는 항상 복수 동사가 온다. (3) either A or B는 동사와 가까운 주어에 수를 일치시킨다. (4) 'not only A but also B'는 등위접속사이므로 문법적으로 같은 것을 써야 한다. stress는 명사이므로, 형용사형으로 고치는 것이 적절하다. (5) but also 뒤의 주어에 일치시킨다. the islands가 복수이다.

06 (1) 이 식당의 음식은 맛있을 뿐만 아니라 건강에 좋다.(건강에 좋을 뿐만 아니라 맛있다) healthy와 delicious는 서로 자리가 바뀌어도 좋다. (2) 거대한 당근을 수확했기 때문에, 그 농부는 그것을 원님에게 기부했다.

교과서

Reading

확인문제   p.82

1 F   2 T   3 T   4 F

확인문제   p.83

1 T   2 F   3 T   4 F

교과서 확인학습 A   p.84~85

01 Psychology   02 unique
03 Chances are
04 human mind, behavior, so, find, to
05 become less
06 big presentation, whole class
07 Feeling, carefully studying
08 came over, to stand tall
09 standing tall, not, anymore
10 In fact, confident that, make
11 become, by standing tall, stressful events
12 bodies, minds, minds, behavior
13 feel confident   14 apart, place, on
15 not only feel sure, but also look confident
16 feel
17 graduates from, professional
18 However, has never told
19 worried that, will not understand
20 Wanting, clear his mind, to take, by himself
21 complete, sitting   22 why he did it
23 However, felt much better   24 Strangely enough
25 because, being judged, seeing
26 that, share with, talking   27 feel much
28 turn, rival into   29 who, not, at all
30 become friends with, came up with
31 rare   32 to lend, a few days
33 deeply
34 Since, not only, but also
35 who do you one favor
36 turn, into, do your rival a favor
37 Instead, to do

교과서 확인학습 B   p.86~87

1 Psychology Answers Your Questions
2 Do you think you have a unique problem?
3 Chances are that many other people have the same problem.
4 Psychology is the study of the human mind and behavior, so it can help you find a solution to your problem.
5 How do I become less nervous?
6 It was five minutes before Jisu's big presentation in front of the whole class.
7 Feeling nervous, Jisu was carefully studying her notes in her chair.

8 Then, her teacher came over and told her to stand tall like Wonder Woman.

9 After standing tall for a few minutes, Jisu did not feel nervous anymore.

10 In fact, she was confident that she would make a great presentation.

11 According to Amy Cuddy, a famous psychologist, we can become more confident just by standing tall for two minutes before stressful events.

12 Our bodies change our minds, and our minds can change our behavior.

13 Do you want to feel confident?

14 Stand with your feet apart, and place your hands on your hips.

15 You will not only feel sure about yourself but also look confident to other people.

16 Who can help me feel better?

17 When he graduates from high school next year, Taeho wants to become a professional farmer.

18 However, he has never told anyone about it.

19 He is worried that his parents or his friends will not understand.

20 Wanting to clear his mind, Taeho decided to take a day trip on a train by himself.

21 On the train, he told a complete stranger sitting beside him about his problem.

22 He had no idea why he did it.

23 However, he felt much better when he got off the train.

24 Strangely enough, we often tell strangers about our problems just like Taeho.

25 That is because we do not have to worry about being judged or seeing them again.

26 If you have a problem that you cannot share with your family or friends, try talking to a stranger.

27 You will feel much better.

28 How do I turn a rival into a friend?

29 Benjamin Franklin once had a political rival who did not like him at all.

30 Franklin wanted to become friends with him, so he came up with a plan.

31 His rival had a rare book.

32 Franklin asked his rival to lend him the book for a few days.

33 When Franklin returned the book, he thanked him deeply.

34 Since that day, his rival became not only a political supporter but also a good friend.

35 Franklin famously said, "Enemies who do you one favor will want to do more."

36 If you want to turn a rival into a friend, don't do your rival a favor.

37 Instead, ask your rival to do you a favor.

시험대비 실력평가 p.88~91

01 ②	02 ③	03 ④	04 ①, ⑤
05 to do	06 ②	07 ①	
08 by himself		09 why → because	
10 (A) less (B) confident (C) apart			
11 Chances	12 ⑤	13 ④	
14 ②	15 ⑤		

16 his rival became a good friend as well as a political supporter

17 professional   18 ④   19 ①

20 ③   21 ③   22 no more → anymore

23 ①, ④

01 이어지는 글의 내용이 긴장하고 있던 지수가 몇 분을 우뚝 선 후에, 더 이상 긴장되지 않았다는 것이므로 '어떻게 하면 긴장을 덜 할 수 있나요?'가 적절하다.

02 psychologist: 심리학자 psychology: 심리학

03 ④ 선생님은 지수에게 다가와서 원더우먼처럼 꼿꼿이 서 있어 보라고 말했다.

04 관계대명사 주격이 필요한 자리이므로 who나 that이 적절하다.

05 ask의 목적격보어로 to부정사가 적절하다.

06 ②번은 Franklin의 정치적 경쟁자를 가리키지만, 나머지는 모두 Franklin을 가리킨다.

07 주어진 문장의 However와 it에 주목한다. However로 앞 문장과 상반되는 내용이 나오며 it이 앞 문장의 내용을 가리키므로 ①번이 적절하다.

08 by oneself: 혼자

09 That is why: 그것이 ~한 이유이다(앞에는 원인이 나오고, 뒤에는 결과가 나옴), That is because: 그것은 ~ 때문이다(앞에는 결과가 나오고 뒤에는 원인이 나옴). 앞 문장의 원인이 이어지므로 That is because가 적절하다. 원인이냐 결과냐를 따지지 말고 해석으로 판단하는 것이 더 좋다.

10 (A) 지수가 원더우먼처럼 꼿꼿이 서 있고 난 후 더 이상 긴장되지 않았다고 했으므로 less가 적절하다. (B) Amy Cuddy를 들어 앞의 내용을 추가 설명하고 있으므로 confident가 적절하다. (C) 원더우먼처럼 꼿꼿이 서려면 양발을 '벌리고' 서야 하므로 apart가 적절하다.

11 Chances are that ~: 아마 ~일 것이다

12 ⓑ와 ⑤번은 분사구문으로 쓰인 현재분사이다. ① 목적격보어로 쓰인 현재분사, ② 진행형에 쓰인 현재분사, ③, ④ 동명사

13 왜 우리의 몸이 마음을 바꾸는지는 대답할 수 없다. ① Amy Cuddy is a famous psychologist. ② By standing tall for a few minutes. ③ She told her to stand tall. ⑤ She stood tall for a few minutes.

14 책을 빌리고 돌려줄 때 진심으로 감사를 표한 후, 경쟁자가 후원자뿐만 아니라 좋은 친구가 되었다는 내용이다.

15 뒤에 days라는 복수 명사가 나오므로 a few가 적절하다. little과 a little은 복수 명사와 함께 쓰이지 않는다.

16 not only A but also B = B as well as A

17 professional: 전문적인, 영영풀이: 전문가는 진보한 교육과 훈련을 요구하는 직업을 갖고 있다.

18 앞에 나오는 내용과 상반되는 내용이 뒤에 이어지므로 However가 가장 적절하다. ① Moreover: 게다가, 더욱이, ③ Therefore: 그러므로, ⑤ In addition: 게다가

19 (A)의 much는 비교급을 강조하는 말로 even, a lot, far, still 등으로 바꿔 쓸 수 있다.

20 ③ 위 글에서 'He had no idea why he did it.'이라고 말하고 있다. ① A professional farmer. ② He has never told anyone about it. ④ Because he wanted to clear his mind. ⑤ By telling a complete stranger about our problem.

21 '선생님이 말씀하신 대로 몇 분을 우뚝 선 후에, 지수는 더 이상 긴장되지 않았다.'고 했으므로 어떻게 하면 긴장을 '덜' 할 수 있나요?가 적절하다.

22 not ~ anymore = ~ no more. 앞에 not이 나와 있으므로 no more를 anymore로 고치는 것이 적절하다.

23 (B)와 ②, ③, ⑤: 동명사, ①, ④: 현재분사

서술형 시험대비   p.92~93

01 a complete stranger

02 Strangely enough

03 we often tell strangers about our problems just like Taeho

04 Because psychology is the study of the human mind and behavior.

05 We can get to be more confident just by standing tall for two minutes before stressful events.

06 Becaus[As, Since] she was feeling

07 with   08 deep → deeply

---

09 his rival became a good friend as well as a political supporter

10 (A) Wanting   (B) sitting   (C) being judged

11 Taeho wants to become a professional farmer

12 He had no idea why he did it.

13 (A) a complete stranger   (B) much better

01 태호가 옆에 앉은 전혀 모르는 사람에게 자신의 고민에 대해서 말한 후 기분이 훨씬 좋아졌다고 했다.

02 Strangely enough: 정말 이상하게도, 기이하게도

03 앞 문장의 내용을 가리킨다.

04 '심리학은 인간의 마음과 행동에 관한 연구이며, 따라서 여러분이 문제에 대한 해결책을 찾는 데 도움을 줄 수 있다.'라고 하고 있다

05 'Amy Cuddy에 의하면, 우리는 스트레스를 받는 상황 이전에 2분 정도 꼿꼿이 서 있는 것만으로도 자신감이 더 생길 수 있다고 한다.'라고 하고 있다

06 Feeling은 'Because[As, Since] she was feeling'을 분사구문으로 고친 것이다.

07 become friends with: ~와 친구가 되다 come up with: (해답 등을) 찾아내다, 내놓다

08 deep: (깊이가) 깊이, 깊게, deeply: ('매우'의 의미로) 깊이, 철저하게

09 not only A but also B = B as well as A

10 (A) 주어인 태호가 원하는 것이므로 능동의 뜻을 갖는 Wanting이 적절하다. (B) 문장의 동사로 told가 나와 있으므로 sitting이 적절하다. (C) 우리가 평가하는 것이 아니라 평가를 받는 것이므로 being judged가 적절하다.

11 ⓐ의 it은 앞 문장에서 언급된 '태호가 전문적인 농부가 되고 싶어 하는 것'을 가리킨다.

12 why he did it(의문사+주어+동사)의 순서로 쓰는 것이 적절하다. have no idea = do not know

13 태호는 전문적인 농부가 되고 싶어 하지만, 부모님이나 친구들이 이해하지 못할까봐 걱정이 된다. 혼자 하루 기차 여행을 하는 동안, 그는 전혀 모르는 사람에게 자신의 고민에 대해서 말했다. 그는 자신이 왜 그랬는지 알 수 없었다. 그러나, 기차에서 내릴 때 기분이 훨씬 좋아졌다.

영역별 핵심문제   p.95~99

01 successful   02 ①   03 ⑤

04 (1) (p)robably   (2) professional   (3) psychology
     (4) (r)are

05 (1) make a presentation (2) stop by (3) stand tall
   (4) Chances are that (5) get off
06 ①   07 ⓔ → help you cook[to cook]
08 ①   09 ②
10 I'm worried about my presentation in history
   class.
11 ⑤   12 (C) → (D) → (B) → (A)
13 His dog chewed them.
14 She advises him to play with him[his dog] more
   often.   15 ④
16 (1) Both the honeybee and the ladybug are in
       trouble
   (2) neither to go to college nor to get a job
17 ②, ③
18 (1) likes (2) dancing (3) or (4) is (5) appears
19 ⑤   20 ②   21 ①   22 ④
23 ②   24 ②   25 ⑤   26 ⑤
27 ③   28 ③
29 He lent his rare book to Franklin.

01 주어진 단어는 명사와 형용사와의 관계를 나타낸
   다. successful: 성공적인, traditional: 전통적인
02 '대학, 학교 등에서 교육을 끝내다'를 가리키는 말은
   graduate(졸업하다)이다.
03 apart: 떨어져
04 probably: 아마도, professional: 전문적인, psychology: 심
   리학, rare: 희귀한
05 chances are that: 아마 ~일 것이다, get off: 내리다,
   stop by: 들르다, stand tall: 당당해 보이다, make a
   presentation: 발표하다
06 by oneself: 혼자서, stop by: 들르다, by 6: 6시까지
07 help는 준사역동사로 원형부정사 또는 to부정사를 목적격 보어
   로 취할 수 있다.
08 stop by = drop by: 들르다
12 (C) 제안 → (D) 수락 → (B) 의무 부인하기 → (A) 반응
13 그의 개가 씹었다.
14 그녀는 Brian에게 개와 더 자주 놀아줄 것을 조언한다.
15 '큰 아파트에 혼자 살고 있는 것'과 '거의 외로움을 느끼지 않는
   것'은 '역접' 관계이다. '양보' 접속사가 적절하다..
16 (1) 꿀벌과 무당벌레 둘 다 거미줄에서 곤경에 처했다. (2) 지호
   는 대학 진학도 취업도 하지 않기로 결정했다.
17 ② Both A and B로 고친다. ③ Either A or B로 고친다.
18 (1) 'not only A but also B'는 B에 동사의 수를 일치시킨다.
   (2) 'not only A but also B'는 문법적으로 같은 것을 받으며,
   준동사도 그렇다. (3), (4) Either A는 or B와 함께 써서 'A 또
   는 B 둘 중 하나'를 가리키며, 동사와 가까운 주어에 일치시킨

다. (5) Not A but B는 B에 동사를 일치한다.
19 분사구문의 부정은 분사 앞에 not을 쓴다. 접속사를 쓸 경우, 접
   속사 뒤에 주어가 오면 분사구문은 쓸 수 없다.
20 분사구문에서의 비인칭 주어 It과 주절의 주어가 다르므로, 'It
   raining all day' 형태의 독립분사구문이 적절하다.
21 ⓐ a solution to A: A에 대한 해결책, to: [행위·동작·작용의
   대상] ~에 대하여 ⓑ told의 목적격보어로 to부정사가 적절하
   다.
22 ② in fact: 사실(앞 문장에 나온 내용에 대해서 자세한 내용을
   덧붙이거나 내용을 강조할 때 사용), ③ 게다가, 더욱이, ⑤ 그
   러므로
23 이 글은 '만약 가족이나 친구들과도 나눌 수 없는 고민이 있다
   면, 낯선 이에게 말해 보면 기분이 훨씬 나아질 것임'을 설명하
   고 있으므로, 주제로는 '고민이 있을 때 기분이 나아지는 법'이
   적절하다.
24 밑줄 친 ⓐ는 내용상 이유를 나타내는 분사구문으로 보는 것이
   적절하다. ⑤번으로 보면 이후의 진행과 연결이 어색하다.
25 '태호는 옆에 앉은 전혀 모르는 사람에게 자신의 고민에 대해서
   말했다. 그는 자신이 왜 그랬는지 알 수 없었다.'라고 되어 있다.
26 앞의 내용에 대안을 제시하고 있으므로 '대신에'가 가장 적절하
   다. ③ Nonetheless: 그럼에도 불구하고
27 주어진 문장의 the book이 ③번 앞 문장의 a rare book을 받
   고 있으므로 ③번이 적절하다.
28 ① wicked: 사악한, ⑤ evil: 나쁜, 흉악한
29 Franklin의 정치적 경쟁자는 Franklin에게 그의 희귀한 책을
   빌려 주었다.

단원별 예상문제   p.100~103

01 ⑤
02 (1) Don't put too much pressure on yourself.
   (2) Stand with your feet apart.
   (3) I'll call the restaurant and make a reservation.
03 He is going to cook seafood spaghetti (for
   dinner).
04 It's because Minsu and Emma already have what
   they need.
05 She will be back home by 6 to help him.
06 (C) → (D) → (A) → (B)   07 You don't have to.
08 ④   09 ⑤   10 ⑤   11 ②
12 ②, ⑤   13 ④   14 ④
15 (1) Using green energy vehicles
   (2) Anne not coming back
   (3) Not having been invited to the final match

16 ③   17 sixty

18 Because[As/Since] we wanted to find the answer to this question,

19 unique

20 Chances are that many other people have the same problem.

21 ③

22 Her teacher advised Jisu to stand tall like Wonder Woman.

23 ⑤

01 '당신을 싫어하면서 당신에게 해를 끼치고 싶어 하는 사람'을 가리키는 말은 enemy(적)이다.

02 put too much pressure on: ~에게 너무 많은 부담을 주다, with your feet apart: 양발을 벌린 채로, make a reservation: 예약하다

03 민수는 저녁으로 해물 스파게티를 요리할 것이다.

04 민수와 Emma는 이미 필요한 것을 갖고 있기 때문에 가게에 들를 필요가 없다.

05 Emma는 6시까지 민수를 도우러 집에 돌아올 것이다.

06 (C) 신발에 생긴 일에 대해 질문 → (D) 설명 및 걱정 표현 → (A) 제안 → (B) 수용 및 바람 표현

07 don't have to: ~할 필요 없다

08 ④ Jack의 엄마는 내일 아침에 쿠키를 구울 것이다.

09 주어진 문장은 매일 연습을 해야 한다고 생각하는가에 대한 질문에 대한 대답으로 알맞으므로 (E)가 적절하다.

10 유리는 Jaden이 매일 연습을 할 필요가 없다고 이야기한다.

11 수영대회는 이번 주 토요일이다.

12 ① Opened → Opening ③ Worked → Working ④ Knowing not → Not knowing

13 but also 뒤에 형용사 generous가 있으므로, 부사 truly(진심으로, 진정으로)는 적절하지 않다.

14 not only 뒤에 과거동사가 나왔으므로, 과거시제 동사가 아닌 것을 찾는다. ④ proud는 형용사이다.

15 부사절을 분사구문으로 만들 때, 일반적으로 접속사를 생략한 후 주어가 같으면 주어도 생략하고, 동사를 V-ing 형태로 바꾸는데 Being은 보통 생략한다. 주절보다 시제가 앞서면 Having been 형태가 되고, 부정문에서 not은 분사 앞에 쓰는 것이 적절하다.

16 'not only A but also B'가 주어 자리에 있을 때는 but also 뒤의 B에 동사를 일치시킨다. 주어가 their mom이므로 동사는 likes가 적절하다.

17 30명의 학생들 중에서 18명의 학생들이 평균 점수를 넘었으므

로 60%이다.

18 이유를 나타내는 부사절로 고치는 것이 적절하다.

19 unique: 유일무이한, 독특한

20 chances are that ~: 아마 ~일 것이다

21 주어진 문장의 After에 주목한다. ③번 앞 문장에서 '선생님이 다가와서는 원더우먼처럼 꼿꼿이 서 있어 보라고 말했'으므로 ③번이 적절하다.

22 지수의 선생님은 지수에게 원더우먼처럼 꼿꼿이 서 있어 보라고 했다.

23 not only A but also B = not only A but B = not simply A but (also) B = not just A but (also) B = not merely A but (also) B cf. not A but B: A가 아니라 B

서술형 실전문제   p.104~105

01 She is looking forward to Sports Day.

02 He is worried that his team may[might] lose because of him.

03 Because she thinks that the 800-meter relay is just a school race and it's not about winning or losing.

04 (1) Walking down the street
   (2) Not knowing what her father meant
   (3) There being any seats left on the plane
   (4) Wanting to clear her mind

05 either / Neither, nor, Not only, but also / both, and

06 Because[As/Since] I didn't have her around

07 Not only did she write a lot about her memories

08 필자는 할머니가 원했던 것처럼 행복해지려고 노력해야 한다는 것을 배웠다.

09 nose

10 (A) getting hotter (B) rises

11 (A) lying (B) Not only do they (C) as if
   (D) rises

01 유리는 운동회를 기대하고 있다.

02 Jaden은 800미터의 마지막 주자로서 그의 팀이 자기 때문에 질까봐 걱정한다.

03 유리는 800미터 릴레이는 학교 경기일 뿐이며 이기고 지고에 관한 것이 아니라고 생각한다.

04 주어진 어휘에 접속사들이 없으므로, 분사구문을 배열하는 문제이다. 각각 (1) 시간, (2) 양보, (3) 조건, (4) 이유 등의 부사절

을 분사구문으로 만든 것이며, (3)의 경우 주절과 종속절의 주어가 다르기 때문에,유도부사 There 등을 문두에 써야 한다.

05 지나가 지훈에게 엄마의 생일을 묻자, 지훈은 11월 10일인지, 12일인지라고 대답해서 지나를 답답하게 한다. 지나는 아빠뿐만 아니라, 동생도 엄마에게 관심이 없다고 말하고, 미안한 지훈이는 어떻게 할지를 묻는다.

06 이유를 나타내는 부사절로 고치는 것이 적절하다.

07 부정어구(not only)로 문장이 시작되면 의문문 형식으로 도치가 이루어진다.

08 본문의 마지막 부분의 내용을 쓰는 것이 적절하다.

09 Pinocchio Effect(피노키오 효과)를 설명하는 대화로 마지막 부분에서 '코가 더 뜨거워지고 눈 주위의 체온이 올라가는 것처럼 느낀다'라고 하고 있으므로 nose가 적절하다.

10 코가 더 뜨거워지고 눈 주위의 체온이 올라가는 것처럼 느끼기 때문이다.

11 (A) '거짓말하다'라는 의미의 자동사 lie가 쓰일 자리이므로 현재분사 lying이 적절하다. (B) 부정어구(not only)로 문장이 시작되면 의문문 형식으로 도치가 이루어지므로 Not only do they가 적절하다. (C) even if: (비록) ~일지라도, (설사) ~이라고 할지라도, as if: 마치 ~인 것처럼, 흡사 ~와도 같이 (D) 체온이 올라간다는 뜻의 자동사 rises가 적절하다. raise는 타동사로 '~을 올리다, 끌어올리다'라는 뜻이다.

창의사고력 서술형 문제 p.106

|모범답안|

01 (A) Grandma's place   (B) bake cookies
   (C) My dad
02 (A) has just moved to a new school   (B) lonely
   (C) Having nobody to talk to
   (D) showed me her notes but also started to talk about herself
   (E) helps you make new friends

01 나는 내일 할머니 댁을 방문하는 것을 기대하고 있다. 우리는 내일 8시쯤에 떠날 것이다. 엄마는 할머니를 위해 쿠키를 만들 계획이다. 아빠는 엄마를 아침 일찍 도와주실 것이다. 나는 할머니를 뵙는 것이 몹시 기대된다.

단원별 모의고사 p.107~111

01 (1) came up with (2) (c)ame over (3) came back

---

02 (1) text message (2) anxious (3) unique
   (4) prepare (5) mind (6) competition
03 (1) Are you interested in the political issue?
   (2) You don't have to prepare your speech every day.
   (3) I'm not worried about our presentation at all.
04 ⑤
05 She is concerned about her presentation in history class.
06 It's because she's prepared a lot.
07 ⑤   08 make a reservation   09 ②
10 (B) → (C) → (D) → (A)   11 ④
12 (A) nervous (B) her swimming competition
   (C) this Saturday
   (D) just relax and enjoy yourself
13 ③   14 ④   15 ④
16 Both Minju[Sam] and Sam[Minju] are interested in joining a club
17 ⑤
18 ④ Having seen him before, Julie decided to make friends with Charles.
19 ⑤ Neither the president nor his secretaries want to know the basic causes of the problem.
20 ② Having, ③ classmates
   이유: ② 주어인 I가 친구가 없는 것이므로 능동의 의미로 쓰여야 한다. ③ 'one of+복수 명사'로 쓰인다.
21 ①   22 ③   23 ②
24 He took a day trip on a train by himself to clear his mind.
25 ②

01 come up with: ~을 떠올리다, come over: (장소에) 들르다, come back: 돌아오다
02 competition: 경쟁 text message: 문자 메시지, prepare: 준비하다, mind: 마음, 생각, anxious: 걱정하는, unique: 독특한
03 political: 정치적인, prepare: 준비하다, be worried about: ~에 대해 걱정하다, not ~ at all: 전혀 ~ 아닌
04 가족이 걱정된다는 말에 서로 이야기할 필요가 없다는 대답은 어색하다.
05 소녀는 역사 시간에 할 발표에 대해 걱정한다.
06 소년은 소녀가 준비를 많이 했기 때문에 잘할 것이라고 생각

한다.

07 엄마가 쿠키를 굽기 위해 내일 몇 시에 일어날지는 대화를 통해 알 수 없다.

10 (B) 긴장한 것 같아 보인다고 이야기함 → (C) 걱정 표현하기 → (D) 격려 → (A) 감사 표현

11 (A) be worried about: ~에 대해 걱정하다, (B) 감정을 나타내므로 과거분사 bored, (C) stop+~ing: ~하던 것을 멈추다, stop+to부정사: ~하기 위해 멈추다

12 소녀는 긴장돼 보였다. 그녀는 수영대회 때문에 매우 걱정이 되었다. 대회는 이번 주 토요일에 열릴 것이다. 소년은 그녀가 수영을 잘한다는 것을 알기 때문에 긴장을 풀고 즐기라고 말하며 그녀를 격려했다. 소년 덕분에 소녀는 안도감을 느꼈다.

13 'not only V-ed but also V-ed' 형태로 영작하는 것이 적절하다. look은 2형식 동사로서 형용사 보어 confident를 받는다. ④의 경우, feel과 Jisu의 위치를 바꾼다면, 정답이 될 수 있다.

14 'not only A but also B' 구문이 주어가 아닌, 문장을 꾸미는 형태에서 Not only가 문두로 나오면, 주어와 동사는 '도치'되므로 정답은 ④가 적절하다.

15 '날씨가 춥지만 맑았다'는 내용과, '우리가 소풍을 갔다'는 내용은 '양보' 접속사 though로 표현하기에 어색하다. '이유'를 나타내는 Because 또는 As 등이 적절하다.

16 Minju와 Sam 둘 모두 동아리에 가입해서 봉사활동을 하는 것에 관심이 있다.

17 ①, ③, ④ '주절과 종속절의 주어가 다르므로, 분사구문의 주어를 쓴다.' ① Watching → Babe watching, ② 주절과 종속절의 주어가 같으면, 주어를 생략한다. She going → Going, ③ Cutting → You cutting, ④ Being → It being

18 분사구문에서 부사절의 주어와, 주절의 주어가 같을 때 분사구문에 주어를 쓰지 않는다. 내용상 '전에 그를 본 적이 있기 때문에, Julie는 Charles와 친구가 되기로 했다'는 것이므로, Julie와 she는 동일 인물이다.

19 'Neither A nor B'는 동사와 가까운 주어에 수를 일치시킨다. secretaries가 복수이므로 wants → want가 적절하다.

21 도와달라고 부탁했을 때 도와주었을 뿐만 아니라 좋은 친구가 되었다고 했으므로 ①번이 적절하다.

22 'Having no friends at school'이라고 하고 있다.

23 이 글은 '모르는 사람에게 자신의 고민에 대해서 말한 후 기분이 좋아졌다.'는 글이므로, 빈칸에 들어갈 말로는 ②번 '누가 내 기분을 낮게 해 줄 수 있나요?'가 적절하다.

25 ②번 다음 문장에서 '그는 부모님이나 친구들이 이해하지 못할

까 걱정이 된다.'라고 하고 있으므로 ②번이 어색하다.

Find Your Passion

01 ⑤   02 pursue   03 ④   04 ①
05 ③   06 ②

01 동의어 관계이다. check: 계산서, bill: 계산서, decide: 결정하다, determine: 결정하다

02 '종종 오랜 시간에 걸쳐, 어떤 특정 목표나 결과를 달성하기 위해 노력하다'는 'pursue(추구하다, 추진하다)'가 적절하다. 더이상 논의할 필요가 없다.

03 ① promise: 약속하다, 다짐하다. 내가 뭘 할 수 있을지 보기는 하겠지만 아무것도 약속할 수는 없어요. ② fix: 수리하다. 전화를 수리하도록 기술자를 보낼게요. ③ slice: 한 조각, 일부. 나는 보통 매일 아침 빵 한 조각을 먹는다. ④ decorate: 장식하다, 꾸미다. 배우들의 사진이 그 레스토랑의 벽을 장식하고 있다. ⑤ provide: 제공하다. 교사들은 아동들에게 본뜰 수 있는 모델을 제시한다.

04 passion: 열정, 흥미 / 너만의 열정을 찾고 너의 꿈을 따라가라.

05 ① scare away: 겁주어 쫓아내다. 그들은 겁을 주어 그 곰들을 간신히 쫓았다. ② fill out: 작성하다. 이 양식들 좀 작성해 주세요. ③ be used to (동)명사: ~에 익숙하다. 저는 한 손으로 쟁반을 나르는 것에 익숙하지 못했어요. be used to 동사원형: ~에 사용되다 ④ take on: 떠맡다. 저는 새로운 책무를 맡을 준비가 안 되어 있는 것 같습니다. ⑤ take classes: 수업을 듣다. 이 수업을 들으려면 컴퓨터를 사용할 수 있어야 한다.

06 take charge of: ~의 책임을 지다, ~을 떠맡다. 네가 그 회사를 맡게 될 거야. of all time: 역대, 지금껏. 내 생각에는 그가 역대 최고의 코미디언 중 한 명인 것 같다. To my thinking: 내 생각에는

01 (1) complain   (2) customer
     (3) appreciate   (4) form

02 (1) complaint   (2) unnatural

03 (1) innovative   (2) decorate
     (3) device   (4) role

04 (1) I have a passion for fashion.
     (2) The new restaurant put up a bright and colorful sign.

(3) Thank you for your understanding and we apologize for any inconvenience.
(4) Now that it's winter, I'm going to go skiing every weekend.

01 (1) complain: 불평하다 / 무엇이나 누군가에 대해 짜증나거나 불만족스럽거나 불쾌하다고 말하다 (2) customer: 고객, 소비자 / 상점, 회사 등으로부터 상품이나 서비스를 구입하는 사람 (3) appreciate: 진가를 알아보다 / 어떤 것의 좋은 점을 인정하여 그것을 좋아하다 (4) form: 서류 / 당신이 정보를 적을 여백을 가진 공식적인 문서

02 (1) '동사 – 명사'의 관계이다. decide: 결정하다 – decision: 결정, complain: 불평하다 – complaint: 불평 (2) '반의어' 관계이다. completely: 완전하게 – incompletely: 불완전하게, natural: 자연스러운 – unnatural: 자연스럽지 않은

03 (1) innovative: 획기적인 (2) decorate: 장식하다 (3) device: 장치, 기구 (4) role: 역할 the main role: 주인공

04 (1) passion: 열정, passion을 추가한다. (2) put up: 세우다, 내붙이다, put을 추가한다. (3) inconvenience: 불편, 애로, thank A for B ~의 형태로 쓰이므로 for를 추가한다. (4) now that: ~이기 때문에, ~이므로, now that으로 접속사 역할을 하도록 that을 추가한다. go ~ing: ~하러 가다

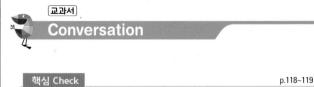

1 I'm not satisfied with the phone.
2 I promise I'll do my best.

1 F   2 T   3 F   4 T

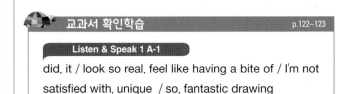

Listen & Speak 1 A-1

did, it / look so real, feel like having a bite of / I'm not satisfied with, unique / so, fantastic drawing

Listen & Speak 1 A-2

How can, help / only a week ago, sometimes turns off by itself / have a look at, inconvenience, take, few hours to / I'm not satisfied with, one / fill out, form

Listen & Speak 2 A-1

myself / better than any other jam / it / would / I promise I'll be

Listen & Speak 2 A-2

were interested in / not anymore, want to / Are, sure / how to act, I promise I'll do

Communicate A

your meal / good, fresh / about / I'm not satisfied with, rare / to bring, another one / be going, have, check / won't have to / I promise we'll provide, with

Progress Check 1

How can I / got, as, I'm not satisfied with / in / one in blue / do, get one

Progress Check 2

take, classes / interested in / not anymore / worry, I promise I'll do / then

Progress Check 3

on / Have, finished / I promise I'll finish

시험대비 기본평가   p.124

01 ②   02 I promise I'll be your first customer.
03 (C) – (B) – (A) – (D)

01 뒤에 나오는 'It's not unique.'로 보아 ②번이 가장 적절하다. 'I'm not satisfied with it'은 불만족을 표현하는 말이다.

02 'I promise I'll be your first customer.'는 다짐을 말할 때 쓰는 표현이다. promise 뒤에는 구체적인 내용을 명사절을 써서 나타내며, "I promise to be your first customer."로 바꿔 쓸 수 있다.

03 '무엇을 도와드릴까요?'라는 주어진 글에 이어서 (C)에서 불만을 말하고, (B)에서 사과하며 '고치는 데 몇 시간 정도 걸릴 거예요.'라며 고쳐 주겠다고 하자, (A)에서 '새것을 원한다'는 말에, (D)에서 '물론.'이라며 '서류만 작성하면 된다.'고 말하는 순서가 적절하다.

시험대비 실력평가   p.125~126

01 ④   02 ①   03 Yes, we do.
04 Do you have one in blue?   05 ⑤
06 ⑤   07 not anymore
08 (C) – (B) – (A) – (D)   09 ④   10 one

01 'not anymore'로 보아 A와 B를 서로 바꾸는 것이 적절하다.

02 다음에 '다른 색상도 있습니다.'라는 말로 보아 색상이 가장 적절하다.

03 뒤에 이어서 남자가 'I'll get one for you.'라고 하고 있으므로 가지고 있다고 했음을 알 수 있다.

04 hat을 대신해서 쓰인 부정대명사 one을 이용하여 one in blue로 영작한다.

05 마지막의 one은 'a hat'을 대신하는 부정대명사이다.

06 빈칸 앞에서 '배우가 되고 싶은 게 확실하니?'라는 질문에 '네, 연기하는 방법을 배울 거예요.'라고 답하고 있으므로 '최선을 다하겠다고 약속할게요.'라는 말이 자연스럽다.

07 not anymore: 더 이상 ~ 아니다, 이젠 ~ 않다

08 손님을 맞이하는 주어진 글에 이어, (C)에서 마음에 들지 않는 색상에 대한 불만족을 말하고, (B)에서 다른 색상도 있음을 설명하고, (A)에서 원하는 색상을 말하고, (D)에서 있다며 하나 가져다 드리겠다고 한 후, 고맙다는 말로 마무리한다.

09 뒤에서 'It's too rare for me.'라고 하는 것으로 보아 불만족을 말하는 것이 적절하다.

10 steak를 대신하는 부정대명사 one이 적절하다.

11 남자가 스테이크를 항상 덜 익은 상태로 제공하는지는 대화를 통해 알 수 없다.

12 'next time'을 하나의 접속사처럼 생각한다.

13 밑줄 친 문장은 다짐을 말할 때 쓰는 표현이다.

서술형 시험대비   p.127

01 (D) → (B) → (C) → (A)
02 You won't have to pay for the steak.
03 Because the steak was too rare for her. 또는 The woman isn't satisfied with the steak because it was too rare for her.
04 I'm not satisfied with the phone.
05 by itself
06 (1) I was. → I did.
    (2) feel like to have → feel like having

01 빵과 샐러드에 대해 언급한 문장에 이어서, 스테이크는 어땠는지 묻는 (D)가 나오고, 스테이크에 대해 불만족을 언급하는 (B)가 나오고, 사과하며 다른 것으로 가져다 드릴지를 묻는 (C)가 나오고, 괜찮다며 가봐야 한다는 (A)로 이어지는 순서가 적절하다.

02 'not have to(~할 필요 없다)'와 'pay for(지불하다)'를 이용한다. 주어의 의지를 나타내는 will과 'not have to'를 'won't

have to'로 쓴다.

03 남자의 '스테이크는 어떠세요?'라는 질문에 여자가 '솔직히, 스테이크는 만족스럽지 않아요. 제겐 너무 덜 익었어요.'라고 하고 있다.

04 'be not satisfied with ~'는 불만족을 나타내는 표현이다.

05 by itself: 스스로, 저절로

06 (1) 일반동사 draw를 받는 대동사이므로 was가 아니라 did로 써야 한다. (2) feel like -ing: ~하고 싶다

[교과서] Grammar

핵심 Check   p.128~129

1 (1) why (2) when
2 (1) However (2) Thus

시험대비 기본평가   p.130

01 ③   **02** (1) in which, where
(2) for which, why   **03** ②
04 (1) However (2) Thus (3) however
(4) However (5) Thus

01 콘서트가 취소된 것과 가수와 팬들이 실망한 것은 인과 관계이다.

02 '전치사+관계대명사'는 관계부사로 표현할 수도 있다. 선행사가 장소일 때 where, 선행사가 이유일 때는 why를 쓴다.

03 관계부사가 오면 뒤의 문장은 완전한 절의 형태여야 한다. 문미에 전치사 in이 남아 있으므로, 관계부사 where가 아닌 관계대명사 which로 고치는 것이 적절하다.

04 접속부사는 앞뒤 문장의 내용을 연결하는 역할을 한다. however는 '대조, 반대' 등의 '역접'을, thus는 '결과, 결론' 등의 '순접'을 의미한다. 해석을 통해 내용의 자연스러운 연결, 또는 반대 연결을 판단하여 어떤 종류의 접속부사로 문맥을 연결할지 결정하는 것이 중요하다.

시험대비 실력평가   p.131~133

01 ③   **02** ④   **03** ②   **04** ⑤
05 ①   **06** (1) For example (2) Moreover
(3) Similarly (4) However (5) However   **07** ⑤
08 ③   **09** ⑤   **10** ③   **11** where
12 when   **13** mother was born in the year when
World War II broke out   **14** why the subway has

not arrived for 30 minutes   **15** ③
16 (1) couldn't understand about the way his mother
cut them straight
(2) to hear how I could be rich

01 선행사 the way와 관계부사 how는 함께 쓸 수 없다. 둘 중 하나를 삭제하면 옳은 문장이 된다.

02 William은 그 공원 옆에서 3년 동안 살았다. (그래서 → 그러나) 한 번도 그곳을 가 본 적이 없다. Thus를 However로 바꾸는 것이 적절하다.

03 그 영화는 실망스러웠다. (그러므로 → 그렇지만), 배우들의 연기는 훌륭했다. Therefore를 However로 바꾸는 것이 적절하다.

04 선행사가 the time이므로 '관계부사' when 또는 '전치사+관계대명사' at which 등으로 연결해서 표현 가능하다.

05 선행사가 the reason일 때, '전치사+관계대명사'로 받을 때는 for which를, '관계부사'로 받을 때는 why를 쓰는 것이 적절하며, the reason과 why 둘 중 하나만 쓰는 것도 가능하다. ④에는 which 앞에 the reason이 필요하다.

06 (1) Shakespeare가 단어들을 만들어 낸 사례들 (2) 추운데다가 바람까지 세차게 불었다. (3) 아들은 아버지를, 마찬가지로 딸은 엄마를 따른다. (4) 소극적인 성격이지만, 불쌍한 사람들을 위해서는 적극적인 Lily. (5) 세계 경제가 불황이라서 사람들이 실직하게 되었다.

07 ① However → Thus ② Thus → However ③ However → Thus ④ Thus → However

08 ① Thus → However ② However → Thus ④ However → Thus ⑤ Thus → However

09 선행사가 the reason일 때, '전치사+관계대명사' 표현은 'for which'가 적절하며, 관계부사 why는 the reason과 함께 써도 되고, 생략도 가능하다.

10 선행사가 the way일 때, 관계부사 how는 같이 쓰지 않으며, 관계부사 앞에 전치사 in을 쓰지도 않는다.

12 두 문장을 연결해 주는 빈칸 뒤에 완전한 문장이 오고, 선행사가 장소일 때는 관계부사 where를, 선행사가 시간일 때는 관계부사 when을 쓰는 것이 적절하다.

13 시간을 나타내는 선행사 the year 뒤에 관계부사 when을 쓴다.

14 이유는 the reason인데 관계부사 why와 함께 쓸 수도 있고, 둘 중 하나를 생략해도 된다. 보기에 the reason이 없으므로, why를 이용하여 알맞게 단어를 배열한다.

15 <보기>는 'Dahyun이 피자 다섯 조각과 햄버거 두 개를 먹었지만 여전히 배가 고프다.'라는 뜻이다. ③ '~에도 불구하고'의 양보 의미를 가진 접속사 Though로 표현된 문장이 가장 가까운 뜻이다.

16 (1) 석봉은 자신의 형편없는 글씨들을 보며, 어떻게 그의 어머니가 그것들을 똑바로 썰었는지 이해할 수 없었다. (2) 내 친구들은 내가 어떻게 부자가 될 수 있었는지 듣고 놀랐다.

01 However

02 (1) However, customers were unhappy because they were used to

  (2) Thus, he invented new machines for his kitchen.

  (3) However, your mind can change your behavior as well.

  (4) Thus, she decided to take a day trip by herself.

03 (1) They found a special cave where their ancestors spent the winter.

  (2) The singer told me how she could be world famous.

  (3) My favorite season is spring when I can see the life coming back.

  (4) Please tell your mom the reason why you hid the the letter from Grace.

  (5) That is the soccer stadium where the Korean national team beat Brazil.

  (6) I remember the day when my first daughter was born.

04 (1) the restaurant where she made a hamburger

  (2) a charity box where a girl putsome money

  (3) the cafe where we talked over teaand coffee

  (4) a laptop where she wrote a marketing report

05 (A) However   (B) However

  (C) However   (D) Thus

06 ④ Thus → However, ⑥ However → Thus

07 the summer vacation when she played in the pool with

02 (1), (3)은 '역접' 관계이므로 접속부사 However를, (2), (4) 는 '순접' 관계이므로 접속부사 Thus를 쓰는 것이 적절하다. 그 외의 단어 배열은 의미와 어법에 알맞게 한다. *be used to: ~ 에 익숙하다 *clear one's mind: 마음을 정리하다

03 (1) 그들은 그들의 조상이 겨울을 보냈던 특별한 동굴을 찾았 다. (2) 그 가수는 어떻게 그녀가 세계적으로 유명하게 되었는지 를 내게 말해줬다. (3) 내가 가장 좋아하는 계절은 생명이 되돌 아오는 것을 볼 수 있는 봄이다. (4) 제발 너의 엄마에게 왜 네가 Grace에게서 온 편지를 숨겼는지 그 이유를 말해라. (5) 저곳 이 한국 국가대표팀이 브라질을 이겼던 축구 경기장이다. (6) 나 는 나의 첫째 딸이 태어난 날을 기억한다.

04 (1) 그녀가 햄버거를 만든 식당에서 한 남자에게 영수증이 건 네졌다. (2) 한 소녀가 돈을 넣는 자선 상자가 있었다. (3) 이 곳은 우리가 차와 커피를 마시며 얘기를 나눴던 카페였다. (4) Brenda는 그녀가 마케팅 보고서를 기록하는 노트북 한 대를 가 져왔다.

05 (A)~(C)는 모두 '역접'이다. 교과서의 원문에는 (A)에는

Unfortunately가, (B)에는 But이, (C)에는 접속사 Although를 이용한 표현이었다. (D)는 내용상 순접이고, Thus가 적절하다.

06 내용상 ④는 '역접'이므로 However를, ⑥은 '순접'이므로 Thus를 쓰는 것이 적절하다.

07 민주는 사촌들과 수영장에서 물놀이를 했던 여름방학을 결코 잊 을 수 없었다.

교과서
Reading

확인문제   p.136

1 T   2 F   3 T   4 F

확인문제   p.137

1 T   2 F   3 T   4 F

교과서 확인학습 A   p.138~139

01 the Cook

02 is known as, painters of all time

03 also

04 few, however, creative

05 twenty-year-old, as

06 took charge of, completely   07 but, like, a few

08 were even decorated with

09 however, were used to, servings

10 As a result   11 A few

12 where, innovative

13 beautifully painted, uniquely written

14 would, appreciate, creative 15 happened

16 to work

17 was given, such as

18 was, put in charge of

19 to be given another, to pursue

20 stop at   21 much more

22 Thus   23 that

24 that, scare, away from   25 were too, too, to

26 to make, which was based on

27 took on, had, been

28 a lot of, cooking, what to put

29 for over, why, to

30 Although, throughout

31 not only, but also

32 Now that, the same way

1 Da Vinci the Cook

2 Leonardo da Vinci is known as one of the greatest painters of all time.

3 He was also a great inventor, scientist, and musician.

4 Very few people, however, know that da Vinci was also a creative cook.

5 In 1473, twenty-year-old da Vinci worked as a cook at a restaurant in Florence, Italy.

6 When he took charge of the kitchen, da Vinci changed the menu completely.

7 He made simple but artistic dishes like fish with a few carrot slices.

8 Some dishes were even decorated with flowers.

9 Customers, however, were unhappy because they were used to dishes with big servings of meat.

10 As a result, da Vinci lost his job.

11 A few years later, da Vinci opened a restaurant with his friend Sandro Botticelli.

12 He wanted to create a place where people could try his innovative food.

13 They put up a beautifully painted sign and made a uniquely written menu.

14 Da Vinci believed that people would soon appreciate his creative cooking.

15 Unfortunately, that never happened.

16 In the early 1480s, da Vinci began to work for Ludovico Sforza in Milan.

17 He was given many different roles, such as a musician, a painter, and an engineer.

18 He was also put in charge of the kitchen.

19 He was happy to be given another chance to pursue his passion for cooking.

20 Da Vinci did not stop at cooking creative dishes.

21 He wanted to cook much more quickly and easily.

22 Thus, he invented new machines for his kitchen.

23 He created machines that could crush vegetables and pull spaghetti.

24 He even made a device that could scare frogs away from the water tank.

25 Surely, they were all very innovative, but most of them were too big or too difficult to use.

26 In 1495, Sforza asked da Vinci to make a grand painting, which was based on the last supper of Jesus, on the wall of a church in Milan.

27 Da Vinci gladly took on the project because he had always been interested in food.

28 He spent a lot of time cooking all kinds of food to decide what to put on the table in his picture.

29 "Da Vinci has wasted his time in the kitchen for over a year. That's the reason why he hasn't finished the painting yet," complained the people from the church to Sforza.

30 Although da Vinci never became a successful cook, he showed great interest in cooking throughout his life.

31 He was not only a great painter but also a creative cook.

32 Now that you know all about his secret passion for cooking, you will never look at The Last Supper the same way.

---

01 ②	02 appreciate	03 ④	04 ③
05 ①	06 to use	07 ⑤	
08 Now that	09 ③		

10 (A) painters (B) a few (C) lost

11 ④	12 ②	13 ⑤

14 Da Vinci not only cooked creative dishes but also wanted to cook much more quickly and easily.

15 that could scare frogs away from the water tank

16 ②	17 ④

18 He spent a lot of time cooking all kinds of food to decide what to put on the table in his picture.

19 ①	20 pursue	21 ③	22 ①

01 이어지는 글에서 다빈치가 '음식점에서 요리사로 일했다'고 하고 있으므로 '창의적인 요리사'가 적절하다.

02 appreciate: ~의 진가를 인정하다 <영영풀이: 그것의 좋은 특성 때문에 그것을 좋아하다>

03 '손님들은 많은 양의 고기 요리에 익숙했었기 때문에 불만족스러워했다. 그 결과, 다빈치는 그의 직업을 잃었다.'라고 하고 있다.

04 ⓐ for: [획득·추구·기대의 대상] ~을 얻기 위해[위한], ⓒ away from: ~에서 떠나서

05 앞 문장의 내용에 대한 결과가 이어지고 있으므로 Thus가 적절하다.

06 too ~ to ...: …하기에 너무 ~한, 너무 ~해서 …할 수 없다

07 (C)의 the project가 주어진 글의 a grand painting을 가리키므로 제일 먼저 오고 (B)에서 어떤 음식을 올릴지 결정하기 위해 모든 종류의 음식을 요리하느라 많은 시간을 쓰고 (A)에서 (B)의 시간 낭비에 대해 불평하는 것이 적절하다.

08 now that: ~이기 때문에, ~이므로

09 앞에서 '다빈치는 1년 넘게 부엌에서 시간을 낭비해 오고 있습니다.'라고 하고 있으므로 complained가 적절하다. complain: 불평하다, commend: 칭찬하다

10 (A) 'one of+최상급+복수 명사'의 형태로 쓰므로 painters가 적절하다. (B) 'a few+셀 수 있는 명사 복수, a little+셀 수 없는 명사 단수'이므로 a few가 적절하다. (C) '손님들은 많은 양의 고기 요리에 익숙했기 때문에 불만족스러워했다.'고 했으므로 lost가 적절하다.

11 da Vinci가 얼마나 오래 요리사로 일했는지는 대답할 수 없다. ① No. ② A cook. ③ He changed the menu completely. ⑤ Customers didn't like the dishes that da Vinci made.

12 ① 두통은 스트레스의 징후일 수 있다. ② 많은 건물 간판이 영어로 쓰여 있다. ③ 그가 엄지손가락을 세우는 몸짓을 해 보였다. ④ 그는 나더러 뜰에 들어오라고 손짓했다. ⑤ 사람이 살고 있는 흔적이 없다.

13 ① common: 일반적인, 평범한 ② routine: 판에 박힌 ③ plain: 평이한 ④ traditional: 전통적인 ⑤ innovative: 혁신적인

14 '다빈치는 창의적인 요리를 만드는 것에 멈추지 않았다. 그는 훨씬 더 빠르고 쉽게 요리하고 싶어했다.'는 것은 '다빈치는 창의적인 요리를 만드는 것뿐만 아니라 훨씬 더 빠르고 쉽게 요리하고 싶어했다.'고 쓸 수 있으므로 'not only A but also B' 구문을 이용한다.

15 scare A away from B: A를 겁주어 B로부터 멀어지도록 하다, that은 주격 관계대명사이다.

16 뒤에서 '"그것이 그가 아직도 그림을 끝내지 못한 이유입니다."라고 교회 사람들이 스포르차에게 불평을 했다.'라고 하고 있으므로 wasted가 적절하다.

17 주절의 내용과 상반되는 내용이므로 Although가 가장 적절하다.

18 spend+시간+~ing: ~하는 데 시간을 보내다, '의문사+to부정사(to put)'가 decide의 목적어가 되도록 배열한다.

19 다빈치가 스포르차에게 무엇을 하도록 요청했는지는 알 수 없다. ② It was based on the last supper of Jesus. ③ Because he had always been interested in food. ④ Da Vinci spend a lot of time cooking all kinds of food to decide what to put on the table in his picture. ⑤ Because we know all about da Vinci's secret passion for cooking.

20 pursue: 추구하다 <영영풀이: 종종 오랜 기간에 걸쳐 특정한 목적이나 결과를 달성하기 위해 노력하다>

21 (B)에서 also로 주어진 글의 내용에 추가되고 있으므로 제일 먼저 오고 (C)에서 Thus로 (B)의 내용에 대한 결과가 나오므로 (B) 다음에 (C)가 이어지고 (A)의 they가 (C)의 machines를 가리키므로 (C) 다음에 (A)가 나오는 것이 적절하다.

22 위 글에서는 과학자로서의 역할에 대해서는 언급하고 있지 않다.

01 It's because customers were not satisfied with his creative dishes.

02 He wanted to create a place where people could try his innovative food.

03 people would soon appreciate his creative cooking

04 He invented new machines for his kitchen.

05 the other → another

06 new machines for his kitchen

07 and it

08 He was a creative cook as well as a great painter.

09 decide what to put on the table in his picture

10 however

11 (A) completely (B) unhappy (C) appreciate

12 da Vinci, Sandro Botticelli

01 손님들이 그의 창의적인 요리에 불만족스러워했기 때문이었다.

02 a place를 선행사로 하는 관계부사 where를 이용하여 영작한다.

03 앞 문장의 내용을 가리킨다.

04 '그는 훨씬 더 빠르고 쉽게 요리하고 싶어했다. 따라서, 그는 그의 주방에서 사용할 새로운 기계들을 발명하였다.'라고 하고 있다

05 the other는 '두 개 중의 나머지 하나'를 일컬을 때 쓰므로 '또 다른 하나'를 말할 때 쓰는 another로 고치는 것이 적절하다.

06 '그의 주방에서 사용할 새로운 기계들'을 가리킨다.

07 계속적 용법의 관계대명사 = 접속사+대명사

08 not only A but also B = B as well as A

09 '그는 그림 속 식탁 위에 어떤 음식을 올릴지 결정하기 위해 모든 종류의 음식을 요리하느라 많은 시간을 썼다.'라고 하고 있다.

10 앞 문장의 내용과 상반되는 내용이며 문장의 중간에 콤마(,)로 삽입되어 있는 형식으로 쓰였으므로 however가 적절하다.

11 (A) 형용사로 쓰일 경우 수식하는 명사나 보어로서의 역할이 없으므로 동사 changed를 수식하는 completely가 적절하다.
(B) 이어서 'As a result, da Vinci lost his job.'라는 것으로 보아 unhappy가 적절하다. (C) 이어서 'Unfortunately, that never happened.'라는 것으로 보아 appreciate가 적절하다. depreciate는 '평가 절하하다, 가치[평가]를 떨어뜨리다'라는 뜻이다.

12 다빈치와 그의 친구인 산드로 보티첼리를 가리킨다.

01 ①   02 decorate   03 unusual, Unfortunately

04 (r)eason, (r)are (1) reason   (2) rare

05 purchase   06 put   07 ③

08 I promise I'll be your first customer.   09 ③

10 ②   11 ④   12 ③   13 ④

14 (1) However   (2) However   (3) Thus

     (4) However   (5) Thus   (6) Thus

15 (1) how da Vinci made his creative cooking

     (2) when I can have a delicious meal with my

       friends

16 ③   17 ①   18 ④   19 ④

20 ②   21 ③

22 He changed the menu completely.

23 such as   24 that[which]

25 most of them were too big or too difficult to use

26 ④   27 ①

28 It was based on the last supper of Jesus.

29 ①   30 where they can use their creativity

01 <보기>와 ①은 '계산서'의 뜻으로 쓰였다. ① 계산서 좀 갖다 주시겠어요? ② 그들은 공항에서 보안 점검을 실시했다. ③ 제가 이 카드를 잘 작성했는지 봐주시겠습니까? ④ 이 수표를 현금으로 바꾸고 싶습니다. ⑤ 자동차는 생산 라인에서 나올 때 점검을 받는다.

02 '어떤 예쁜 것을 올려놓아 어떤 것을 더 매력적으로 보이게 만들다'라는 의미로 'decorate(장식하다, 꾸미다)'가 적절하다.

03 (1) 형용사 usual에 un을 붙여 반의어가 된 어휘이다. unusual: 흔치 않은. 거대한 소행성이 지구에 너무 가까이 접근하는 것은 흔치 않은 일이다. (2) 문장 구성상 부사가 적절하다. unfortunately: 불행하게도. 형용사 fortunate에 un을 붙여 반대의 뜻을 갖는 형용사가 되고 거기에 ly를 붙여 부사가 된 어휘이다. 불행히도, 저는 그 회의에 참석할 수 없을 거예요.

04 (1) reason: 이유. 누군가가 어떤 것을 하기로 결정한 이유, 또는 일어난 어떤 것에 대한 원인이나 설명. 그렇게 늦은 것에 대한 이유가 있니? (2) rare: 덜 익은, 살짝 익힌. 잠깐 요리된; 속이 아직 붉은. 우리 아버지는 속이 약간 분홍빛이 도는 덜 익은 고기를 좋아하신다.

05 반의어 관계이다. rare: 덜 익은, well-done: 잘 익은, sell: 팔다, purchase: 구입하다

06 • put ... in charge of ~: …에게 ~의 책임을 맡기다 / 그들은 그에게 그 공원을 책임지게 했다. • put up: 내붙이다, 게시하다 / 그는 "반려동물 출입 금지"라는 팻말을 내걸었다. • put out: (불을) 끄다 / 소방차들이 화재를 진화하기 위해 도착했다. • put on: 입다 / 내게 네가 입을 수 있는 스웨터가 있어.

07 '배우가 되고 싶다'는 말에 '최선을 다하겠다고 약속한다'는 것은

08 'I promise ~'는 다짐을 말할 때 쓰는 표현으로 promise 뒤에는 구체적인 내용을 명사절을 써서 나타낸다.

09 (C)의 it이 주어진 글의 this blueberry를 가리키므로 가장 먼저 나오고, (B)에서 'Really?'로 (C)에서 한 말에 대해 놀라움을 나타내고, (A)에서 (B)에서 말한 '팔아도 되겠다'는 말에 대해 '사람들이 이걸 살 거라고 생각하는지' 묻고, (D)에서 '물론'이라는 말로 답하는 순서가 적절하다.

10 'I made it myself.(직접 만든 거야.)'라고 하고 있다.

11 '큰 아파트에 혼자 살고 있는 것'과 '거의 외로움을 느끼지 않는 것'은 '역접' 관계이다. '역접'의 접속부사 Nevertheless가 쓰인 문장이 적절하다.

12 which를 where로 바꾸거나 which 앞이나 stayed 다음에 in이 있어야 한다.

13 'space or building in which'에서 which 뒤의 절이 불완전하므로 in which를 which로 바꾸어야 한다.

15 (1) 사람들은 다빈치가 어떻게 그의 창의적인 요리를 만드는지 관심이 없었다. (2) 학교에서, 나는 친구들과 맛있는 식사를 할 수 있는 점심시간이 제일 좋다.

16 선행사 the way와 관계부사 how는 함께 쓸 수 없다.

17 관계부사 where 뒤에는 완전한 절의 구조가 와야 하는데, 전치사 in이 있으므로 where를 which로 고치는 것이 적절하다.

18 시간을 나타내는 선행사 뒤에 관계부사를 찾는 문제이다. ①은 부사절 접속사 ②, ③, ⑤는 의문사로 사용되었다.

19 '그의 설명이 명확하지 않아서 이해를 못했다'는 것은 '순접'의 인과 관계이다. Since, As, Because 등의 접속사를 이용해서 한 문장으로 만드는 것이 적절하다.

20 '(a) few+셀 수 있는 명사 복수, (a) little+셀 수 없는 명사 단수'이며 'few와 little'은 '부정'의 의미이고 'a few와 a little'은 '긍정'의 의미이므로 few가 적절하다. however로 앞부분과 상반되고 있음을 확인한다.

21 주어진 문장의 however에 주목한다. however로 앞 문장과 상반되는 내용이 나오므로 ③번이 적절하다. 또한 ③번 다음 문장에서 As a result로 주어진 문장의 결과가 나오고 있음에도 유의한다.

22 When he took charge of the kitchen, da Vinci changed the menu completely.

23 like = such as: ~와 같은

24 주격 관계대명사가 필요한 자리이다. 선행사가 사물이므로 that이나 which가 적절하다.

25 'too ~ to ...(…하기에 너무 ~한, 너무 ~해서 … 할 수 없다)' 구문을 이용한다. most of them: 그것들 중 대부분

26 '선행사로 the reason이 나와 있으므로 관계부사 why가 적절하다.

27 주어진 문장의 the project가 ①번 앞 문장에서 언급한 '웅장한 그림을 밀라노에 있는 교회의 벽에 그리는 것'을 말하고 있으므로 ①번이 적절하다.

28 '그것은 예수의 최후의 만찬을 바탕으로 한 것이었다.'라고 하고 있다.

29 ⓐ와 ①: 형용사적 용법 ②, ⑤ 부사적 용법 ③, ④ 명사적 용법

30 관계부사 where를 이용하여 'they can use their creativity'가 선행사 a place를 수식하도록 한다.

단원별 예상문제 p.155~159

01 ③ 02 ⑤ 03 charge
04 (1) of all (t)ime (2) (u)sed to (3) (u)nique
05 ② 06 ⑤
07 I feel like having a bite of the bread. 08 ①
09 She asks the man to let her just have the check.
10 ① 11 (1) however (2) Thus (3) Thus
(4) However (5) Thus 12 ③ 13 the reason why he hadn't finished the painting earlier
14 (1) Jamaica is a country where international reggae festivals take place every summer.
(2) Show your brother how you solved the puzzle in such a short time.
(3) Everyone but me knows the day when I will be transferred to Jeju island.
(4) Katherine won't tell her teacher the reason why she ran out of the classroom.
15 where people have to line up all night to eat pizza
16 He wanted to create a place where people could try his innovative food.
17 ② 18 ⑤ 19 at 20 ④
21 painting → cooking
22 most of them were so big or so difficult that people couldn't use them

---

01 ③번은 동의어 관계이다. 나머지는 모두 반의어 관계이다. check: 계산서, bill: 계산서 ① inconvenience: 불편, convenience: 편리함 ② sell: 팔다, purchase: 구매하다 ④ satisfied: 만족한, dissatisfied: 불만족한 ⑤ creative: 창의적인, uncreative: 창의적이지 않은

02 ① appreciate: 진가를 알아보다, 고마워하다 / 무엇이든 문제가 있으면 알려주시면 고맙겠습니다. ② feel like -ing: ~할 마음이 나다 / 정말 더 이상 일하고 싶지 않아요. ③ not ~ anymore: 더 이상 ~ 아니다 / 그곳은 더 이상 조용한 섬이 아니야. ④ have a bite of: 한 입 베어 물다 / 이 버거를 한 입 먹

어보고 싶지 않나요? ⑤ now that: ~이기 때문에, ~이므로 / 이제라도 내가 알았으니까 너를 챙겨 줄게.

03 • put ~ in charge of: ~에게 …의 책임을 맡기다 / 나는 사무실 책임자를 맡게 되었다. • take charge of: ~의 책임을 지다, ~을 떠맡다 / 아버지가 돌아가신 후 그가 농장을 책임지게[떠맡게] 되었다.

04 (1) of all time: 역대, 지금껏 (2) be used to 동명사: ~하는 것에 익숙하다 (3) unique: 독특한, 고유의, 특유의

05 look+형용사: ~처럼[하게] 보이다 really를 real로 고쳐야 한다.

06 소녀가 독창적이지 않다고 할 뿐 무엇이 독창적인지는 알 수 없다.

07 feel like ~ing: ~하고 싶다

08 ①을 제외한 모두는 불만족을 표현하고 있다. pitiful: 동정적인, 처량한

09 여자는 'Let me just have the check, please.'라고 말하고 있다.

10 여자는 '빵은 괜찮았고, 샐러드는 신선했어요.'라고 하고 있다.

11 (1) 레오나르도 다빈치는 역대 가장 위대한 화가들 중의 한 명이자 위대한 발명가, 과학자, 그리고 음악가로 알려졌다. 하지만, 극히 소수의 사람들만이 그가 창의적인 요리사였다는 것을 안다. (2) 다빈치의 창의적인 음식을 본 손님들은 많은 양의 고기 요리에 익숙했었기 때문에 불만족스러워했다. 그래서, 다빈치는 그의 직업을 잃었다. (3) 다빈치는 창의적인 요리를 더 빠르고 더 쉽게 요리하고 싶어 했다. 따라서, 그는 채소를 으깨고 스파게티를 뽑을 수 있는 새로운 기계들을 발명했다. (4) 다빈치는 살아 있을 때, 결코 성공적인 요리사는 되지 못했다. 그러나, 그는 그의 생애 내내 요리에 대한 큰 흥미를 보여 주었다. (5) 나는 다빈치의 요리에 대한 비밀스런 열정에 대해 배웠다. 그러므로, 나는 결코 예전과 같은 방식으로 '최후의 만찬'을 바라보지 않을 것이라고 생각한다.

12 ③은 '의문사+to부정사' 형태의 what이 적절하다. ① 계속적 용법의 관계대명사 which, ② 인과 관계를 나타내는 접속사 because. ④ 선행사 the reason, ⑤ 부사 yet이다.

13 사람들은 다빈치가 너무 많은 시간을 음식에 낭비했고 그것이 그가 그림을 더 일찍 끝내지 못한 이유라고 불평했다.

14 각각의 선행사에 맞게 관계부사를 쓰되, the way는 how와 같이 쓸 수 없으므로, (2)에서 선행사 없이 관계부사가 이끄는 절만 쓰는 것에 유의한다.

15 저기가 사람들이 피자를 먹으러 밤새 줄을 서는 그 유명한 식당이다.

16 a place를 선행사로 하는 관계부사 where를 이용하여 한 문장으로 바꾼다.

17 be[get] used to+명사 = be[get] accustomed to+명사: ~

29

에 익숙하다[익숙해지다]

18 이 글은 '다빈치가 창의적인 요리사였지만 요리사로서 성공하지는 못했다'는 내용이므로, 제목으로는 '다빈치의 이루지 못한 꿈'이 적절하다. Jack of all trades: 팔방미인

19 stop at cooking: 요리를 만드는 것에 멈추지 않다, stop cooking: 요리하는 것을 멈추다. 요리를 멈춘 것이 아니라 요리를 만드는 것에 멈추지 않고 그 이상을 했다는 의미가 적절하다.

20 ④ Because da Vinci wanted to cook much more quickly and easily. 나머지는 모두 대답할 수 없다.

21 '그는 요리를 향한 그의 열정을 추구할 또 다른 기회를 얻게 되어 행복했다.'라고 하고 있다.

22 'too ~ to … = so ~ that 주어 can't …'. use의 주어로 일반 사람을 나타내는 people을 쓰는 것이 적절하다.

01 turns off by itself

02 inconvenience

03 I'm not satisfied with the phone.

04 (1) where　(2) when　(3) how　(4) why　(5) when

05 (1) In other words　(2) However　(3) In addition
　　(4) Thus　(5) For example

06 As a result

07 twenty-years-old → twenty-year-old

08 Because customers were unhappy with his dishes.

02 '당신을 귀찮게 하거나 악영향을 주는 어떤 것에 의해 일어나는 문제들'은 'inconvenience(불편, 애로)'이다.

03 'I don't like ~', 'I'm not satisfied with ~'는 모두 불만족을 표현하는 말이다.

04 각각의 선행사가 (1) 장소, (2) 시간, (3) 방법, (4) 이유, (5) 시간 등이다.

05 (1) 다빈치는 늘 독특하고 창의적인 음식을 만들었다. 즉, 그는 실험적 요리사였다. (2) 다빈치는 성공적인 요리사가 되고 싶었다. 그러나, 사람들은 그를 요리사로 여기지 않았다. (3) 다빈치는 채소를 으깨는 장치를 고안했다. 게다가, 그는 파스타를 뽑아내는 기계를 발명했다. (4) 다빈치는 요리에 관심이 있었다. 그래서 그는 <최후의 만찬> 테이블에 무슨 음식을 놓을지 오래 생각했다. (5) 다빈치는 다양한 분야에서 그의 재능으로 알려졌다. 예를 들어, 그는 화가이자, 건축가, 수학자, 그리고 음악가이다.

06 앞 문장에 대한 결과가 이어지고 있으므로 As a result가 적절하다.

07 twenty-year-old처럼 하이픈(-)으로 연결되어 뒤에 나오는 명

사를 수식하는 경우 형용사처럼 쓰이는 것이므로 복수형 years 라고 하지 않는다.

08 '다빈치는 기꺼이 그 작업을 맡았는데, 그가 항상 음식에 흥미를 가졌기 때문이었다.'라고 하고 있다.

|모범답안|

01 (1) drawing, I don't like the color.
　(2) steak, It's too rare.

02 (1) This is not the place where I eat the apple.
　(2) This is the day when I don't eat the apple.
　(3) The witch asked the mirror how she could
　　　make Snow White eat the apple.

02 (A) an artist　(B) using technology　(C) technical
　(D) my first exhibition

02 보기의 단어들을 적절히 조합하여 그림과 어법에 맞게 영작한 답이면 된다.

01 provide　02 crush　03 ④　04 ⑤

05 throughout　06 fix

07 I'll learn how I should act.

08 I will make sure that I'll do my best.

09 It's because he wants to become an actor.

10 ②　11 It sometimes turns off by itself.

12 It would take a few hours.　13 ③

14 ④　15 ④　16 ④

17 (1) However, it was so painful that the dog ran away.
　(2) Thus, Sumi asked for a lot of side dishes.

18 ③　19 He made simple but artistic dishes.

20 ⑤　21 ③　22 ④

01 surely: 확실히 – certainly: 확실하게, supply 제공하다 – provide 제공하다

02 '어떤 것을 세게 눌러서 깨지거나 손상되게 하다'는 'crush(으깨다, 쭈그러뜨리다)'가 적절하다. 그 승용차는 트럭에 깔려 완전히 쭈그러졌다.

03 • 우리는 평생 행복을 추구한다. • 나는 그가 불평하는 것을 들어본 적이 없다. pursue: 추구하다, 추진하다. complain: 불평하

다, determine: 결정하다, provide: 제공하다, decorate: 장
식하다

04 put ~ in charge of: ~에게 …의 책임을 맡기다, of all time:
역대, 지금껏

05 throughout: ~ 동안 내내

06 fix: 수리하다. 망가지거나 제대로 작동하지 않는 것을 수리하다.
수리할 사람을 보내 주시겠습니까?

07 의문사+to부정사 = 의문사+주어+should+동사원형

08 'I promise ~'와 'I will make sure that ~'은 모두 다짐을 말
하는 표현으로 쓸 수 있다.

09 소년은 'I want to go to an arts high school. I want to
become an actor.'라고 하고 있다.

10 '제가 좀 봐도 될까요?'라는 뜻의 주어진 문장은 ②번 다음 문장
인 '불편을 드려 죄송합니다. 고치는 데 몇 시간 정도 걸릴 거예
요.'의 앞에 들어가는 것이 자연스럽다.

11 'I bought this phone only a week ago, but it sometimes
turns off by itself.'라고 하고 있다.

12 'It'll take a few hours to fix it.'이라고 하고 있다.

13 'Sam이 아침식사를 하지 않은 것'과 '배고픔을 느끼지 않는 것'
은 '역접' 관계로서 '접속부사' however가 쓰였다. 이것을 한 문
장으로 바꾸면, '역접'의 '접속사' Though를 활용한 ③번 문장이
가장 적절하다.

14 '학생들이 환자와 PC방에서 밀접한 접촉을 가진 것'이 원인이
고, '그들이 바이러스에 감염된 것'이 결과이므로, '순접'의 '인과
관계'를 나타내는 접속사 Because, As, Since 등으로 한 문장
을 만드는 것이 적절하다. ②와 ③은 보기의 문장과 내용이 조
금 바뀌었으므로, 유의하도록 한다.

15 선행사가 the way일 때, how는 같이 사용하지 않는다.

16 '선행사'가 the day일 때, 전치사는 in이 아니라, on을 쓰는 것
이 적절하다.

17 (1) 고슴도치는 그저 그 개와 잘 지내고 싶었을 뿐이었다. 그렇
지만, 너무 아파서 그 개는 도망을 갔다. (2) 오늘은 수미의 부모
님이 급식 당번을 하는 날이다. 그래서, 수미는 반찬을 많이 달
라고 했다.

18 '조각가'가 아니라 '과학자'로 소개하고 있다.

19 '그가 부엌을 책임지게 되었을 때, 다빈치는 메뉴를 완전히 바꿔
버렸다. 그는 약간의 당근 조각을 곁들인 생선과 같이 단순하지
만 예술적인 음식을 만들었다.'라고 하고 있다.

20 a special moment(시간)를 선행사로 하는 관계부사 when이
적절하다.

21 주어진 문장의 Thus가 ③번 앞 문장에서 언급하고 있는 내용의
결과를 이끌고 있으므로 ③번이 적절하다.

22 'I entered Korea Art College.'라고 언급되었다.

교과서 파헤치기

Lesson 4

단어 TEST Step 1　　　　　　　　p.02

01 온실　　02 수확하다　　03 광고
04 전시회, 박람회　05 수중의, 물속에서　06 해양의, 바다의
07 전국적인　　08 해외의
09 홍보하다, 촉진하다　　10 교량, 다리
11 지역 공동체　12 감동받은　13 유산
14 환경　15 해산물　16 몇몇의
17 생계를 책임지는 사람, 가장　18 여성의
19 화산의, 화산 작용에 의한　20 세계적으로
21 완성[완료]하다　22 호흡하다　23 파괴하다
24 폭포　25 좁은 길
26 무형의, 만질 수 없는　27 해파리
28 누르다; 언론, 기자　29 지하의　30 적합한, 적절
31 청중　32 과로하다　33 경로, 길
34 깨닫다, 인식하다　35 ~을 기원하다　36 우연히 ~하다
37 ~을 따라 걷다　38 두 서너 개의　39 ~에 들어가다
40 ~에 적절하다　41 강의하다, 연설하다
42 조금, 약간　43 ~에 유익하다

단어 TEST Step 2　　　　　　　　p.03

01 waterfall　02 ad(=advertisement)
03 path　04 overwork　05 bridge
06 trail　07 underground　08 worldwide
09 volcanic　10 greenhouse　11 destroy
12 exhibition　13 promote　14 complete
15 several　16 breadwinner　17 suitable
18 female　19 press　20 community
21 intangible　22 underwater　23 jellyfish
24 marine　25 harvest　26 audience
27 heritage　28 breathe　29 nationwide
30 overseas　31 realize　32 tightly
33 beat　34 good harvest　35 go on vacation
36 get into　37 happen to　38 walk along
39 be good for　40 keep -ing　41 cheer up
42 give (someone) a hand
43 give a presentation

단어 TEST Step 3　　　　　　　　p.04

1 harvest, 수확하다　2 underground, 지하의
3 complete, 완성[완료]하다　4 beat, (북 등을 치는) 소리
5 waterfall, 폭포　6 suitable, 적합한　7 breathe, 호흡하다

8 community, 지역 공동체　9 heritage, 유산
10 intangible, 무형의, 만질 수 없는　11 overseas, 해외의
12 seafood, 해산물　13 destroy, 파괴하다　14 ad, 광고
15 bridge, 다리　16 breadwinner, 생계를 책임지는 사람, 가장

대화문 TEST Step 1　　　　　　　　p.05~06

Listen & Speak 1 A-1

look at, bridge, ad, where the photo was taken / How do, know / went there with, last summer

Listen & Speak 1 A-2

Look over I wonder why, waiting in line / waiting to get into / famous / on / should try, then

Listen & Speak 2 A-1

I'd like to borrow / Here, are / explain how to use it / Press, what to do

Listen & Speak 2 A-2

Are, going somewhere / going to, walk along / Could you explain what that is / long hiking path around / enjoy your trip

Communicate A

I wonder where, coming from / over there, check it out / strong beat, traditional / called, a kind of community / Could you explain a little bit / traditionally, cheer up, wish for. good harvest / are dancing to, rhythm / part of, completes / Let's join / Why not

Progress Check 1

I wonder why there are so many cars / Lots of, going on vacation / why don't we, too

Progress Check 2

Excuse, copy machine / how to make double-sided copies / Press, double-sided copies, press

대화문 TEST Step 2　　　　　　　　p.07~08

Listen & Speak 1 A-1

G: Wow, look at the bridge in this ad. I wonder where the photo was taken.
B: That's Gwangandaegyo in Busan.
G: How do you know that?
B: I went there with my family last summer.

Listen & Speak 1 A-2

B: Look over there. I wonder why there are so many people waiting in line.

G: They're waiting to get into the new bakery there.

B: Why? Is it famous?

G: Yes. It was on a TV program.

B: Really? We should try their bread then.

G: Sure.

W: Excuse me, I'd like to borrow an audio guide.

M: Here you are.

W: Could you explain how to use it?

M: Sure. Press this button, and it'll tell you what to do.

B: Are you going somewhere this summer?

G: I'm going to Jejudo to walk along the Jeju Olle Trail.

B: The Jeju Olle Trail? Could you explain what that is?

G: It's a long hiking path around Jejudo.

B: Oh, I see. I hope you enjoy your trip!

Jaden: Do you hear that? I wonder where that music is coming from.

Yuri: I think it's coming from over there. Do you want to go and check it out?

Jaden: Yes, I love that strong beat. Is it traditional Korean music?

Yuri: Yes, it's called nongak. It's a kind of community band music.

Jaden: Nongak? Could you explain a little bit more about it?

Yuri: It's traditionally used to cheer up farmers and wish for a good harvest.

Jaden: I see. Look! Some people are dancing to the rhythm.

Yuri: Yes, that's a big part of nongak. Dancing together completes the music.

Jaden: Let's join them.

Yuri: Sure. Why not?

W: Look over there. I wonder why there are so many cars on the road.

M: Lots of people are going on vacation this weekend.

W: Really? Then, why don't we go somewhere, too?

M: O.K.

B: Excuse me, I'd like to use a copy machine.

W: O.K. You can use this machine.

B: Could you explain how to make double-sided copies?

W: Sure. Press the button for double-sided copies, and then press the start button.

B: Thank you.

---

01 Haenyeo, Female Divers

02 several, underwater, promoted, worldwide

03 female, harvest, without, breathing

04 made, Intangible, Heritage list

05 last, interviewed, experience, taking

06 become interested in taking

07 One day, happened to   08 was surprised to find

09 Until, seen, looked, tired

10 kept laughing, been, over

11 realized, should take   12 isn't it difficult to

13 At, why I wanted

14 looked pretty in, wetsuits

15 So, very special

16 show, culture to, world

17 opened up, then

18 make them look beautiful

19 tell us more about   20 so special about

21 can tell you, things

22 symbol, strong women

23 volcanic, suitable, farming, breadwinners

24 form, own, each other

25 example, more-experienced, less-experienced

26 stay, without, breathing, catch

27 good for, underwater environment

28 marine, time, destory, place

29 what, planning, do, future

30 attended, exhibition, talk, lives

31 finished, held, hand tightly

32 said to, so much

33 such a special person

34 crying with happiness

35 was deeply moved

36 never forget, moment, continue

37 more beautiful stories about

01 Female Divers

02 underwater photographer, has promoted, worldwide

03 female divers, without any breathing devices

04 made UNESCO's Intangible Cultural Heritage list

05 was interviewed, experience of taking picutres

06 become interested in taking

07 One day, happened to

08 was surprised to find, was enjoying

09 Until then, had only seen, looked very tired

10 kept laughing, for over five hours

11 realized, should take pictures

12 isn't it difficult to take pictures

13 At first, why I wanted

14 looked pretty in their wetsuits

15 very special   16 show, to

17 opened up, then

18 Of course, make them, beautiful

19 more about   20 so special

21 can tell you

22 symbol of strong women

23 which, is not suitable for, have become the breadwinners for

24 form, own communities, each other

25 more-experienced, less-experienced

26 because, without, breathing devices, can't catch

27 is good for, underwater environment

28 Catching, at one time in one place can destory

29 what, planning to do

30 attended, overseas exhibition, give a talk

31 held my hand tightly

32 so much

33 whole life, such a special person

34 crying with happiness

35 was deeply moved

36 can never forget, continue to take

37 more beautiful stories about them

1 해녀, 한국의 여성 잠수부

2 지난 몇 년 동안, 수중 사진작가 Zin Kim은 제주 해녀 문화를 전 세계에 홍보해 왔다.

3 해녀는 어떤 호흡 장치도 사용하지 않고 해산물을 채취하는 한국의 여성 잠수부들이다.

4 그들의 문화는 2016년에 유네스코 무형문화유산에 등재되었다.

5 지난주 그녀의 작업실에서, Zin Kim과 해녀의 사진을 찍는 그녀의 경험에 대해 인터뷰를 했다.

6 Q. 어떻게 해녀의 사진을 찍는 것에 관심을 가지게 되었나요?

7 어느 날, 저는 우연히 한 해녀의 사진을 찍게 되었어요.

8 저는 그녀가 자신의 일을 즐겁게 하는 것을 보고 놀랐습니다.

9 그때까지, 저는 흑백 사진 속의 아주 지친 모습의 해녀만 봐 왔죠.

10 하지만, 그녀는 다섯 시간이 넘도록 물속에 있은 후에도 계속 웃었어요.

11 저는 그때 해녀의 사진을 찍어야겠다고 깨달았어요.

12 Q. 작가님은 아름다운 해녀 사진들을 찍으시는데, 그들의 사진을 찍는 것이 어렵진 않으신가요?

13 처음에, 그들은 제가 왜 자신들의 사진을 찍으려고 하는지 이해하지 못했어요.

14 그들은 잠수복을 입은 자신들의 모습이 예뻐 보인다고 생각하지 않았으니까요.

15 그래서, 제가 그들에게 말했죠, "여러분들은 아주 특별해요.

16 저는 여러분의 문화를 세계에 알리고 싶어요."

17 그들은 그때 제게 마음을 열었어요.

18 물론, 저 또한 그들에게 제 사진 속에서 그들을 아름답게 보이도록 하겠다고 약속했지요.

19 Q. 해녀에 대해서 더 말씀해 주시겠어요?

20 그들은 무엇이 그렇게 특별한가요?

21 세 가지를 말씀 드릴게요.

22 첫 번째로, 해녀들은 강인한 여성의 상징이에요.

23 제주도는 화산섬이고, 이는 농사에 적합하지 않아서 많은 해녀들이 가족들의 생계비를 버는 가장이 되어 왔어요.

24 둘째로, 해녀들은 그들 자신의 공동체를 조직하고 서로 도와요.

25 예를 들어, 경험이 더 많은 해녀들이 경험이 적은 해녀들을 훈련시키지요.

26 세 번째로, 어떤 호흡 장치도 사용하지 않고 물속에 머물기 때문에, 해녀는 많은 해산물을 채취할 수가 없어요.

27 이것은 수중 환경에 좋은 것이지요.

28 한 번에 한 장소에서 너무 많은 해양생물을 채취하는 것은 바다를 파괴할 수 있으니까요.

29 Q. 마지막으로, 앞으로 계획하고 있는 것에 대해 말씀해 주세요.

30 예전에 두 명의 해녀들과 함께 그들의 삶에 대해 이야기하기 위해 해외에서 열리는 박람회에 참가한 적이 있어요.

31 제가 연설을 마쳤을 때, 해녀 중 한 분이 제 손을 꼭 잡았어요.

32 그분이 말했죠, "너무 고마워.

33 내 평생 내가 이렇게 특별한 사람이라는 걸 미처 알지 못했어."

34 그녀는 행복해서 울고 있었어요.

35 청중들 모두가 깊은 감동을 받았어요.

36 전 그 순간을 절대 잊을 수가 없기 때문에 해녀의 사진을 계속해서 찍을 거예요.

37 저는 그들에 대한 더 많은 아름다운 이야기들을 세계의 더 많은 사람들에게 알려 주고 싶어요.

1 Haenyeo, Female Divers of Korea

2 For the past several years, the underwater photographer Zin Kim has promoted the culture of Jeju haenyeo worldwide.

3 Haenyeo are Korean female divers who harvest seafood without any breathing devices.

4 Their culture made UNESCO's Intangible Cultural Heritage list in 2016.

5 At her studio last week, Zin Kim was interviewed about her experience of taking pictures of haenyeo.

6 Q. How did you become interested in taking photos of haenyeo?

7 One day, I happened to take pictures of a haenyeo.

8 I was surprised to find that she was enjoying her job.

9 Until then, I had only seen black-and-white photos of haenyeo who looked very tired.

10 However, she kept laughing even after she had been in the water for over five hours.

11 I realized then that I should take pictures of haenyeo.

12 Q. You take beautiful pictures of them, but isn't it difficult to take pictures of haenyeo?

13 At first, they didn't understand why I wanted to take their pictures.

14 They didn't think they looked pretty in their wetsuits.

15 So, I said to them, "You're very special.

16 I want to show your culture to the world."

17 They opened up to me then.

18 Of course, I also promised them that I would make them look beautiful in my pictures.

19 Q. Could you tell us more about haenyeo?

20 What's so special about them?

21 I can tell you three things.

22 First, haenyeo are a symbol of strong women.

23 Jejudo, which is a volcanic island, is not suitable for farming, so many haenyeo have become the breadwinners for their families.

24 Second, haenyeo form their own communities and help each other.

25 For example, more-experienced haenyeo train less-experienced haenyeo.

26 Third, because they stay in the water without any

27 breathing devices, haenyeo can't catch a lot of seafood.

27 This is good for the underwater environment.

28 Catching too much marine life at one time in one place can destroy the ocean.

29 Q. Lastly, please tell us what you're planning to do in the future.

30 I once attended an overseas exhibition with a couple of haenyeo to give a talk about their lives.

31 When I finished my talk, one of the haenyeo held my hand tightly.

32 She said to me, "Thank you so much.

33 I've never known in my whole life that I was such a special person."

34 She was crying with happiness.

35 Everyone in the audience was deeply moved.

36 I can never forget that moment, so I'll continue to take pictures of haenyeo.

37 I want to tell more beautiful stories about them to many more people in the world.

Communicate – B Talk and Play

1. what these are
2. called songpyeon
3. explain more about
4. traditional Korean rice cakes

After You Read A

1. Photographer Who Loves
2. an underwater photographer, has promoted, worldwide
3. decided to take pictures, when she met, who was enjoying
4. It, easy taking, at first
5. However, that, their culture to the world, finally opened their minds
6. At an overseas exhibition, gave a talk
7. one of, was crying with happiness
8. would continue to take

Write

1. makes coffee drinks for a living
2. became a barista, had found out about his passion
3. His favorite part of, decorating coffee with, watching, enjoying
4. planning to open

Communicate – B Talk and Play

1. A: I wonder what these are.
2. B: They're called songpyeon.
3. A: Could you explain more about them?
4. B: They're traditional Korean rice cakes.

After You Read A

1. A Photographer Who Loves Haenyeo
2. Zin Kim, an underwater photographer, has promoted the culture of Jeju haenyeo worldwide.
3. She decided to take pictures of them when she met a haenyeo who was enjoying her job.
4. It was not easy taking their pictures at first.
5. However, when she told them that she wanted to show their culture to the world, the haenyeo finally opened their minds.
6. At an overseas exhibition, she gave a talk about the lives of haenyeo.
7. After her speech, one of the haenyeo was crying with happiness.
8. Zin Kim said that she would continue to take pictures of haenyeo.

Write

1. Kim Minho is a barista. He makes coffee drinks for a living.
2. He became a barista after he had found out about his passion for coffee.
3. His favorite part of his job is decorating coffee with hot milk and watching his customers enjoying it.
4. He is planning to open his own coffee shop.

Lesson 5

01 해산물, 해물	02 불안해하는	03 경쟁, 대회
04 적	05 휴식을 취하다	06 졸업하다
07 실제로	08 무력한	09 전문적인
10 대신에	11 판단하다	12 낯선 사람
13 행운인, 운이 좋은	14 안도하는	15 유명하게
16 준비하다	17 마음, 정신	18 불안해하는
19 자신감 있는	20 행동	21 독특한
22 심리학자	23 조심스럽게	24 정치적인
25 지원자	26 (거리·공간·시간상으로) 떨어져	
27 (음식을) 씹다	28 발표	29 해결책
30 편리한	31 드문, 희귀한	32 경쟁자
33 스트레스가 많은	34 심리학	35 내리다
36 발표하다	37 ~에 들르다	38 결코 ~가 아닌
39 혼자서	40 (해답 등을) 찾아내다, 내놓다	
41 예약하다	42 A를 B로 바꾸다	43 A뿐만 아니라 B도

01 graduate	02 behavior	03 confident
04 solution	05 decide	06 enemy
07 chew	08 famously	09 professional
10 actually	11 psychologist	12 rare
13 stressful	14 relax	15 supporter
16 seafood	17 political	18 relieved
19 helpless	20 carefully	21 psychology
22 competition	23 instead	24 relay
25 presentation	26 judge	27 convenient
28 rival	29 stranger	30 unique
31 lucky	32 prepare	33 lend
34 guess	35 according to	36 turn A into B
37 make a presentation		
38 not only A but also B		39 by oneself
40 come up with	41 not ~ at all	
42 make a reservation		43 not ~ anymore

1 rare, 드문, 희귀한　2 bake, 굽다　3 enemy, 적

4 stranger, 낯선 사람　5 chew, (음식을) 씹다

6 supporter, 지원자　7 helpless, 무력한

8 convenient, 편리한　9 graduate, 졸업하다

10 presentation, 발표　11 relieved, 안도하는

12 psychology, 심리학　13 lend, 빌려주다

14 relax, 휴식을 취하다　15 confident, 자신감 있는

16 rival, 경쟁자

대화문 TEST Step 1　p.25~26

Listen & Speak 1 A-1

happened to, Aren't / chewed, all the time, worried about / bored, Why don't you play with / hope, stop chewing

Listen & Speak 1 A-2

nervous / worried about, swimming competition / worry, relax, enjoy / much better

Listen & Speak 2 A-1

what time, Grandma's place / About, bake cookies / get up early / don't have to

Listen & Speak 2 A-2

Shall we try / Why, call, make a reservation / don't have to, online / How convenient

Communicate A

can't wait / actually worried / Aren't, good at / worried, relay / What, mean / last runner, What if, because of / putting too much pressure on / practice / don't have to do / winning, losing / right, lucky, like

Progress Check 1

nervous / worried about, presentation, history class / prepared a lot, do, job / feel much better

Progress Check 2

seafood spaghetti / stop by, on the way / You don't have to, what, need / back home by, help, cook

---

대화문 TEST Step 2　p.27~28

Listen & Speak 1 A-1

G: What happened to your shoes? Aren't they new?

B: Yes, but my dog chewed them. He does it all the time. I'm worried about him.

G: He was probably bored. Why don't you play with him more often?

B: O.K., I will. I hope he will stop chewing my shoes.

Listen & Speak 1 A-2

B: You look a bit nervous.

G: I'm worried about my swimming competition this Saturday.

B: Don't worry. You're such a good swimmer. Just relax and enjoy yourself!

G: Thanks. I feel much better now.

Listen & Speak 2 A-1

B: Mom, what time are we going to Grandma's place tomorrow morning?

W: About 8 a.m. I'm going to bake cookies for her before we go.

B: Then, should I get up early to help you?

W: You don't have to. Your dad will help me.

B: O.K, then. Good night, Mom!

Listen & Speak 2 A-2

W: Shall we try that new Mexican restaurant tomorrow?

M: Why not? I'll call the restaurant to make a reservation for us.

W: You don't have to call them. You can do it online.

M: Oh, I see. How convenient!

Communicate A

Yuri: Hi, Jaden. Sports Day is next Friday. I can't wait!

Jaden: Really? I'm actually worried about it.

Yuri: Why? Aren't you good at sports?

Jaden: Yes, I am, but I'm worried about the 800-meter relay.

Yuri: What do you mean?

Jaden: I'm the last runner. What if our team loses because of me?

Yuri: I think you're putting too much pressure on yourself.

Jaden: Really? Don't you think I should practice every day?

Yuri: No, you don't have to do that. It's just a school race. It's not about winning or losing.

Jaden: I guess you're right , Yuri. I'm lucky to have a friend like you.

Progress Check 1

B: You look a bit nervous.

G: Well, I'm worried about my presentation in history class.

B: Don't worry. You've prepared a lot. You'll do a great job.

G: Thanks. I feel much better now.

M: Shall we have seafood spaghetti for dinner?

W: Sure. I'll stop by the store on the way home.

M: You don't have to do that. We already have what we need.

W: Oh, I see. Then, I'll be back home by 6 to help you cook.

본문 TEST Step 1 p.29~30

01 Psychology Answers, Questions

02 think, have, unique

03 Chances, many other, same

04 human mind, behavior, solution

05 become less nervous

06 presentation, front, whole class

07 Feeling nervous, carefully studying

08 came over, stand tall

09 standing tall, not, anymore

10 In fact, confident, presentation

11 According, standing tall, stressful

12 bodies, minds, change, behavior

13 want to feel confident

14 with, apart, place, on

15 not, sure, but, confident

16 help, feel better

17 graduates from, become, professional

18 However, has never told

19 worried that, will, understand

20 Wanting, clear, by himself

21 complete stranger sitting beside

22 why he did it

23 felt much better, off

24 Strangely enough, strangers, like

25 because, being judged, seeing

26 share with, try talking   27 feel much better

28 turn, rival into   29 political, not, at all

30 friends with, came up   31 rival, rare book

32 to lend, for, few

33 returned, thanked, deeply

34 Since, only, supporter, also

35 famously, Enemies, favor, more

36 turn, into, rival, favor

37 Instead, rival, do, favor

본문 TEST Step 2 p.31~32

01 Psychology Answers, Questions

02 unique problem

03 Chances are

04 human mind, behavior, so, help, find, to

05 become less nervous

06 big presentation, front, whole class

07 Feeling nervous, carefully studying

08 came over, to stand tall like

09 standing tall, a few, not, anymore

10 In fact, confident that, make, presentation

11 According to, become, by standing tall for, stressful events

12 bodies, minds, minds, behavior

13 feel confident

14 feet apart, place, on

15 not only feel sure, but also look confident, other people

16 feel better

17 graduates from, next year, professional

18 However, has never told

19 worried that, will not understand

20 Wanting, clear his mind, decided to take, by himself

21 complete, sitting beside   22 why he did it

23 However, felt much better, got off

24 Strangely enough, often tell strangers

25 because, not have to, being judged, seeing

26 that, share with, talking, stranger

27 feel much better   28 turn, rival into

29 political rival who, not, at all

30 become friends with, came up with

31 rare

32 to lend, a few days   33 deeply

34 Since, not only, but also

35 famously, who do you one favor

36 turn, into, do your rival a favor

37 Instead, to do, favor

본문 TEST Step 3 p.33~34

1 심리학이 당신의 물음에 답하다

2 여러분은 당신만의 유일무이한 고민을 가지고 있다고 생각하는가?

3 아마 많은 다른 사람들이 여러분과 똑같은 고민을 가지고 있을 것이다.

4 심리학은 인간의 마음과 행동에 관한 연구이며, 따라서 여러분이 문제에 대한 해결책을 찾는 데 도움을 줄 수 있다.

5 어떻게 하면 긴장을 덜 할 수 있나요?

6 지수가 반 전체 앞에서 발표를 하기 5분 전이었다.

7 지수는 긴장이 되어, 의자에 앉아 자신의 필기를 열심히 들여다보고 있었다.

8 그때 선생님이 다가와서는 원더우먼처럼 꼿꼿이 서 있어 보라고 말했다.

9 그렇게 몇 분을 우뚝 선 후에, 지수는 더 이상 긴장되지 않았다.

10 사실, 그녀는 발표를 멋있게 할 수 있을 것이라는 자신감이 생겼다.

11 유명한 심리학자인 Amy Cuddy에 의하면, 우리는 스트레스를 받는 상황 이전에 2분 정도 꼿꼿이 서 있는 것만으로도 자신감이 더 생길 수 있다고 한다.

12 우리의 몸은 마음을 바꾸고, 마음은 우리의 행동을 바꿀 수 있다.

13 자신감이 생기기를 원하는가?

14 양발을 벌리고, 허리께에 손을 올려 보아라.

15 자신에 대한 확신이 생길 뿐만 아니라 다른 사람이 보기에도 자신감에 차 보인다.

16 누가 내 기분을 낫게 해 줄 수 있나요?

17 내년에 고등학교를 졸업한 이후에 태호는 전문적인 농부가 되고 싶어 한다.

18 하지만, 누구에게도 그것에 대해 한 번도 말하지 않았다.

19 그는 부모님이나 친구들이 이해하지 못할까 걱정이 된다.

20 마음을 정리하기 위해서, 태호는 혼자 하루 기차 여행을 떠나기로 결심했다.

21 기차에서, 그는 옆에 앉은 전혀 모르는 사람에게 자신의 고민에 대해서 말했다.

22 그는 자신이 왜 그랬는지 알 수 없었다.

23 그러나, 기차에서 내릴 때 기분이 훨씬 좋아졌다.

24 정말 이상하게도, 우리는 태호처럼 우리의 문제에 대해 낯선 사람에게 말할 때가 있다.

25 그것은 우리가 평가받거나 그 사람을 다시 볼 것이라는 걱정을 할 필요가 없기 때문이다.

26 만약 가족이나 친구들과도 나눌 수 없는 고민이 있다면, 낯선 이에게 말해 보아라.

27 기분이 훨씬 나아질 것이다.

28 라이벌을 어떻게 친구로 만들 수 있을까요?

29 Benjamin Franklin에게는 한때 그를 전혀 좋아하지 않는 정치적 경쟁자가 있었다.

30 Franklin은 그와 친구가 되고 싶어서, 계획을 세웠다.

31 그의 경쟁자는 희귀한 책을 가지고 있었다.

32 Franklin은 그의 정적에게 그 책을 며칠 동안 빌려달라고 부탁했다.

33 Franklin이 그 책을 돌려줄 때, 그는 그에게 진심으로 감사를 표했다.

34 그날 이후로, 그의 경쟁자는 정치적인 후원자뿐만 아니라 좋은 친구가 되었다.

35 Franklin은 "당신을 한 번 도운 적은 더 돕고 싶어 하게 된다."

라는 유명한 말을 했다.

36 여러분이 경쟁자를 친구로 만들고 싶다면, 경쟁자의 부탁을 들어주지 마라.

37 대신, 경쟁자에게 부탁을 해 보아라.

---

1 Psychology Answers Your Questions

2 Do you think you have a unique problem?

3 Chances are that many other people have the same problem.

4 Psychology is the study of the human mind and behavior, so it can help you find a solution to your problem.

5 How do I become less nervous?

6 It was five minutes before Jisu's big presentation in front of the whole class.

7 Feeling nervous, Jisu was carefully studying her notes in her chair.

8 Then, her teacher came over and told her to stand tall like Wonder Woman.

9 After standing tall for a few minutes, Jisu did not feel nervous anymore.

10 In fact, she was confident that she would make a great presentation.

11 According to Amy Cuddy, a famous psychologist, we can become more confident just by standing tall for two minutes before stressful events.

12 Our bodies change our minds, and our minds can change our behavior.

13 Do you want to feel confident?

14 Stand with your feet apart, and place your hands on your hips.

15 You will not only feel sure about yourself but also look confident to other people.

16 Who can help me feel better?

17 When he graduates from high school next year, Taeho wants to become a professional farmer.

18 However, he has never told anyone about it.

19 He is worried that his parents or his friends will not understand.

20 Wanting to clear his mind, Taeho decided to take a day trip on a train by himself.

21 On the train, he told a complete stranger sitting beside him about his problem.

22 He had no idea why he did it.

23 However, he felt much better when he got off the train.

24 Strangely enough, we often tell strangers about our problems just like Taeho.

25 That is because we do not have to worry about being judged or seeing them again.

26 If you have a problem that you cannot share with your family or friends, try talking to a stranger.

27 You will feel much better.

28 How do I turn a rival into a friend?

29 Benjamin Franklin once had a political rival who did not like him at all.

30 Franklin wanted to become friends with him, so he came up with a plan.

31 His rival had a rare book.

32 Franklin asked his rival to lend him the book for a few days.

33 When Franklin returned the book, he thanked him deeply.

34 Since that day, his rival became not only a political supporter but also a good friend.

35 Franklin famously said, "Enemies who do you one favor will want to do more."

36 If you want to turn a rival into a friend, don't do your rival a favor.

37 Instead, ask your rival to do you a favor.

Listen & Speak 2 - Think and Talk

1. A: What don't I have to do on Stress-Free Day?

2. B: You don't have to clean the classroom.

3. C: You don't have to come to school by 8:30.

Link

1. How confident do you feel about yourself?

2. Wanting to find the answer to this question, we created a test about confidence.

3. Thirty students took the test. The average score was nine.

4. Eighteen students scored above the average score.

5. Thus, sixty percent of the students felt quite confident about themselves.

Write

1. The hardest time in my life

2. The hardest time in my life was when my grandmother passed away five years ago.

3. When I was younger, she took care of me most of the time.

4. Not having her around, I felt sad and lonely.

5. One day, I found my grandmother's diary.

6. She not only wrote a lot about her memories but also wished that I would lead a happy life.

7. From this experience, I have learned that I should try to be happy just as she wished.

Listen & Speak 2 - Think and Talk

1. don't, have to do

2. don't have to clean

3. don't have to come to school by

Link

1. How confident, feel about yourself

2. Wanting to find, created a test

3. took the test, average score

4. scored above the average score

5. Thus, felt quite confident about themselves

Write

1. The hardest time

2. hardest time in my life, passed away, ago

3. younger, took care of, most of

4. Not having her around, nfelt sad, lonely

5. One day, found

6. not only wrote a lot, but also wished

7. From this experience, have learned, try to be happy, as she wished

단어 TEST Step 1

p.41

01 독특하게	02 계산서	03 으깨다
04 불행하게도	05 확실히, 분명히	
06 진가를 알아보다, 고마워하다		07 환상적인
08 수리하다	09 웅장한, 위대한	10 일어나다
11 완전하게	12 불편, 애로	13 추구하다, 추진하다
14 고객, 소비자	15 발명가	16 이유
17 창의적인, 창조적인		18 역할, 배역
19 사실적인	20 덜 익은, 살짝 익힌	21 만족한
22 솔직하게, 솔직히	23 불평하다	24 열정, 흥미
25 끝마치다	26 지불하다, 지급하다	
27 획기적인	28 ~ 동안 내내	29 제공하다
30 서류	31 한 조각, 일부	32 신선한
33 기꺼이	34 성공적인	35 작성하다
36 겁주어 쫓아내다	37 ~이기 때문에, ~이므로	
38 결과적으로	39 역대, 지금껏	40 내붙이다, 게시하다
41 ~에 익숙하다	42 최선을 다하다	
43 ~의 책임을 지다, ~을 떠맡다		

단어 TEST Step 2

p.42

01 passion	02 appreciate	03 check
04 throughout	05 rare	06 pay
07 fix	08 form	09 surely
10 inconvenience	11 completely	12 gladly
13 pursue	14 reason	15 role
16 happen	17 complain	18 decorate
19 fantastic	20 meal	21 fresh
22 honestly	23 creative	24 crush
25 innovative	26 slice	27 successful
28 unfortunately	29 grand	30 customer
31 uniquely	32 supper	33 provide
34 satisfied	35 be used to	36 fill out
37 not anymore	38 as a result	39 of all time
40 do one's best	41 feel like -ing	42 put up
43 scare away		

단어 TEST Step 3

p.43

1 role, 역할, 배역　2 rare, 덜 익은, 살짝 익힌
3 meal, 식사　4 provide, 제공하다
5 supper, 만찬, 저녁 식사　6 throughout, ~동안 내내
7 check, 계산서　8 appreciate, 진가를 알아보다

9 crush, 으깨다　10 customer, 고객, 소비자
11 decorate, 장식하다, 꾸미다　12 fix, 수리하다
13 form, 서류　14 inventor, 발명가
15 complain, 불평하다　16 pursue, 추구하다, 추진하다

대화문 TEST Step 1

p.44~45

Listen & Speak 1 A-1

draw, did, it / look so real, feel like having a bite of / I'm not satisfied with, unique / so, fantastic drawing

Listen & Speak 1 A-2

How can, help / bought, only a week ago, sometimes turns off by itself / have a look at, inconvenience, take, few hours to fix / I'm not satisfied with, like, one / course, fill out, form

Listen & Speak 2 A-1

did, buy / myself / better than any other jam / should sell it / would, to buy / I promise I'll be

Listen & Speak 2 A-2

thought, were interested in / not anymore, want to become / Are, sure / how to act, I promise I'll do my best

Communicate A

your meal / good, fresh / about / I'm not satisfied with, rare / Would, like, to bring, another one / be going, have, check / won't have to pay for / I promise we'll provide, with, experience

Progress Check 1

How can I / got, as, I'm not satisfied with / in different colors / one in blue / do, get one

Progress Check 2

take, classes / interested in / not anymore, chef / hard work / worry, I promise I'll do / then

Progress Check 3

on / Have, finished / I promise I'll finish

대화문 TEST Step 2

p.46~47

Listen & Speak 1 A-1

B: Wow! Did you draw this?
G: I did. Do you like it?
B: Yes, the bread and the milk look so real. I feel like having a bite of the bread.
G: Thanks, but I'm not satisfied with it. It's not unique.
B: I don't think so. I think it's a fantastic drawing.

Listen & Speak 1 A-2

M: Hello, ma'am. How can I help you?

W: I bought this phone only a week ago, but it sometimes turns off by itself.

M: Oh, I see. May I have a look at it? (Pause) We're sorry for the inconvenience. It'll take a few hours to fix it.

W: I'm not satisfied with the phone. I'd like a new one.

M: Of course. I just need to fill out this form.

Listen & Speak 2 A-1

G: Wow, I like this blueberry jam. Where did you buy it?

B: I made it myself.

G: Really? This is better than any other jam I've ever had. You should sell it.

B: Do you think people would want to buy this?

G: Of course. I promise I'll be your first customer.

Listen & Speak 2 A-2

B: Mom, I want to go to an arts high school. I want to become an actor.

W: What? I thought you were interested in science.

B: I was but not anymore. I want to become a movie star.

W: Are you sure you want to be an actor?

B: Yes, I'll learn how to act. I promise I'll do my best.

Communicate A

Man: Are you enjoying your meal?

Woman: Well, the bread was good, and the salad was fresh.

Man: How about your steak?

Woman: Honestly, I'm not satisfied with the steak. It's too rare for me.

Man: I'm sorry. Would you like me to bring you another one?

Woman: That's O.K. I need to be going. Let me just have the check, please.

Man: I'm really sorry. You won't have to pay for the steak.

Woman: O.K. Thanks.

Man: I promise we'll provide you with a better experience next time you visit.

Progress Check 1

M: Hello, ma'am. How can I help you?

W: I got this hat as a gift yesterday, but I'm not satisfied with the color.

M: Oh, I see. We have this hat in different colors.

W: Do you have one in blue?

M: Yes, we do. I'll get one for you.

W: Thanks.

Progress Check 2

B: Mom, I want to take cooking classes.

W: What? I thought you were interested in sports.

B: I was but not anymore. I want to become a chef.

W: Are you sure? Cooking is hard work.

B: Don't worry. I promise I'll do my best.

W: O.K., then.

Progress Check 3

G: Dad, I want to watch a movie on TV now.

M: Have you finished your homework?

G: No, but I promise I'll finish it after I watch TV.

본문 TEST Step 1   p.48~49

01 Vinci the Cook

02 known as, greatest, time

03 also, inventor, musician

04 few, however, that, creative

05 In, worked as, at

06 took charge, changed, completely

07 simple, artistic, like, slices

08 dishes, even decorated with

09 because, used, with, servings

10 As, result, lost, job

11 few, later, opened, with

12 create, where, try, innovative

13 put up, uniquely written

14 believed, appreciate, creative cooking

15 Unfortunately, never happened

16 In, early, work for

17 different roles, such as

18 put in charge of

19 another chance, pursue, passion

20 stop at cooking creative

21 much more quickly, easily

22 Thus, invented, machines

23 created, crush vegetables, pull

24 device, scare, away from

25 innovative, most, too, to

26 grand, based on, wall

27 took, because, been interested

28 spent, kinds, what, put

29 wasted, over, reason, complained

30 Although, successful, interest, throughout

31 not only, but also

32 that, secret, same way

01 the Cook

02 is known as, greatest painters of all time

03 also, inventor, scientist

04 few, however, creative cook

05 twenty-year-old, as a cook

06 took charge of, changed, completely

07 but, like, a few carrot slices

08 were even decorated with

09 however, were used to, with, servings

10 As a result   11 A few, later

12 to create, where, innovative

13 put up, beautifully painted, uniquely written

14 would, appreciate, creative

15 Unfortunately, happened   16 early, to work

17 was given, roles, such as

18 was, put in charge of

19 to be given another, to pursue, passion

20 stop at   21 much more

22 Thus, invented   23 that, crush

24 that, scare, away from

25 were too, too, to use

26 to make, which was based on

27 took on, had, been interested in

28 a lot of, cooking, what to put

29 for over, why, to

30 Although, interest in, throughout

31 not only, but also, creative cook

32 Now that, secret passion, the same way

1 요리사 다빈치

2 레오나르도 다빈치는 역대 가장 위대한 화가들 중의 한 명으로 알려져 있다.

3 그는 또한 위대한 발명가, 과학자, 그리고 음악가였다.

4 하지만, 극히 소수의 사람들만이 또한 그가 창의적인 요리사였다는 것을 안다.

5 1473년, 스무 살의 레오나르도 다빈치는 이탈리아 플로렌스에 있는 음식점에서 요리사로 일했다.

6 그가 부엌을 책임지게 되었을 때, 다빈치는 메뉴를 완전히 바꿔 버렸다.

7 그는 약간의 당근 조각을 곁들인 생선과 같이 간단하지만 예술적인 음식을 만들었다.

8 몇몇 음식들은 심지어 꽃으로 장식되었다.

9 하지만, 손님들은 많은 양의 고기 요리에 익숙했었기 때문에 불만족스러워했다.

10 그 결과, 다빈치는 그의 직업을 잃었다.

11 몇 년 후, 다빈치는 그의 친구인 산드로 보티첼리와 함께 음식점을 열었다.

12 그는 사람들이 그의 획기적인 음식을 먹어 볼 수 있는 장소로 만들기를 원했다.

13 그들은 아름답게 그려진 간판을 내걸었고 독특하게 써진 메뉴를 만들었다.

14 다빈치는 사람들이 곧 그의 창의적인 요리의 진가를 알아볼 것이라고 믿었다.

15 불행히도, 그런 일은 결코 일어나지 않았다.

16 1480년대 초반에, 다빈치는 밀라노에서 루도비코 스포르차를 위해 일하기 시작했다.

17 그는 음악가, 화가, 그리고 공학자와 같은 많은 역할들을 부여받았다.

18 그는 또한 주방을 책임지게 되었다.

19 그는 요리를 향한 그의 열정을 추구할 또 다른 기회를 얻게 되어 행복했다.

20 다빈치는 창의적인 요리를 만드는 것에 멈추지 않았다.

21 그는 훨씬 더 빠르고 쉽게 요리하고 싶어했다.

22 따라서, 그는 그의 주방에서 사용할 새로운 기계들을 발명하였다.

23 그는 채소를 으깨고 스파게티를 뽑는 기계들을 만들었다.

24 그는 심지어 개구리를 겁주어 물탱크에서 쫓아낼 수 있는 기구도 만들었다.

25 확실히 그것들은 모두 매우 획기적이었지만, 그것들 중 대부분은 사용하기에 너무 크거나 너무 어려웠다.

26 1495년, 스포르차는 다빈치에게 웅장한 그림을 밀라노에 있는 교회의 벽에 그려 달라고 부탁했는데, 그것은 예수의 최후의 만찬을 바탕으로 한 것이었다.

27 다빈치는 기꺼이 그 작업을 맡았는데, 그가 항상 음식에 흥미를 가졌기 때문이었다.

28 그는 그림 속 식탁 위에 어떤 음식을 올릴지 결정하기 위해 모든 종류의 음식을 요리하느라 많은 시간을 썼다.

29 "다빈치는 1년 넘게 부엌에서 시간을 낭비해 오고 있습니다. 그것이 그가 아직도 그림을 끝내지 못한 이유입니다."라고 교회 사람들이 스포르차에게 불평을 했다.

30 다빈치는 결코 성공적인 요리사는 되지 못했지만 그는 그의 생애 내내 요리에 대한 큰 흥미를 보여 주었다.

31 그는 훌륭한 화가일 뿐만 아니라 창의적인 요리사였다.

32 이제 여러분은 요리에 대한 그의 비밀스런 열정을 모두 알게 되었기 때문에 〈최후의 만찬〉을 절대 같은 식으로는 보지 않을 것이다.

1 Da Vinci the Cook

2 Leonardo da Vinci is known as one of the greatest painters of all time.

3 He was also a great inventor, scientist, and musician.

4 Very few people, however, know that da Vinci was also a creative cook.

5 In 1473, twenty-year-old da Vinci worked as a cook at a restaurant in Florence, Italy.

6 When he took charge of the kitchen, da Vinci changed the menu completely.

7 He made simple but artistic dishes like fish with a few carrot slices.

8 Some dishes were even decorated with flowers.

9 Customers, however, were unhappy because they were used to dishes with big servings of meat.

10 As a result, da Vinci lost his job.

11 A few years later, da Vinci opened a restaurant with his friend Sandro Botticelli.

12 He wanted to create a place where people could try his innovative food.

13 They put up a beautifully painted sign and made a uniquely written menu.

14 Da Vinci believed that people would soon appreciate his creative cooking.

15 Unfortunately, that never happened.

16 In the early 1480s, da Vinci began to work for Ludovico Sforza in Milan.

17 He was given many different roles, such as a musician, a painter, and an engineer.

18 He was also put in charge of the kitchen.

19 He was happy to be given another chance to pursue his passion for cooking.

20 Da Vinci did not stop at cooking creative dishes.

21 He wanted to cook much more quickly and easily.

22 Thus, he invented new machines for his kitchen.

23 He created machines that could crush vegetables and pull spaghetti.

24 He even made a device that could scare frogs away from the water tank.

25 Surely, they were all very innovative, but most of them were too big or too difficult to use.

26 In 1495, Sforza asked da Vinci to make a grand painting, which was based on the last supper of Jesus, on the wall of a church in Milan.

27 Da Vinci gladly took on the project because he had always been interested in food.

28 He spent a lot of time cooking all kinds of food to decide what to put on the table in his picture.

29 "Da Vinci has wasted his time in the kitchen for over a year. That's the reason why he hasn't finished the painting yet," complained the people from the church to Sforza.

30 Although da Vinci never became a successful cook, he showed great interest in cooking throughout his life.

31 He was not only a great painter but also a creative cook.

32 Now that you know all about his secret passion for cooking, you will never look at *The Last Supper* the same way.

Write

1. an artist who uses technology

2. special moment, decided what I wanted

3. Back in, small statue using technology

4. great chance to learn, using technology

5. decided to, technical high school

6. After, graduated from, entered, learned, arts, technology

7. This year, held, exhibition

8. am, satisfied with

Link

1. the most important thing to consider, choose their career

2. come up with, design new things

3. work at a place where, use their creativity

Watch and Think Share

1. is known for using, during

2. few people, however, historian, painter, writer

3. won, Nobel Prize in Literature

Write

1. My name is Kim Jieun. I am an artist who uses technology.

2. There was a special moment when I decided what I wanted to be.

3. Back in 2030, I made a small statue using technology.

4. It was a great chance to learn about using technology for arts.
5. Thus, I decided to go to a technical high school.
6. After I graduated from high school, I entered Korea Art College and learned more about arts and technology.
7. This year, I held my first exhibition.
8. I am very satisfied with my life.

Link

1. Some people think creativity is the most important thing to consider when they choose their career.
2. They like to come up with new ideas and design new things.
3. Thus, they want to work at a place where they can use their creativity.

Watch and Think Share

1. Winston Churchill is known for using the Prime Minister of the United Kingdom during World War II.
2. Very few people, however, know that he was also a historian, a painter, and a writer.
3. He even won the Nobel Prize in Literature in 1953.

MEMO

MEMO

MEMO

적중100

영어 기출 문제집

정답 및 해설

미래 | 최연희